D1613109

Clinical *H*ypnotherapy

THE AUTHORS

DAVID B. CHEEK, M.D., F.A.C.S., F.A.C.O.G.: Diplomate, American Board of Obstetrics and Gynecology; Fellow and Past President, American Society of Clinical Hypnosis; Attending Staff, Childrens Hospital, San Francisco, California.

LESLIE M. LeCRON, B.A.: California State Certified Psychologist; former Fellow, Society of Clinical and Experimental Hypnosis.

THE BOOK

CLINICAL HYPNOTHERAPY supplies practical applications as taught in courses given by *Hypnosis Symposiums.*

Clinical *H*ypnotherapy

by

David B. Cheek, M.D.

and

Leslie M. LeCron, B.A.

Grune & Stratton
A Subsidiary of Harcourt Brace Jovanovich, Publishers
Orlando   San Diego   San Francisco
New York   London   Toronto   Montreal
Sydney   Tokyo   São Paulo

Books by Leslie M. LeCron

HYPNOTISM TODAY (Written with Jean Bordeaux)
EXPERIMENTAL HYPNOSIS (A collection of articles by leading authorities,
    edited by Leslie M. LeCron)
TECHNIQUES OF HYPNOTHERAPY
SELF HYPNOTISM, THE TECHNIQUE AND ITS USE IN EVERYDAY LIVING
HOW TO STOP SMOKING WITH SELF HYPNOSIS
HOW TO MAKE THE NEXT TEN YEARS THE BEST YEARS OF YOUR LIFE
BETTER HEALTH THROUGH SELF HYPNOSIS

Grune & Stratton, Inc.
Orlando, Florida 32887

Distributed in the United Kingdom by
Grune & Stratton, Ltd.
24/28 Oval Road, London NWI

Library of Congress Catalog Number 68-16304
International Standard Book Number 0-8089-0097-8
Printed in the United States of America

Contents

Part I: The Facts about Hypnosis

Part II: The Clinical Applications of Hypnosis

Foreword

by James F. Kuntz, M.D.

STEMMING FROM THE Eighteenth Century activities of Franz Mesmer and his notion of animal magnetism, throughout its entire history, hypnosis has been subject to cycles of intense interest and of deep disrepute. Hailed by some as a great discovery in the treatment of human ailments, it has been regarded by others as charlatanism and pure quackery. The names of prominent men and recognized authorities will be found as strong advocates on the one hand and equally well-recognized names as severe critics on the other hand.

During the past two decades there has been a great revival of interest in the subject of hypnosis, and it has become an acceptable modality, although many still regard it with skepticism. The dramatic nature of some of the phenomena, together with the controversial nature of its potential value for human behavior and in medical practice has stimulated much carefully controlled scientific investigation. This is being conducted in university laboratories and in private practice throughout the world. For the dissemination of such knowledge, both experimental and empirical, two excellent journals may be mentioned: the *International Journal of Clinical and Experimental Hypnosis* and the *American Journal of Clinical Hypnosis*. In this country as well as abroad, there are numerous societies whose members are interested in and concerned with the phenomena and applications of hypnosis.

Scientific research on hypnosis has been directed toward three important aspects: (1) the intrinsic nature of hypnosis, (2) its possible value and applications in surgical and medical practice, and (3) its use in hypno- and psychotherapy. Regarding the intrinsic nature of hypnosis, uncertainty still prevails, giving rise to numerous explanatory theories. Concerning the second aspect, hypnosis has been labeled a psychic analgesic with real value in the control of pain. Moreover, its value in removing preoperative as well as postoperative anxiety and complications is a generally accepted fact. The importance of these features in the treatment of patients certainly deserves careful consideration. As for the third phase, of hypno- and psychotherapeutic procedures, attention is directed toward personality improvement and development toward maturity. To assist in age integration, the improvement of the self-image, the development of self-reliance and self-confidence (in a word, the improvement of morale), it is obviously of tremendous value.

Some years ago I attended, mainly out of curiosity, one of the courses in hypnotic techniques offered by Hypnosis Symposiums. Impressed with the possibilities demonstrated there, I immediately began to apply what I had learned. (I am in general medical practice.) As a result, I have been able to help many patients when orthodox medical treatment could do very little. Therefore I believe I am a much better physician.

I have found hypnotherapy to be no panacea but of great value. I have used it in the treatment of various psychosomatic ailments, in obstetrics, gynecological conditions, infertility, frigidity, impotence, and in surgery. I have set aside certain hours for its use, including some evening hours. Most of my hypnotic patients are seen in half-hour sessions. One of its greatest values in my experience is in the treatment of obesity. In the past, my overweight patients might reduce but most soon regained the lost weight. Since using hypnosis in its treatment, not one of my patients, so far as I know, has failed to maintain proper weight after reducing.

As a matter of interest, I have also taught a number of college and law students how to employ self-hypnosis in studying. With it they are able to concentrate far better, to absorb and then recall. Their grades as a result have improved greatly.

The content of this work should prove enlightening to anyone interested in the healing arts. The reader will find the content presented in a clear and understanding manner. Therefore, for anyone engaged in the healing arts, as well as those who are professionally qualified to use hypnosis and are concerned with the problems of mental health, both preventative as well as curative, the perusal of this work should prove challenging and genuinely self-rewarding. To the realization of these desirable objectives, the careful study of the present volume is sincerely recommended. It offers in writing the same material taught in the Hypnosis Symposiums given by Cheek, LeCron and their panels of instructors. I might add that it is easy to learn hypnotic induction. Many beginners expect this to be difficult. This will be readily accomplished with a very few practice sessions, using the techniques given in the following pages.

Introduction

THE PURPOSE of this book is to offer a working concept of hypnosis as a valuable natural phenomenon in human ecology, to formulate simple plans of attack on clinical problems, and to discuss its applications and results with the combination of light hypnosis and the ideomotor questioning techniques developed by the authors.

This is not an attempt to cover the entire field of application of hypnosis to medicine, dentistry, and clinical psychology. There are too many variations in disease and too many factors affecting the interchange between therapist and patient to permit any author or combination of authors to draw final conclusions about all the values and all the limitations of hypnosis.

Essentially we are offering a course of instruction in hypnotic techniques in clinical application. It is not intended as a textbook on hypnosis; several of these have already been published. Here we are putting into writing what we have taught in courses given by Hypnosis Symposiums, more than ninety of them given in all sections of this country and in Canada, Mexico, Puerto Rico and Jamaica.

The first part of the book is a discussion of hypnosis itself, presenting the information the practitioner should know in order to utilize it. Part II deals with its clinical applications in general practice and in many specialties, including dentistry. After a bit of experience with the induction of hypnosis, the reader will be prepared to use this modality in his practice. More than 6,000 physicians, dentists and psychologists have attended our courses and have learned the clinical applications of hypnosis as they are offered here in book form. Although a book cannot replace the practice sessions and clinical demonstrations of an actual verbal course, we present here and discuss significant case examples of various hypnotherapeutic methods.

Only recently has hypnosis been accepted by the medical profession as a valuable and legitimate means of therapy. Like the general public, physicians often regard it as something mysterious and mystical, to be avoided as savoring of quackery. Hence, in the past it has carried a stigma. Many physicians have also felt that its techniques would be difficult to master. This is not the case.

In 1955 the British Medical Association adopted a resolution approving the use of hypnosis and urging physicians to learn its techniques. It also stated that hypnosis should be taught in medical schools. In 1958 our American Medical Association followed suit with a similar resolution. For the first time in its history, hypnosis became accepted as legitimate, although sharp warnings about its presumed dangers were broadcast by the Association's Committee on Hypnosis; this committee was disbanded in 1962.

Despite these resolutions, medical schools in both countries have failed to provide instruction. This situation is gradually changing and a few are beginning to offer such courses on a postgraduate level. The same situation has applied to dental schools.

Prior to World War II, there were probably only about 200 professional men in this country who were utilizing hypnosis in their work. Soon after the war, LeCron began arranging small classes in hypnosis for physicians and dentists who had become interested in the subject. As interest developed further, it seemed that the purpose of instruction could best be served if courses were given on a larger scale with a panel of 3 or 4 instructors. Accordingly, such a group was organized under the name Hypnosis Symposiums. It seemed that this would be a service to professional men who found instruction unavailable in the schools where it properly belongs.

Several psychiatrists, other physicians, and dentists have been included on the panel of instructors, in addition to ourselves. It is our belief that clinical demonstrations are an important part of instruction and that these should be with actual patients, showing the practical applications of hypnotherapy in a group setting. Others have contended that this is dangerous and embarrassing to patients and the audience. This has not been substantiated in our experience. The patients volunteer, usually being members of the class, or from members of their families or from among the patients of local physicians in the area where a symposium is held.

We believe that instructors should work together as a panel through a course in order to avoid repetition and in order to fill in material or clarify points. Thus information can be coordinated and integrated. Large and imposing rosters of instructors are more impressive than effective because individual instructors tend not to audit the talks of their colleagues.

Two national professional societies have been formed in this country since 1947, and there are now many similar associated societies throughout the world. These two are the American Society of Clinical Hypnosis and the Society for Clinical and Experimental Hypnosis. Both publish excellent quarterly journals and both offer workshops from time to time.

A technique which will be described and which will be found of the very greatest value is the use of ideomotor signalling as an uncovering technique in psychotherapy. This involves setting up a means of rapid and direct communication with the subconscious part of the mind, obtaining from it replies to questions by means of unconsciously controlled signals. The causes or motives for psychosomatic illnesses and other neurotic disturbances can usually be learned very quickly in this way.

One important chapter deals with the alleged dangers in hypnosis. While there are some dangers they have been greatly exaggerated by some psychiatrists. The critics who have stressed these dangers have not been noted for positive contributions to the literature on hypnosis. With the many psychiatrists and others who are real authorities, agreement is almost unanimous that dangers are minimal and can be avoided. In some instances there have been bad results, but they have come because of personality difficulties of the hypnotist, authoritative, coercive misuse of hypnosis, or lack of knowledge. Patients will protect themselves from harm when the therapist shows respect for their ability to do so.

The authors believe that most successful therapy in disease results from the innate capacity of human beings to adapt well to a threatening world when given hope. The value of all hypnotherapeutic methods probably should be assigned to the enormous power of the placebo, the strength from sincerely given hopeful suggestions.

We all know that hope may be abandoned and hope-giving therapy rejected by people who are subconsciously convinced they should suffer or die. The ease of breaking self-destructive resistances has been impressive, however, with help from the ideomotor questioning methods. Sick human beings may refuse help for themselves but many willingly overcome pain and disease for the benefit of loved ones when permitted to weigh values at a subverbal horizon of thought.

Memories recalled in deep hypnosis may evoke great emotional responses. Breuer and Freud believed such abreaction was necessary for the ventilation of traumatic experiences and development of insight. Such memories tend to be of the *complete age-regression* type. Little insight can be gained in the light of adult perspectives and maturing judgment when the experience is relived with the age level of understanding of that time or, as is usually the case, an age slightly greater than that of the experience. The complete type of age-regression seems to occur initially also with memories recalled at a subverbal level of awareness reflected by finger movements or the swing of a pendulum. The subject may feel and look uncomfortable and may indicate an unwillingness to know about the event at a conscious level of awareness. The feeling and appearance of alarm may disappear and the subject signal a willingness to know about the event when asked to look at it from the viewpoint of the time of interview.

There are other possible explanations, but it seems reasonable that the human mind can select several viewpoints for experience. All the advantages of vivid recollection in dramatic but sometimes harmful reliving an event during deep hypnosis are more rapidly gained with ideomotor methods. Additional value is obtained from the usually incomplete type of age-regression occurring most of the time with light hypnosis aided by use of ideomotor signals indicating the beginning and end of an experience. Patients can become therapists for themselves as they review an unpleasant experience with greater poise and perspective long after the event.

It has been known for many years that unconscious attitudes may be reflected by physiological responses and unconscious gestures. This is the reason for development of the polygraph machine for detecting telling a lie. Milton H. Erickson deserves credit for recognizing that any subconscious review of an experience will tend to evoke ideomotor and ideophysiologic responses appropriate to that experience, that subconscious review of sequential experiences also induces a hypnotic-like state. He was the first to write about the use of symbol movements of the head for "yes" and "no" answers when patients were unable to talk during hypnotic interview. He added movements of the hands when he recognized that specific meanings could be attached to such gestures and that the subject would not be aware of the gestures while in hypnosis.

LeCron had been observing similar characteristics of behavior with use of a Chevreul pendulum and added specific uses of unconsciously controlled finger movements to obtain "yes," "no" and "I don't want to answer" responses. He should be credited with the simple and rapid methods of interrogation used in this book and applied by some hundreds of his former students. Variations of his methods have permitted consistent break-through of the amnesia associated with general chemo-anesthesia and experiences of very early life.

Part I

The Facts about Hypnosis

Chapter 1

Hypnosis: Its Values and the Misconceptions about It

SPONTANEOUS SELF-HYPNOSIS

Since hypnosis has been used and well-publicized for nearly 200 years, it is strange that so many misconceptions and false ideas are held by the public and even by professional men. Hypnosis may seem mysterious, but everyone has been spontaneously in self-hypnosis under certain conditions. This probably happens to all of us every day of our lives. Though these situations are not labeled hypnosis, that is just what they are.

At times everyone daydreams. This definitely is a trance state. (In dealing with patients, it is better not to use the word "trance," but hypnosis is a trance state.) Whenever we become absorbed in what we are doing, we slip into hypnosis. Self-hypnosis results when you become absorbed in reading a book, in your work, in watching a motion picture or TV program, while listening to an interesting talk, even during some religious ceremonies. Any strong emotion may also produce hypnosis. A state of shock certainly is similar to a trance state. A realization that we enter hypnosis in these circumstances will give a better understanding of it.

What has been called "highway hypnosis" is another common condition. All drivers have probably had such an experience. On the open road where one can relax at the wheel, the monotonous hum of the motor while keeping the eyes fixed on the white line of the road is conducive to hypnosis. You probably can remember a time when you were driving and had passed through some town, then found yourself beyond it with no recollection of having gone through it. Many accidents blamed on falling asleep at the wheel have resulted from highway hypnosis. Some people are very prone to this.

COMMON MISCONCEPTIONS

Most people expect to pass out and be unconscious when hypnotized. Actually there never is loss of consciousness even in the deepest stages of hypnosis. The formally hypnotized subject is just as fully aware as are those in spontaneously occurring hypnotic-like states of daydreaming, shock and disorientation.

Many people expect to be under the control of the hypnotist, in his power. They think any suggestion given must then be carried out. In fact there is no surrender of will-power. Any suggestion given is strictly censored, both consciously and subconsciously. In general it may be said that no one will do anything under hypnosis that is against his moral code or that he may not want to do. This matter will be considered at more length in a later chapter. It applies to hypnosis as ordinarily used but not to brainwashing or dictator-persuasion long continued.

It should be mentioned here that the usual psychiatric term for the inner part of the mind is *unconscious*. Other words have also been applied to it. The word unconscious has two meanings: the inner part of the mind and also a state of unconsciousness. Therefore we prefer the word *subconscious*, as it has only one meaning, and we will use this term throughout the book.

Another common misconception is that the mind may be weakened by being hypnotized. No one's mind has ever been weakened even when hypnosis has been induced many times. Instead, strong-minded people make better subjects. Hypnosis can even be used to strengthen the mind and bring out its latent abilities.

Often there is confusion in people's minds between hypnotizability and gullibility. Gullibility is the quality of being easily fooled and certainly it is not an asset. A very hypnotizable person may not be at all gullible. Hypnotizability is an asset rather than a liability.

Some patients may fear they will talk and betray "state secrets" or say something they might not want known while in hypnosis, as may happen with some drugs. Since one is fully aware at all times when hypnotized, there is no such tendency.

Another fear often expressed is that awakening from hypnosis may be difficult or impossible. There never is any difficulty awakening a subject except in very, very rare cases. More will be said of this rare happening in the chapter as to dangers. Actually it is not a danger and with knowledge of how to handle the situation the subject can always be awakened.

Any of these false ideas may cause one to be fearful of being hypnotized. He may refuse hypnosis or fear may cause unconscious resistance to its induction. The practitioner may need to discuss the misconceptions and eliminate whatever fears may be entertained by a patient.

THE USES AND VALUES OF HYPNOSIS

What are the uses and values of hypnosis in the practice of medicine, dentistry and psychology? One of the main applications is in psychotherapy. It should be realized that hypnosis is not a method of treatment but is a valuable tool which can shorten treatment to a very great degree with any method used.

All physicians do not wish to become psychotherapists, yet it is impossible to practice without some psychotherapy being involved. Even your bedside manner is in this category. On leaving medical school and beginning to practice, every physician soon finds that many of the conditions he encounters are psychosomatic in origin. They have an emotional or psychological background and treatment may be ineffective unless the causes are learned.

It is not necessary for the physician to have any extensive knowledge of psychotherapeutic methods in order to use hypnosis. Of course the more he knows in this field the better a physician he will be, whether or not he uses hypnosis. With the methods and techniques given in the second part of this book, psychosomatic ailments may be successfully treated with only a superficial understanding of psychotherapy. Most physicians know the basic principles involved.

Here is a partial list of some of the uses of hypnosis in treatment. It is not complete, for tension and stress may be a factor in almost any illness, even the infectious ones.

Any illness classed as psychosomatic.

Resistance to infection can be improved.

Pain can be alleviated.

Inflammatory responses can be decreased with suggestions decreasing pain and making tissues "feel cool."

Muscle spasm either causing or caused by pain may be relieved by suggestion.

Emotional factors influencing the function of any of the systems can be discovered and corrected.

There are other applications of hypnosis. In the chapter on obstetrics it will be seen that it undoubtedly is the best method of childbirth, as has been noted by every obstetrician who has employed it. Another field where it is of great value is in anesthesia and surgery. Dentistry is another area where it can be of great value.

Some possible applications have been little explored, for instance in diagnosis and in affecting physical bodily changes. These matters and the dental uses will all be covered in Part II.

Chapter 2

What Is Hypnosis?

ALTHOUGH MANY BOOKS have been written about hypnosis, no one as yet has been able to formulate a theory about it which is entirely satisfactory. Several have been advanced which have some merit but none is completely accurate when all its many aspects are considered. All fall short in some way. One of the difficulties in reaching a workable theory is that a light state of hypnosis differs greatly from a deep one. We can describe and define hypnosis but a workable theory is something else again. However, you will have a better understanding of hypnosis if you know something of the theories which have been evolved, so they will be discussed briefly. From them it will be seen that hypnosis is a very complex phenomenon.

THE PAVLOVIAN THEORY: HYPNOSIS AS A FORM OF SLEEP

According to Pavlov, hypnosis and sleep are almost identical, both involving inhibition in some cerebral areas. Others have believed that hypnosis is at least a modified form of sleep. These ideas are based on the fact that rhythmic repetition of stimuli induces relaxation and the focusing of attention causes immobilization and inhibits some brain functions.

This theory falls by the wayside because research has shown that physiologically the two states are different. In hypnosis there is no loss of reflexes such as the knee jerk, which is lost in sleep. Another important difference is that there is no loss of consciousness even in the deepest stages of hypnosis, although there is some alteration of awareness. The differences are even greater in light stages of hypnosis.

HYPNOSIS AS CONDITIONED RESPONSE

Pavlov also believed that hypnosis is based on conditioning and is a reaction stimulated by past experiences. Words can act as stimuli for conditioned reflexes. Verbal stimuli can produce both organic and psychological reactions. Any hypnotic induction talk tends in some ways to induce conditioned responses to the words, tone and ideas. Certainly this theory has merit but fails to explain some important and complex factors seen in hypnosis. It also does not explain the great differences between a light state and a deep one.

THE PSYCHOANALYTIC THEORY

Analysts, such as Ferenczi, have studied hypnosis along analytic lines. Ferenczi claimed that there is regression to childhood during hypnosis, the subject unconsciously associating the hypnotist with the strong father, if induction was of aggressive, commanding type, or the mother, if it was permissive in form. In other words, transference is involved. The subject then unconsciously wishes to obey the parent figure based on love and fear of the parent image.

With this theory self-subordination is present together with the Oedipus complex and there is then a sexual factor in hypnosis. There have been claims of definite eroticism exhibited by the subject when in hypnosis. This observation has not been substantiated by other experienced hypnotherapists and probably is an individual response which certainly is not generally present. It must be concluded that the operator in some unconscious way promoted such behavior.

There is no doubt that a subject may experience erotic fantasies, but to say that these are always present or that the subject regresses to childhood is untrue. If the operator is a male and the subject a female, erotic fantasies are more likely to develop, but this is also true in any physician-patient relationship. Experienced subjects able to enter a deep state often deny any such tendencies. Voice tone and inflection should be carefully studied by those using hypnosis in order to avoid sounding unctious or condescending or seductive.

These ideas are more of a description of some possible unconscious processes than a theory. They do not take into consideration some hypnotic phenomena or self-hypnosis.

HYPNOSIS AS DISSOCIATION

In the past, this theory has had many supporters and certainly has some meritorious aspects. It seems to be founded on the idea that hypnosis abolishes volition and is a form of automatism. It regards the conscious mind as dissociated when a person is under hypnosis, some other part of the mind having taken over. Post-hypnotic amnesia for what occurred during the trance, or amnesia in carrying out a post-hypnotic suggestion tends to confirm this theory.

Here we encounter difficulty in explaining the difference between light and deep hypnosis. There are elements of dissociation in the deep stage but almost none in the light trance. Some deep trance phenomena seem to be dissociative. This theory at present has little support.

HYPNOSIS AS ROLE-PLAYING

Several psychologists, including White, Sarbin and Barber, claim that hypnosis is merely role-playing on the part of the subject. They state that any hypnotic phenomena can be produced in the waking state as, for instance, in cases of hysteria. For the most part, this is true, although such things as voluntary control of physiological processes is only possible under hypnosis and is not subject to volition (for instance, change of heartbeat). Briefly stated, this theory is that the hypnotized person acts and behaves as he thinks a hypnotized person should behave.

Role playing has some points in common with the Pavlovian theory of conditioned responses, and, in fact, most of our suggestions directed toward improving physiological responses are based on using previously learned reactions to appropriately chosen types of suggested environment. To categorize all hypnotic phenomena as "role playing" is unscientific, however, because hypnotized subjects may burst into tears when asked to recall a happy experience or may become dyspneic with an asthmatic episode when told to remember some unpleasant experience in childhood.

The factor of rapport with the hypnotist does enter here and almost every subject tries to cooperate and to please the operator. In a light stage there is at times some role-playing. However, to us this theory seems highly ridiculous. It completely ignores the possible changes in bodily processes due to hypnotic suggestion and the positive Babinski reflex which occurs with hypnotic age regression to infancy. It also ignores the fact that a person can be hypnotized by indirect methods so that he is unaware of being hypnotized. Furthermore, a child of 4 or 5 years can be deeply hypnotized and would have no conception of how a hypnotized person would behave. It even ignores auto-hypnotic spontaneous states.

There have been some other postulations advanced which can explain some facets of hypnosis, but it will be seen from a consideration of all these theories that no completely workable explanation of hypnosis has yet been formulated. It is a very complex matter.

WHAT THE HYPNOTIZED SUBJECT EXPERIENCES

While we cannot explain hypnosis, we can describe it. It is undoubtedly a state of altered awareness, although consciousness is retained most of the time. Suggestibility is increased under hypnosis, the greater the degree, the deeper the trance. There is an alteration of reality. If hallucinations are suggested, they seem real. In hypnosis, the subject tends to relax spontaneously to a greater degree than he can voluntarily, although some subjects can remain in a rigid form of catalepsy during hypnosis.

The main sensation experienced by the subject is one of listlessness or lethargy. It seems to be too much trouble to move, although, if sufficiently motivated, movement is possible. But he doesn't wish to be bothered by making the effort. Speech may be difficult. If told to make some movement, perhaps to lift an arm voluntarily, it will be done very slowly. These signs and feelings are greater in the deeper stages.

If the subject's eyes are opened while in a deep trance, there is usually a tunneling of vision. Instead of peripheral vision extending in an arc of almost 180 degrees, it may tunnel to perhaps 90 degrees, with peripheral vision lost or narrowed down. Ideomotor questioning reveals that peripheral vision is maintained unconsciously while the more conscious (verbal level) reported vision is tunneled.

As a person enters a light state of hypnosis, one of the most usual indications is a fluttering of the eyelids, which ends as the person goes deeper. This may be slight or there may be considerable movement of the lids. Most subjects say this is not uncomfortable, but others find it so. Hence, if it continues, suggestions should be made of relaxation of the muscles of the lids.

In a first induction and sometimes in later ones, there is an increase in heartbeat and in the rate of breathing. Probably this is due to anxiety, as most people have some apprehension over a new experience. With greater depth and more relaxation, heart and breathing rates slow down to less than normal. Breathing tends to become more abdominal in type. Possibly with slower rate the pulse becomes stronger. The pulse in the neck may not be observable visually at first, then may become quite apparent and can be timed by watching it.

If a patient has been in hypnosis for some time, perhaps for the greater part of an hour, if asked how long it has been since it was induced he will probably greatly underestimate the length of time that has passed. Often it will be guessed as having been only 10 or 15 minutes.

As the subject drifts deeper into hypnosis and relaxation becomes greater, the lines of the face smooth out. It becomes mask-like and without expression. In a deep state, this becomes very noticeable. Then, if his eyes are opened, they will have a peculiar glassy look and seem to be in a fixed stare. When closed, the eyeballs often will be seen to have rolled up. Sometimes the lids will open slightly and the whites of the eyes are visible. Wandering movements of the eyes beneath the lids are often seen when patients are recalling events in age regression.

Subjects frequently will comment after awakening that they felt as though they were very light and were floating in the air. More often the opposite effect is experienced. A feeling of heaviness develops, particularly in the limbs. The person may try to lift an arm and find it too heavy; the effort to lift it is too great.

When one has become used to being hypnotized, it is almost invariably felt to be a most comfortable, enjoyable state. People frequently say they were reluctant to awaken. Sometimes it will be noted that a subject enters a deeper stage when he is told he is about to be awakened.

It is very common during induction for the subject to give a slight sigh as he slips into hypnosis. On awakening this may be repeated. Many people will rub their eyes on awakening, as if emerging from normal sleep.

One of the main signs of hypnosis is the disinclination to move. Unless some movement is suggested, the person may lie for hours without making the slightest movement, something almost impossible to do voluntarily. Movements are frequent during the lighter stages of normal sleep. Even if there is discomfort, there is likely to be no movement. If a fly should alight on a person's face while he is in a deep state, there probably would be no attempt to brush it off, as we have seen happen. The subject may be uncomfortable for some reason but almost never will take the trouble to mention it until he is awakened.

Any movement by the subject should be noted by the operator. It might indicate discomfort, and he should ask about that possibility. Usually it is a matter of the subject reassuring himself or even more likely is a sign of unconscious resistance. Resistance is sometimes manifested by the development of an itch on the face which the subject will then rub or scratch. Still another sign of resistance is when the subject laughs or smiles during induction, though a smile may only be a sign of self-consciousness.

Throughout the hypnotic session, the operator should take pains to observe the subject, watching for these signs and for anything in the person's behavior that will give him information. His procedure will largely depend on his observations. Attentiveness to the subject should be continued while therapy is conducted.

It is usual for a subject to underestimate the depth of hypnosis he has reached. In a light state or even a medium one, the subject will frequently state after awakening that he was not hypnotized, although the operator has noted definite signs and indications of hypnosis. Knowing that hypnosis has developed, the operator may be inclined to dispute this. It is better not to contradict the subject in this situation. Using ideo-motor questioning, the subject's subconscious can be asked if he was hypnotized. When it replies affirmatively, this is very convincing to the subject and he accepts it as a fact.

Chapter 3

The History of Hypnosis

PRACTITIONERS OF HYPNOSIS should be familiar with its history, which is quite interesting.

THE EARLY HISTORY OF HYPNOSIS

All primitive cultures, both ancient and modern, have been aware of hypnosis. Priests and witchdoctors have made it a stock in trade since early in the history of the human race. There were "sleep temples" in ancient Greece and in Egypt where patients were hypnotized or were talked to during their sleep and given curative suggestions. The Druids, the Celtic priesthood, are supposed to have been experts in its use. In primitive cultures, trance induction has always been by means of rhythm: drums, dancing, chanting, etc.

ITS MODERN HISTORY

This is considered as beginning with Mesmer, the terms *mesmerism* or *animal magnetism* being applied to it for nearly a century. James Braid, a British physican, coined the word hypnosis from the Greek word for sleep, *hypnos*. Mesmer began his work with it in 1773, not realizing that suggestion is involved. He first practiced in Vienna, then moved to Paris when he encountered strong opposition from his medical colleagues. His method of treatment was often successful at a time when nothing was known of psychotherapy. He became the idol of Paris and patients flocked to him, especially the nobility. He wanted the French Academy of Science to investigate his work, but this was at first refused.

Later on, an investigation was made, but Mesmer was disgruntled and refused to cooperate. The Academy's committee, which included Benjamin Franklin as a member, investigated some of Mesmer's followers instead and then reported unfavorably, discrediting Mesmer. The committee ignored the results being obtained and said that they came only from imagination. This was in 1784 and Mesmer's contributions were forgotten for some time. He died in Switzerland in obscurity.

Braid, working in the 1840s, found that a trance could be produced by eye fixation and suggestion instead of mesmeric passes. He was the first to understand that suggestion plays a large role in induction.

About this time, Elliotson, a prominent British surgeon, became interested in mesmerism and performed many operations with hypnotic anesthesia. James Esdaile, still another British surgeon, working in a prison hospital in India, began experimenting with mesmerism in 1845. This was before chemo-anesthesia had been accepted and prior to Lister's campaign against infection. Esdaile had read that pain could be relieved in the mesmeric trance and proved the mesmeric relief of pain.

Esdaile performed over 3,000 operations, more than 300 of them being major surgery, using nothing but hypnosis. Writing in 1847, his book *Mesmerism in India* is a classic example of thoughtful observation. It was recently republished by Julian Press under the title *Hypnosis in Medicine and Surgery*. In it he describes in detail his methods and results.

At that time, surgeons washed their hands after surgery rather than before. Mortality from infection following an operation ranged between 25 per cent and 50 per cent. In India, Esdaile had 50 per cent mortality in his own work. To his amazement, when he began using hypnotic anesthesia, his fatalities dropped to only 5 per cent. This was very puzzling. He had no idea why it occurred, and the only explanation today seems to be that with hypnotic anesthesia the subconscious mind must develop in the body greater resistance to infection. This phenomenon has been noted again and again in modern times.

On his return to England, Esdaile was persecuted by his associates. He was tried by the British Medical Association and lost his license. During his trial it was even stated that he was blasphemous for controlling pain; God intended people to suffer!

The history of hypnosis has been a series of peaks of interest followed by valleys of disinterest. Although the few professional men who used it found it so valuable that they would not give it up, the resulting persecution kept many others from learning about it. Mesmer created great interest for a few years. This subsided when he was discredited. Another high point in interest came in the 1830s in Europe and in the 1840s in England and America. The first extraction of a tooth under hypnosis was in 1823, and 3 years later a woman went through painless childbirth while under hypnosis. This wave of interest subsided until the 1880s, a period when interest probably reached its highest until the present day.

In France, Hippolyte Bernheim was at the top of the medical profession. He was mortified when a country doctor named Liebeault, living in Nancy, was successful in curing one of Bernheim's patients through hypnosis where Bernheim had failed of a cure. Bernheim went to Nancy to denounce Dr. Liebeault as a quack. Bernheim was so impressed with what he learned that he became a convert to hypnotherapy. He moved to Nancy and, with Liebeault, set up the famous Nancy Clinic, using only hypnosis in therapy. The results were so good that physicians came from all over Europe and America for instruction in hypnosis. Freud was one of them. Their therapeutic method was to use direct suggestion to alleviate the patient's symptoms or illness. It produced good results but there were some failures as well.

In the 1890s when Freud first began to practice, he worked with a general practitioner named Breuer, one of the best medical hypnotists of that time. Freud knew little about hypnosis, was a poor operator and had the mistaken idea that a deep trance was necessary for good results. Only about one in ten of his patients would enter a deep trance and Freud found this frustrating. Breuer was having far better results. There was much rivalry between them and Freud could not tolerate this situation. He therefore sought other methods, gave up hypnosis, and developed free association and dream interpretation.

Although Freud's contributions to our knowledge of the mind and of psychotherapy are great, his abandoning hypnosis was harmful, for he blocked hypnotherapy for nearly fifty years. Today many psychiatrists and most analysts have minimal interest in hypnosis. They know nothing about it and believe it worthless because Freud first used it and then gave it up. Many of them firmly believe that hypnotherapy is only a matter of suggesting away symptoms, as Bernheim used it. Hence it is often claimed that hypnotherapy has only temporary results, although Bernheim and other physicians of that day certainly proved this idea false.

THE PRESENT SITUATION

In the first half of this century interest in hypnosis was in such eclipse due to Freud's abandoning it that it was little used. Very few physicians continued to practice hypnosis. During World War I, some interest developed when it was found very effective in the treatment of "shell shock" or battle fatigue as it is now called. It was not until the Second

World War that interest again developed. Oddly it was the dentists who showed more enthusiasm for it than did the medical profession. In 1945 it is doubtful if there were more than 200 qualified practitioners of hypnosis in this country.

When the British Medical Association officially endorsed hypnosis in 1955 and the American Medical Association followed suit in 1958, the picture was completely changed. For the first time in its history, hypnosis became acceptable, though today many physicians still regard it with lifted eyebrow. This attitude is gradually diminishing as medical journals now publish papers on hypnosis in every medical specialty. At last a modality which has helped hundreds of thousands of patients is coming into its own.

REFERENCES

Bernheim, H.: Suggestive Therapeutics. New York, G. P. Putnam's Sons, 1899.
Esdaile, J.: Hypnosis in Medicine and Surgery. New York, Julian Press, 1957.
Kline, M. V.: Freud and Hypnosis. New York, Julian Press, 1958.

THE STUDENT OF HYPNOSIS may ask, "Will I be able to hypnotize my patients? Will there be frequent failures which might damage my professional prestige?" He may have read of very complete and thoughtful studies on the hypnotizability of volunteer college students, some of whom were not hypnotizable and wonder from these conclusions whether it is even worthwhile for him to try using hypnosis in his professional practice.

It should be stressed here that the state of hypnosis with its increased suggestibility, literalness of understanding and willingness to comply with optimistic suggestions is a quality of behavior that appears spontaneously in human beings at critical times of fear, illness and unconsciousness. Studies on hypnotizability made with volunteers can be valid only for volunteers under the test circumstances of the laboratory. They have nothing to do with the hypnotizability of patients when the therapist feels that hypnosis could prove valuable. The most unhypnotizable volunteer student will enter hypnosis at an adequate level if the therapist presents hypnosis to him with honest conviction that hypnosis will work and will work with this immediate indication. The experienced hypnotherapist approaches an untested patient with the philosophy that all people are in hypnosis at frequent intervals and "I might as well show this person how to use it constructively now."

With this attitude, one can hypnotize essentially 90 per cent of his patients on the first visit. After uncovering and correcting resistances, it should be possible to use hypnosis successfully in nearly 100 per cent of the patients on the second office visit. This is not to be misunderstood as meaning that hypnotherapy will achieve its goal in nearly 100 per cent of one's patients, merely that it will be possible to help a patient achieve at least a light state of hypnosis and be able to appreciate some of the phenomena of hypnosis by the second visit in nearly all the patients.

The stages of hypnosis are usually considered as light, medium, or deep, the latter often called the somnambulistic state. Fortunately only a light state is needed for most purposes. In some situations it may even be better than a deep one where lethargy may be so great that communication is difficult. The use of hypnosis would be impractical if we had to depend on the patient reaching a deep stage, because only about one person in eight or ten will enter this stage under ordinary circumstances of office consultation.

It is difficult to say why some people enter a very deep trance very quickly on the first induction, while others who are willing and motivated may only reach a light state on repeated attempts. Again we must distinguish between the motivation and willingness of experimental volunteers and the seeming readiness of the patient who is injured, sick or in pain. Patients coming to the office for control of habits will approximate the behavior of experimental volunteers, while those who are in great pain or are seen during times of emergency will, for all practical purposes, be in a light state of hypnosis *before* being introduced to formal hypnosis. Unconscious human beings under general chemo-anesthesia are unable to demonstrate phenomena and are unable to communicate, but they are able to hear and react physiologically to suggestions as has been demonstrated by Wolfe, Hutchings and Pearson. We can only speculate that a form of hypnosis occurs spontaneously under such circumstances and that we have only to recognize the possibility in order to use it helpfully for the patient.

Laboratory studies of hypnotizability by Andre and Geneva Weitzenhoffer and by Ernest Hilgard have shown that there is no difference between the sexes and that no one race is any more susceptible than another. Children make the best subjects and most of them will enter a deep trance within short periods of time although they may outwardly appear unhypnotized. The most responsive period seems to be from ages 6 to 12.

RESISTANCES TO INDUCTION OF HYPNOSIS

1. *Unconscious resistance* is often an obstacle even though the individual may be consciously eager to be hypnotized. Fears may be present though unrecognized. These are usually based on the common misconceptions about hypnosis. Therefore, it is well for the operator to explain away these mistaken ideas before an induction is attempted.

2. *Previous frightening experiences* may cause resistance, seemingly because the human mind has retreated into a hypnotic-like state and the

induction of hypnosis later reminds him of the unpleasant cause of the earlier spontaneous state. This speculation is supported by repeated observations of subjects who have uncovered their reasons for feeling uncomfortable and wanting to avoid initial experiences with formally induced hypnosis. Such subjects quickly lose their feelings of fear and are able to enter hypnosis as soon as they learn they need not be reminded of the unpleasant experience again.

3. *Fear of loss of control* is another reason for initial resistance. There never is such a loss, for the subject is fully aware and, indeed, can awaken himself at any time if he desires to do so. Fear of talking too much and telling "state secrets" is a misconception quickly dispelled by explanation that it is hard to talk in hypnosis anyhow and protective forces within the subject are to be respected by the hypnotherapist.

4. *Personality factors* may interfere with induction. The methods of talking and presenting ideas by the operator may irritate the subject and interfere with results which could easily be obtained by another, more relaxed therapist. Unpleasant personality traits in the operator could lead to distrust and failure to achieve the necessary rapport.

5. *Motivation,* mentioned last but of greatest importance, has to be considered in relation to hypnotizability as it does with therapy in general. Primary motivation must come with the therapist. Even an enthusiastic patient can be cooled by a therapist who is uninterested in the task at hand. In contrast, an uninitiated and scoffing patient may slip right into hypnosis as he picks up the convictions and positive motivations of an interested therapist. Dentists and anesthesiologists are fortunate in having a high percentage of their subjects very highly motivated toward using hypnosis. Fear of pain and fear of the unknown are strong forces on the side of permitting easy induction into hypnosis.

It must also be remembered that symptoms may be unconscious mechanisms of defense or may serve some other purpose. While the patient may consciously wish to be helped, unconsciously the need for a symptom may be so strong that resistance develops in fear that the symptom may be taken away. Actually the purpose of therapy is not to eliminate the symptom when it is needed but to make it unnecessary through a revision of viewpoints and better insight.

The following results are to be expected for an operator of average skill at the first session:

5%	unhypnotizable
45%	able to enter light state
35%	able to enter medium state
15%	able to enter deep trance

These estimates are, of course, subject to great variation. For instance, unhypnotizable subjects who are completely refractory alone may become good subjects after seeing someone else hypnotized. The attitude of the operator is also of great importance because his subject is highly sensitive to minimal cues of voice tone, inflection and timing of words. An uncomfortable operator will make his subject uncomfortable. The therapist who is afraid of causing dangerous reactions in his patient will either find that none of his subjects can be hypnotized or he will be shocked by his high percentage of frightening reactions.

If we were to graph hypnotizability, the graph line would rise very sharply from the age of 3 to ages 8–10, which would be the peak. The line would then descend very gradually with increasing age. Elderly people are harder to hypnotize. However, hypnotizability depends entirely on the individual. Sometimes even a child will be very resistant. Some people in their eighties will be able to reach a very deep state. Thus, statements as to hypnotizability can only be general. Of course the skill of the operator enters as a factor.

Naturally the beginner with hypnosis is not very confident, but confidence comes quickly with practice and results then are better. It should be remembered that everyone who uses hypnosis, including the most expert, went through the beginner stage and had to develop confidence. Most professional men soon develop it.

Almost everyone seems to have the opinion that he will be a poor subject. Perhaps it is an unconscious means of reassuring oneself, or the subject may believe he has too strong a mind to be "controlled." Regardless of this, the person may then enter a deep trance. His belief seems to have no bearing on the result. The loudest skeptic may be an excellent subject.

One's station in life may have a bearing on hypnotizability. Again this depends entirely on the individual. In general, those who customarily give orders to subordinates will not be as good subjects as those accustomed to receive them. For instance, an army officer would be less likely to be a good subject than a private.

When a patient proves to be a poor subject or induction fails, ideomotor response to questions may be utilized to find the reasons. Unconscious resistances or any other cause may be uncovered in this way and possibly removed.

With experience most operators become able to sense how good a subject a patient will be. This may come from subconscious intuition as well as from observation of the patient. Such an ability is a part of the stock in trade of the stage hypnotist. He quickly determines which volunteer will be resistant and sends others back into the audience, keeping only those who he is sure will be good subjects. A quick test or two will help him decide that one or two others will not be good enough for his purpose and they, too, are dismissed.

A case of LeCron's could be mentioned which shows how unconscious resistances can sometimes be overcome by learning the reason behind them. A 21-year-old girl was referred for hypnotherapy and he was sure she would be a fine subject. On attempted induction, to his surprise she could not even be lightly hypnotized. Resorting to the questioning technic, he was able to learn the reason. At the age of 14 she had attended a stage demonstration of hypnosis and had volunteered as a subject. She had proved to be a somnambulist. Her brother had attended with her and on their return home he told their mother of his sister's experience. The mother was horrified, having the usual misconceptions about hypnosis. She scolded the girl, ordering her never to let herself be hypnotized again. Unconsciously she had been obedient and had carried out her mother's command. When this had been learned and her mother agreed that hypnosis could help the daughter, the girl was again able to enter a deep trance.

TESTS OF HYPNOTIZABILITY

Much research has been conducted as to tests of hypnotizability. Some are too involved and require too much time to be practical. Those who use hypnosis should be familiar with some of the simpler ones. There are situations where they can be of value, but usually the busy practitioner will not bother with them.

One has been called the *sway test*. With it the subject is asked to stand with his back to the operator and to close his eyes. It is then suggested that he will begin to feel as if the operator were pulling him backward, that he will find himself beginning to sway backward and forward and then will fall backward. First he should be assured that he will be caught and not allowed to fall. Almost everyone responds in varying degree to this suggestion. The greater and quicker the response, the higher the degree of hypnotizability. The subject must not be allowed to fall, of course. Strangely, some people will respond to the suggestion but will do so in their own way, starting to fall forward instead of backward. The operator must be prepared for this. When the response is best, the subject will not step back as he finds himself falling. Both feet will remain on the floor as he goes backward. A susceptible person may enter hypnosis as these suggestions are given and then may be caused to sit down and the trance deepened, or he may be awakened.

A test called *eye closure* or *eye catalepsy* is an interesting one. It can be a way of testing hypnotizability with the subject awake or can be a means of showing the hypnotized subject that something is happening to him. This test consists of having him shut his eyes, squeezing the lids tightly together, then suggesting that they cannot be opened. Enough time must be allowed for the suggestions to become effective. Speaking slowly and emphatically the wording of the suggestions could be as follows.

"Now as your eyelids are squeezed tightly together, I am going to count to three and you will be unable to open your eyes. Wait until I tell you when to try and then try hard, but the harder you try to open your eyes the tighter the lids will stick together. (This invokes the Law of Reversed Effect.) One, your eyelids are becoming glued together, glued fast together, gluing tighter and tighter together. Two, now it is as though the lids were welded together, welded into one piece and you couldn't possibly open them, welded tightly together. Three, the lids are locked together now, locked tight. They are tight, tight, tight. Now try to open them, but you can't; they are locked tight, tight, tight. Now stop trying. Now they are free again and you can open them."

It is surprising how many people even in the waking state will be unable to open their eyes with these suggestions. Those who do not will be the better subjects. Do not allow more than two or three seconds for the subject to try, then suggest that the eyes can open again.

A very similar test has been called the *handclasp test*. The person is asked to clasp his hands together in front of him with fingers interlaced and palms pressed tightly together. The suggestions given would be the same as above but substituting the words "hands" for "eyes."

Sometimes an experienced practitioner of hypnosis is asked to speak on this subject and to demonstrate. In our opinion, such talks should be given only to professional groups, not to laymen. Either of these two tests provides a way for the lecturer to select a good subject for his demonstration. The handclasp test is probably the best because it is easier to observe the results. Watching those in the audience closest to him, the lecturer undoubtedly will see someone straining fruitlessly to separate his hands. He can then be asked to serve as a subject.

These two tests are good indications of hypnotizability but are by no means infallible. Both are challenges to the subject. Some of us almost instinctively react to a challenge of this kind by opening our eyes or unclasping our hands, yet such a person may prove to be a good subject even if the test failed. In our opinion an operator should usually avoid challenges, even if the subject is in hypnosis. A failure is a setback.

One way of making such a test which avoids a challenge can be used while the subject is hypnotized. He could be told he is to be shown how he can respond to his own suggestions. The operator tells the subject what he is to suggest to himself and states that he will respond to this.

The same suggestions as given above are then given slowly, with pauses between the counting so that the subject can repeat the words to himself, using the word "I" instead of "you." He need not speak aloud, merely think the words. When the subject gives these suggestions to himself, no challenge is involved and results should be better.

Another test both of suggestibility and hypnotizability (they go hand in hand) does not involve a challenge. This is to ask the person to hold both arms out in front of him, fists closed, and with his eyes shut. He is then told to imagine that he is holding a heavy briefcase full of books in his dominant hand. If the subject is a woman, a large handbag can be suggested. The case or bag is said to be heavy and the weight will be felt pulling his arm down. Repetition of the suggestions will probably cause the arm to move down several inches. The subject is then asked to open his eyes and note how well he has responded to the idea of weight on that arm, although there was no difference in the actual weight of the two arms.

A variation of this test is to say that a cord is tied to the subject's arm closest to the operator and that he will feel the operator pulling on the cord, the arm responding to the imaginary pull. Usually it will drift over toward the operator, moving away from the other outstretched arm.

A variation of the sway test is to suggest to the subject, standing with his eyes closed, that he has something heavy in one hand, very heavy. Continuing to repeat this idea, the subject will usually bend or lean to that side.

When any test fails, it does not necessarily mean that the person will be a difficult subject, though the chances are that a deep trance will not be produced. Some challenging tests can be of aid in preparing the patient for hypnosis, but if time does not allow testing, induction may proceed without spending time on tests.

REFERENCES

Cheek, D. B.: Removal of subconscious resistance to hypnosis using ideomotor questioning techniques. Amer. J. Clin. Hypn. 3: 103-107, 1960.

Hilgard, E.: Hypnotic Susceptibility. New York, Harcourt, Brace & World, 1965.

Hutchings, D.: The value of suggestion given under anesthesia. Amer. J. Clin. Hypn. 4: 26-29, 1961.

Pearson, R. E.: Response to suggestions given under general anesthesia. Amer. J. Clin. Hypn. 4: 106-114, 1961.

Weitzenhoffer, A., and Weitzenhoffer. G.: Sex transference and susceptibility to hypnosis. Amer. J. Clin. Hypn. 1: 15-24, 1958.

Wolfe, L. S.: Hypnosis in Anesthesiology. In: Techniques of Hypnotherapy, (L. M. LeCron, Ed.). New York, Julian Press, 1961.

Chapter 5

Inducing Hypnosis

THERE ARE MANY METHODS of inducing hypnosis. The induction talk may be given in a positive commanding way or be spoken very permissively. The latter is usually a slower method but generally better for the beginner. With it the voice is kept low and the subject almost coaxed into the trance. The cadence is slow and a monotone should be used. With the commanding type of induction, the tone is louder and authoritative. The words should be spoken more rapidly and forcefully. The stage hypnotist always uses this approach because of the quick results. He cannot take more than two or three moments for an induction or his audience would become bored. Objection to the forcing type of induction is that it overwhelms the possible resistances of the subject and may cause resentment that would interfere with therapeutic results.

For induction, the subject should be in a comfortable position so that he can relax well. Clothing should not be too tight and the discomfort of a full bladder would be a handicap. It makes no difference whether the subject sits up or is reclining. A so-called "reclining chair" which will tip back and which has a footrest is excellent for induction, for the patient can sit up if he prefers or can lie back at any preferred inclination of the chair.

EYE FIXATION METHODS

With most induction methods it is desirable for the subject to close his eyes as distractions are then shut out. However it is not essential for the eyes to be closed.

There can be many variations of the eye fixation method. The subject can be asked to gaze into the eyes of the operator or he can direct his attention to some object. This can be almost anything as long as there is no discomfort in gazing at it. A picture on the wall, a spot on the ceiling, a doorknob, anything will serve. A colored light bulb which is not too bright is sometimes used, perhaps set in the ceiling above the chair. One of the best objects is a clear plastic-ball pendulum which will be described later.

Many gadgets are available which may aid in induction, although they are quite unnecessary. Perhaps the best of these is a spiral disk mounted on a phonograph turntable revolving at slow speed. Another good object is a lighted candle, the flickering flame helping somewhat in the process of induction. Most effective therapists use imagery rather than actual objects for limitation of attention.

Eye fixation can also be achieved by means of some bright object held in the hand of the operator. A wristwatch, a dental hand mirror, a colored Christmas tree ornament, anything bright will serve. Bernheim asked his subjects to look at the ends of his fingers, holding his forefinger and thumb extended about a foot in front of the person's eyes.

A variation of this method would be to move the hand up and down, letting the patient's eyes follow and thus tiring the eyes. Apparently tiring the eyes is advantageous, though perhaps this is merely because the subject thinks it will induce hypnosis: a matter of indirect suggestion.

Another way to tire the eyes is to ask the subject to open and close them as the operator counts backward from one hundred. The eyes are to close on the even numbers, open on the odd ones. The speed in counting should be varied, slow at first, then speeded up, then slowed again. This can be repeated, depending on how long the count is continued. It should be terminated when the subject is seen to be having difficulty continuing to open and close his eyes.

When the subject has taken a comfortable position and is gazing at some object, the operator begins his induction talk. As he speaks he should observe the subject closely. The speech is fitted to the results indicated by the behavior of the subject. The length of the talk will depend on these observations. If the patient's eyes close quickly and he is seen to be well-relaxed and does not move, the talk would be shorter than otherwise. The length of time might be only two or three minutes or it could be continued for 15 or 20 minutes, or even longer. As an average, it will probably require about ten minutes. The following wording is an example of what might be said.

"Now that you are comfortable, let yourself relax as much as possible. Take a good deep breath which helps you relax. The more you can let go, the better it will be. Keep your eyes fixed on what you are watching. Let your eyes go out of focus if you can. Take another deep breath.

"Probably you will find yourself winking at times. You may find your vision blurring. As you continue to look you'll find your eyelids beginning to feel heavy. They'll get heavier and heavier. The muscles will relax more and more and the lids feel heavier and heavier. Let them wink whenever they want to and soon they will be so heavy they will close. Let them close whenever you wish. Soon they will be too heavy to hold open, and it's good to shut out the light and let them close.

"Now you are more relaxed and very comfortable. You will probably feel a pleasant, drowsy, listless feeling creep over you as you relax more and more. Your eyelids grow heavier and heavier. Take another deep breath. You may feel a heaviness in your arms and legs; perhaps your whole body will feel heavy. As you relax more and more, the heaviness will increase. Your hands and arms become heavy, your legs feeling heavy. Your eyelids may be so heavy it's hard to hold them open. Let them close now. Now close your eyes.

"As you relax more and more, your breathing becomes slower. You may notice that it's slower now and you tend to breathe more from the bottom of your lungs, the way a singer learns to breathe. You feel so list-less and comfortable. Drowsy and comfortable. It's too much trouble to move, just too much trouble. Listen only to my voice. Pay no attention to outside sounds. They will go in one ear and out the other.

"Now you can relax still more. Begin with your right leg and let all the muscles go loose and limp, the toes and foot relaxing, the ankle, the calf muscles, the knee, and the thigh. Let the leg relax completely from the toes up to your hip. And now let the left leg relax in the same way, from the toes up to your hip.

"Your whole body can now relax more. Let your stomach and abdom-inal muscles loosen, then your chest and breathing muscles. Let them go loose and limp. The muscles of your back can loosen. Now your shoulders and neck muscles. Often we have tension in this area. Feel the tension going out of these muscles as they loosen. And now your arms from the shoulders right down to your fingertips. The arm muscles will relax completely. Even your facial muscles will relax. The more relaxed you are the more comfortable you are. All tension is leaving you and you are so very comfortable.

"Often there is a flickering of the eyelids when you are in hypnosis. It's one of the signs of hypnosis. If yours are flickering, they will soon relax still more as you go deeper. The flickering will soon stop.

"Notice that you have a feeling of well-being, as though any troubles have been set aside and nothing seems to matter. It's a pleasant feeling of comfort. Some people seem to feel heavier and heavier the more they relax, but others reverse this and may feel very light, so light they seem to be floating. It doesn't matter which feeling you have.

"Now you can drift a bit deeper. Let go and drift still deeper into this pleasant state. Let go and go deeper with each breath you take. Deeper and deeper. The deeper you go, the more comfortable and pleasant it will seem to you.

"Suppose you use your imagination now. In your mind's eye, imagine that you are standing in front of an escalator such as are in some stores. See the steps moving down in front of you and see the railings. You're all alone. It's your private escalator. I'll count backward from ten to zero, and as I start to count, imagine that you are stepping on the escalator and then stand with your hand on the railing as the steps move down carrying you with them deeper and deeper. With each count you'll go deeper and deeper. When I reach zero in the count, imagine you've reached the bottom and step off the escalator.

"One, and you step on. Two, etc. Five, deeper and deeper. Six, etc. Zero, and you step off at the bottom. Now drift still deeper with each breath. Deeper and deeper."

Some women do not like to ride an escalator. A question can determine this in advance. In this case suggest walking slowly down a staircase instead. The escalator technique is a deepening method. Others will be described which could then be added to the induction talk. Some tests that could also be made have been described in the previous chapter.

The beginner in the use of hypnosis should not bother to memorize this talk. If you will note how progressive suggestions are made, with repetition, the general idea can be followed and put into your own wording. In your first practice of induction, this talk might even be read to a subject. With its general idea you can soon fit your own wording to it and either lengthen or shorten it as seems indicated.

INDUCTION WITH THE SUBJECT STANDING

An induction method frequently used by us is valuable because it requires only a brief time and gives the operator much information as he proceeds. It also permits the subject to realize that something is happening to him.

This consists of having the subject stand in front of a chair. He is told to relax as much as possible while on his feet, letting his arms dangle at his sides and looking into the eyes of the operator for visual fixation. Then he is to count backward aloud from 100. This is to be a slow count, without hurrying it. As the subject counts, the operator talks to him. At the same time his hands are placed on the subject's shoulders and he is moved around slowly in a clockwise circle.

The response to this circular movement immediately provides information. If the movement is resisted and it is difficult to move the subject, it is a sign that he is unconsciously resisting induction. A longer induction talk is then required. If the subject can easily be moved, induction will be much quicker.

As the subject starts to count backward he will probably begin in a normal tone of voice. If he counts too rapidly, he should be told to slow the cadence. As he begins to enter hypnosis his voice will usually dwindle off in tone, perhaps to a whisper, and will tend to count slower. Sometimes he finds he cannot continue to count.

As the operator talks he also listens to the counting. Confusion frequently develops as the subject enters the trance. A number may be skipped over, or even a series of numbers. There will be hesitation and groping for the next number. These signs are not always shown but they are quite usual. From them the operator notes the progress being made. The subject is fully aware of the difficulty he is having in remembering and in saying the numbers in proper sequence. He realizes something is happening to him.

As soon as signs of hypnosis appear, the subject is told to close his eyes. If this is not carried out at the first request, it should be repeated. If there is no response to a third request, it is a sign that the subject prefers to keep his eyes open. The operator should accept this and not insist further.

As deeper hypnosis is reached, it may be necessary to hold the subject upright as he is being moved around in the circle. He may become something of a deadweight, completely relaxed, although his knees do not give way. This indicates that he is well into hypnosis, probably at a medium depth or possibly even deeper. This or further confusion in the counting indicates that the subject can now be directed to sit down in the chair behind him. As he stands directly in front of it, he need not open his eyes. He can be told to place his hands on the arms of the chair, then sit down and relax in a comfortable position. The operator, his hands still on the subject's shoulders, guides him into the chair and then releases him. After being seated, the subject is told to relax more and more while deepening techniques are used, including the imaginary escalator.

With this method, a very susceptible subject may be in hypnosis by the time he has counted only three or four numbers. The average subject will be hypnotized by the time he has reached about 60 in his count. Resistance may cause the count to go farther, the operator continuing his suggestions until he sees signs of response. Counting to 60 requires no more than about two minutes, hence this is a rapid method of induction. With deepening techniques, only a total of five or six minutes is required for the average subject.

STAGE METHODS OF INDUCTION

Among other direct methods which are very rapid are the various ones employed by stage hypnotists. You should be aware of these methods and their principles, but they should be avoided in professional practice. However, it is possible to learn more about induction from stage hypnotists who certainly are adept at rapid inductions. Otherwise their knowledge of hypnosis is usually quite superficial. It will be noted that a stage hypnotist always exudes confidence and plays on his reputation as an "expert."

Most stage techniques are based on a startle effect. The subject literally is frightened so that he enters hypnosis. These methods are not recommended for use, but they should be understood and recognized as avenues through which a hypnotized state may be achieved.

A very good rapid method can be used which has a slight startle effect but is not at all objectionable. It is very successful and sometimes this is true when a previous, more persuasive technique has failed. Here the subject is asked to sit upright, either in a chair or on a couch. Suggestions would be something like this:

"I'd like you to look at the ends of my fingers as I hold my hand in front of your face (about two feet away). I'm going to bring my hand slowly closer to your head and move it on beyond your vision. Let your eyes follow it until you can't see my hand anymore. That leaves you looking up. Continue to look up toward the ceiling. In a moment then you'll feel like winking. As soon as you want to wink, let your eyes close."

The patient may wink within a few seconds or may continue to stare upward for a moment or so. As soon as his eyes close, the operator places his left hand at the back of the subject's neck with his right hand or fingers pressing on the forehead. He then suddenly moves the subject's head around sharply and rapidly in a clockwise circle, telling him to relax his neck and shoulder muscles and to let go completely. The tone should be positive and the words should be spoken rapidly. Having one's head seized unexpectedly and rotated in this way produces a mild startle effect.

After rotating the head a few times, the subject should be pushed back in the chair, until his head rests comfortably or supported back into a reclining position on the couch. The operator then continues in a more permissive way to induce more relaxation and resorts to deepening techniques. This method is both rapid and effective and is unobjectionable, although the subject will be somewhat startled.

INDIRECT METHODS OF INDUCTION

The induction techniques we have described are direct methods. Indirect ones are also available. With them the patient may not even realize he has been hypnotized. Some professional men who use hypnosis do not wish to be known as "hypnotists." They will resort to indirect methods to avoid this.

One difficulty in this situation is that the patient may have some knowledge of hypnosis and may realize that he has been hypnotized. Possibly he might then feel resentment if permission for this were not sought. One physician lost a valuable patient because of this, although if he had been better informed he could have made explanations which could have removed the resentment.

This physician was visited by a patient who mentioned that she had a headache at the time. By the use of an indirect technique, she was hypnotized, and suggestions quickly terminated the headache. At the end of the session she asked the physician if he had hypnotized her and he acknowledged that this was true.

"Doctor," she remarked, "if you had told me you could help my headache through hypnosis I would have had no objections to your using it. As it is you've tricked me and taken advantage of me, for I might not have wanted to be hypnotized. I feel that you can't be trusted." She never returned.

The proper handling here would have been to explain that he knew her headache could be relieved if she relaxed completely and lost her tension. She had relaxed and had done so well that she had slipped into hypnosis, as may happen spontaneously with great relaxation. Her headache had disappeared and now she must feel relieved. This would have led her to believe that hypnosis had developed spontaneously. She probably would have accepted this without resentment, although it was subterfuge. However it is our belief that a patient should be informed when hypnosis is to be used, thus avoiding trickery or deceit.

The most usual indirect induction method is merely to avoid the word hypnosis and talk only about relaxation. Suggestions would be much the same as in the sample induction talk given previously. In terminating hypnosis with this method, no mention should be made of awakening. The patient can be told he will open his eyes and will then be fully alert and normal in every respect, which would cause him to awaken.

Another indirect technique is possible but ordinarily there would be little opportunity for it to be applied in professional practice. This is to talk to a sleeping person, bringing him out of normal sleep into hypnosis.

It is successful with adults but much more so with children. Probably a parent could utilize it with a child.

Still another indirect method has been called the *confusion technique*. Some skill is needed in utilizing it, for it is difficult to handle properly. It may be very successful with even a difficult subject, for with it he is unable to mobilize his resistances and doesn't realize he is being hypnotized. The aim of this method is to produce such confusion in the subject's mind that he escapes into a trance to avoid the bewilderment which develops.

The operator talks rapidly so the subject doesn't have time to analyze and digest what is being said. Misstatements are made, the operator contradicting himself at times. He says one thing and a moment later will say exactly the opposite. Attention is called to something, then to something else and again to something entirely different, too quickly to be followed. The subject becomes more and more bewildered. The operator is always a step ahead of him, never giving him time to follow the ideas presented.

As a sample of such an induction, here is a possible wording: "Sometimes it is pleasant to sit back and relax, to let your muscles go loose and limp and to let go. As you listen to me and concentrate on what I'm saying, a spontaneous relaxation takes place. At times you can be aware of certain things and at other times you may not be aware of them. For instance, you might be aware of a picture on the wall if you look at it. You might be looking at it but if your attention is elsewhere, as on that window over there, you might not be aware of the picture. You might be aware of it subconsciously even if you are not looking at it. There is something right now you are unaware of until I mention it and then you become very much aware of it. That is of having shoes on your feet. Now you feel them. And you can be aware of me and of what I'm saying or may say, or might have said, or you may not be aware of some things I say, but your subconscious could be very well aware of them.

"You can be aware of time or unaware of it. You can be aware of the present or the past or the future. You can remember various things about the present or the past or the future when that becomes the past. Day before yesterday, yesterday was tomorrow and that was the future, and then yesterday became today and was the past. And tomorrow will soon be today and then yesterday or tomorrow and yesterday can become today. Or even the day after tomorrow. And you may remember last January first when you wrote 1967 when it was really 1966. (This talk about time is a good introduction for inducing complete age regression.)

"It may be interesting for you as you sit here to recall that the time is (whatever the hour is). And as you sit and think about the time, it is interesting to realize that today is (give the date). Yesterday at this hour you probably were doing something else. You may have been at home, or at your business, or someplace else. And perhaps you were relaxed as you are now. And you may be reminded today of how relaxed you were, just so relaxed. And you might have been rather listless and drowsy and sleepy, really relaxed. And how pleasant it was to relax completely and to let go completely and forget about today. You may have found your eyes closing as you relaxed. You were very comfortable and it is always good to relax and let all your muscles go loose and limp. And you can remember times when you were very sleepy. And how pleasant it is to drift off and relax and sleep. And sleep deeply, deeply, and soundly. And you can probably feel those feelings growing stronger and can relax completely now."

This may be continued with similar remarks. Until relaxation is mentioned, the talk should be so rapid that the patient does not have time to think and follow what is being said. When talking relaxation, the voice can be lowered and a monotone maintained. It would be well for the beginner to wait until he has become skillful before trying this technique.

Many operators use the word "sleep" during the induction. It is a perfectly good word for the purpose, but it should be mentioned to the subject that hypnotic sleep is meant rather than normal sleep. Even children will be able to distinguish between the two meanings.

In primitive societies, hypnosis is always produced by rhythm, drumbeat or other percussion instruments, dancing, chanting, etc. This fact can be utilized in the office. Soft, slow music can help with any form of induction. A metronome set with slow beat and not too loud can be used. With practice the operator can learn to set up a rhythm in his voice as he talks, stressing a word here and a syllable there. A monotone is very effective and the voice can be kept very low so the subject must strain somewhat to hear. This focuses his attention better.

MESMERISM

In the days of Mesmer and for some decades after, induction was accomplished by means of passes. This was with the idea that there was a force called animal magnetism in everyone, greater and stronger in some individuals. It was thought that this could be projected through the hands. Therefore the operator made passes with his hands over the body of the subject. The mesmerist moved his hands down the subject's body from head to foot, sometimes holding them centered over the head or the solar plexus for a moment. Usually the hands were held a few inches above the body, sometimes contact was made. These passes might be continued over a long period of time until results were seen, though usually it was for only about half an hour. Awakening was accomplished by reversing the direction of the passes. Braid was the first to show that it was not the passes but expectation and suggestion bringing on the trance.

The British surgeon, Esdaile, who had such great success with hypnotic anesthesia, had his subjects lie down and seated himself so he could breathe on the person's face. With his hands held in a claw-like position, he moved them slowly an inch from the body from the back of the head to the pit of the stomach, keeping his hands suspended there for some time. Though some patients were quickly hypnotized, he found most required about two hours of continued passes, some even a much longer time. Obviously he produced a very deep state by taking such a long time. He awakened his subjects by blowing sharply on the eyelids or sprinkling the face with cold water. As he found continuing the passes boring and tiring, he trained hospital servants and others to do this for him. When surgery was intended, Esdaile would come now and then to the subject and prick him sharply with a pin. If he flinched, he was not yet deep enough and the passes were continued until a spontaneous anesthesia had developed. No verbal suggestions were given.

In modern times no one has taken the trouble to try in the same way to reproduce Esdaile's results. It would make interesting research.

TRANCE DEEPENING

A very good subject may enter a medium trance, sometimes a very deep one, within a very short time, perhaps only three or four minutes. A few more minutes might be needed for further deepening. With some, a longer time for deepening would be needed.

For some purposes, as in obstetrics or when preparing a patient for surgery with only hypnotic anesthesia, depth is important, and as deep a state as possible should be obtained. For most purposes, depth is not too important. However, it is well to spend a few moments during the first session in deepening the state obtained.

One of the best techniques for this is the use of the imaginary escalator or staircase. Here the escalator does the work, if it is the method, the subject merely standing while in his imagination the steps move down taking him deeper. Sometimes a subject may ask if he can go up instead of down the escalator. Such a request is always accepted. Then the word "deeper" should be avoided. It can be said that he is going farther into hypnosis instead of deeper.

Another deepening method is to inform the subject that you are going to place your hands on his shoulders and will push him deeper. It is often remarked afterward that the person felt himself sinking deeper with this pressure. It should be mentioned that it is always well to tell a subject when he is to be touched in any way, which will avoid startling him.

Stroking the forehead of the subject with suggestions of going deeper will be found effective, especially with children. It seems to be very soothing.

Verbal suggestions of going deeper and deeper will be of aid. This can be varied by saying that you will say nothing at all for two or three moments while the subjects keeps drifting deeper.

Any of the tests of hypnosis which are successful tend to deepen the trance. This is also true when any hypnotic phenomena are induced. If the person is judged to be in a medium or deep state, the production of hypnotic anesthesia in one hand, called glove anesthesia, usually will bring greater depth.

LEARNING THE DEPTH OF HYPNOSIS REACHED BY A SUBJECT

In the next chapter, hypnotic phenomena will be discussed. The most reliable way of ascertaining the depth a patient has reached is the induction of different phenomena. Some are characteristic of a light state, others will indicate a medium depth, and still others will indicate the deep state.

Usually an experienced hypnotist can sense the depth his subject reaches. However this ability comes only with much experience. For the beginner and even at times for anyone using hypnosis, it is advantageous to be able to determine quickly how deeply the subject may be in hypnosis. Some years ago LeCron worked to develop a way of doing this and reported it in a paper.

Here is the method. If we give the subconscious part of the mind a yardstick with which to measure, it should be able to determine the depth reached. As a yardstick we can use an imaginary 36-inch yardstick. Somewhat arbitrarily we can say that a light state is the first foot on the yardstick, 1 to 12 inches. A medium state is 12 to 24 inches, and a deep one is 24 to 36 inches. Explaining this to the hypnotized subject, he can then be asked to answer questions by ideomotor signals and by this means the depth reached can be learned.

When a person is in hypnosis, depth will fluctuate. At one moment he will be deeper than at another. In a deep trance there even seems to be a kind of wave pattern, the trance lightening then deepening. Questions as to the depth reached can be worded to learn the situation at the moment or to find the greatest depth attained during the session. This is carried out with the ideomotor responses to questions, which will be described later.

The questions are worded so that they can be answered affirmatively or negatively. The first question might be "Have you been as deep or deeper at any time during this session as 20 inches on our yardstick?" If the operator believes this unlikely, the question could be as to 15 inches instead of 20. If the answer to this question is affirmative, the next should be as to 25 inches, jumping five inches. If negative, the next question would be as to 15 inches. In this way, a bracket is established. Obtaining a bracket within five inches is close enough for all practical purposes, although some subjects will narrow this down to a single number if the questioning is continued.

This method of learning depth permits a quick evaluation of approximate depth. It has also proved valuable as a means of involving the patient with therapy. It seems that the acceptance of estimated depth brings better cooperation.

THE PLENARY TRANCE

While it is usually said that there are three stages of depth in hypnosis, this is merely an arbitrary division. Each merges into the other. There is still a deeper stage which has been called a plenary trance. Considering it in relation to our yardstick, it would be well beyond the 36-inch mark. It is seldom introduced because it requires a very long time even with the best subjects. Unfortunately there has been no scientific investigation of this state. In our era hardly anyone has ever even seen it.

While we can only generalize about the plenary trance, it is doubtful if even one person out of 25 could ever reach such a depth. At its deepest it would seem to be almost a state of suspended animation. It probably is similar to the state or condition produced experimentally with drugs or with freezing.

Esdaile apparently induced this plenary trance with many of his surgical patients. In the 1890s, a Swedish physican named Wetterstrand utilized such a state at times. He reported keeping some subjects in it continuously for as long as two weeks, using it for some conditions as a kind of Weir Mitchell treatment. Its possibilities are unknown but the hypnotic practitioner should be aware that there is such a state.

LeCron has experimented with this with two subjects. It required about three hours of continued induction to produce it. One subject was a young woman who remained in the state for 36 hours, being brought back to a lighter level once to eat a meal and to go to the bathroom. Her pulse was reduced to about 50 beats a minute and her breathing rate dropped to only three breaths a minute, hardly discernible. It required almost half an hour at the end of the session for her to become fully awake. She reported being fully aware at all times but that her mind seemed to be a blank unless spoken to. A friend stayed with her during the night. Questioning with ideomotor replies indicated that she did not sleep while in this deep trance.

TESTS FOR HYPNOSIS

The production of hypnotic phenomena is one way of testing to find the depth of trance reached or merely to learn if the subject is hypnotized. Eye catalepsy or the handclasp test is often used. Another which is one of the best because it is not a challenge, is *arm levitation.* It is suggested to the hypnotized individual that one of his arms will begin to lose all sensation of weight. The arm selected should be the one closest to the operator. Wording could be as follows.

"Your arms are probably feeling rather heavy now, but your right arm, the one closer to me, is going to begin to lose the feeling of weight. It's as though all the weight were draining out of it. It begins to feel lighter and lighter, lighter and lighter. In a moment it will begin to lift. It will lift of its own accord, without conscious effort. Your hand will start to float up toward your face, lifting until the fingers touch your face. The arm is becoming lighter and lighter.

"Think of some part of your face where you would like to have your fingers touch when your hand reaches your face. It can be your forehead, your ear, your nose, any place. But your inner mind will cause your fingers to touch some other part of your face. Let's see where it will touch. A different place than the one you thought of consciously.

"Now your arm is getting still lighter. (It is well to lift the arm somewhat, letting it rest on your own hand.) Your hand will begin to float up away from my hand. It's as light as a feather. I'll give it a start and it will continue to lift until the fingers touch your face. (The arm should be pushed up slightly.) It is bending at the elbow, floating up toward your face, lifting higher and higher. Floating on up. In a moment you'll feel your fingers making contact at a different spot than the one you thought of."

Such suggestions can be continued as the hand lifts. With some subjects only a moment will be required for the hand to begin to move upward. With others the suggestion must be continued. When the fingers touch the subject's face, he should be told to lower his arm to some comfortable position.

Sometimes a subject will lift his hand voluntarily, trying to cooperate. This can be detected at once, and he should be instructed not to move it voluntarily, that it will come up of its own accord. If the movement is involuntary (ideomotor), the hand will move upward with slight jerky motions. The movement will perhaps be very slow, only an inch at a time. When the arm is lifted intentionally, the movement is smooth and rapid. The difference is easily detected.

Suggesting that the hand will touch a different place than the one consciously selected allows the subject to learn that his inner mind can make its own decisions. Perhaps this will also bring better cooperation from that part of his mind. As the arm lifts, the subject may be aware of its position and that it is moving or sometimes will lose track of the arm entirely, dissociating it.

If the arm fails to respond, as occasionally happens, it is a sign of resistance. When the operator lifts it and lets it rest on his own hand or finger, it is easy to sense if there is any response to the suggestions. If it continues to feel heavy after spending two or three minutes in suggesting lightness, the test should be abandoned, perhaps saying that you do not want to take too much time for this. Failures are seldom with this technique. Many who use hypnosis make this test almost routinely during a first induction.

SUBSEQUENT INDUCTIONS

A busy practitioner will not wish to spend on inductions any more time than is necessary. The first session may require perhaps as long as 20 minutes. Later inductions do not require more than three to five minutes, or even less. During the first session a posthypnotic suggestion is given that in the future when the subject is willing to be hypnotized he will enter hypnosis quickly, responding to some signal which is specified. This can be a word or phrase or some touch or movement. For instance, the suggestion could be that when the phrase "relax now" is said to him and repeated, he will let his eyes close and will at once relax and go into hypnosis. We find it well to combine such a phrase with some touch or movement. As the phrase is said, his arm will be lifted by the operator until the fingers touch his face. The combination is more effective than a single signal. When this suggestion has been made, the subject should later be awakened and the signal given so that the result is well established. In other words, it should be practiced once, which will make it more effective in later sessions. Such a posthypnotic suggestion saves much time in subsequent inductions.

TRANCE ENDING

Before the hypnotized person is awakened, all suggestions which have been given should be removed, with the exception of those intended to be posthypnotic in effect. De-hypnotizing is usually simple, and it is rare for a subject to fail to awaken at once. However, it is essential to be sure the person is fully awake before he is dismissed. Almost everyone requires no more than a moment or two to become completely alert, but if the person has been in a deep trance, a few more moments may be required.

The usual method of awakening is to suggest that the person will awaken at the count of three or perhaps five. This should be spoken slowly, allowing time for him to become wide awake. The wording could be as follows.

"I'm going to count to three and you will then be wide awake and fully alert. You'll notice how refreshed you feel, relaxed and clearheaded, feeling exceptionally well. One, you are coming awake. Two, now you are almost awake. Three, wide awake now. Wide awake, alert and feeling fine."

These suggestions will prevent the patient from feeling dull or fatigued and also will prevent a headache from developing as is sometimes noted otherwise. This is not a common result of hypnosis, but a few people do complain of a slight headache afterward. The reason for this is not clear.

The rare instances of difficulty in de-hypnotizing will be considered in the chapter on possible dangers in hypnosis, although this is not a real danger, for it can easily be handled.

SELECTION OF AN INDUCTION METHOD

Most of those who practice hypnosis find with experience some method with which they seem to have the best results, and they then favor it. This is natural and advantageous but should not be overdone. Often an operator will work out some variation of his own. The skilled hypnotist tries to fit his method of induction to the individual subject's needs and character. In selecting the form of induction to be used, the decision should rest on the observations he makes as to the patient. He considers the type of person with whom he is dealing. It would be a mistake to use a forceful, dominating technique with one who is positive and aggressive in his behavior.

If the patient is a woman, it might be interpreted and resented as seductive to use the standing technique where the subject is moved around in a circle, or the rapid technique where she would be pushed back on a couch.

The time available to the operator in a first session would also be a factor in deciding as to method. Ordinarily it is best to allow about 20 minutes for a first induction, even if it might not be required. This would not be true if it seemed apparent that the patient would be a good subject and was perhaps experienced. Yet there could be some circumstances when this much time is not available where a rapid method would be indicated.

In general, for office practice the slower, permissive, "lullaby" type of induction is best, but this depends on the patient and the situation. It would be indicated with a patient who seems frightened or apprehensive about being hypnotized. Yet the degree of such an emotion might have a bearing. Remembering that stage hypnotists usually frighten or startle their subjects into hypnosis, sometimes the rapid technique would be a good one, taking advantage of the feeling of apprehension if it is not too great. When anyone is under an emotion he is apt already to be in a light state of hypnosis.

The practitioner should always keep his prestige and be aware that he has prestige with the patient. Otherwise that person would not have come to him. He should always show confidence. When there is a failure in induction, prestige can be maintained by an explanation that not everyone can be hypnotized on first attempt, that this is an ability which improves with practice. Blame for failure should not be placed on the patient but on the circumstances. Something has caused him unconsciously to resist, though he has consciously been cooperative. Something acted to prevent him from being hypnotized.

The practitioner must always realize that there will be failures and should not be discouraged when these occur. Even the most adept operator at times will fail in an induction. It is "par for the course" and should not be disturbing.

Inductions which are rapid and practical in clinical situations are presented later. We feel that time-honored induction techniques should be mastered before attempting the more advanced methods involving subconscious review and ideomotor questioning.

REFERENCES

Braid, J.: Neurypnology, London, Geo. Redway, 1899.

Erickson, M. H.: Deep hypnosis and its induction. In: Experimental Hypnosis (L. M. LeCron, Ed.). New York, Macmillan, 1952.

LeCron, L. M.: A method of measuring the depth of hypnosis, J. Clin. Exp. Hypn. 1: 4-7, 1953.

Wetterstrand, O.: Hypnotism and Its Application to Practical Medicine, New York, Putnam, 1897.

Chapter 6

Trance Phenomena

CERTAIN PHENOMENA have been assigned as characteristics of the different stages of hypnosis. However, it should be understood that this depends entirely on the individual subject. Sometimes phenomena attributed to the deep state will be evidenced in only a light state. In other instances light trance phenomena cannot be elicited with a subject in a very deep trance. Anesthesia sufficient to permit a woman to go through childbirth painlessly usually requires a deep state, but not infrequently the patient will be free of pain while only lightly hypnotized. This variation is true of all hypnotic phenomena. Motivation may be a consideration in this effect.

RAPPORT

Rapport is not only related to hypnosis but is a factor in all good physician-patient relationships. Rapport seems to become stronger when one is under hypnosis and will even be present in the first session when the subject may have had no previous acquaintance with the hypnotist.

Rapport can be said to be empathy on the part of the subject with a strong desire to please the operator. It is closely related to what Freud called transference. This regard and attitude toward the operator is of great advantage in therapy.

In the earlier days of hypnosis, one aspect of rapport was the idea that a hypnotized person would pay no attention to anyone but the hypnotist unless instructed to do so, if rapport were transferred. Suggestions given by another would be disregarded. A question would not be answered. This situation is rarely seen today, though it can be shown. It depends on the subject's attitude and desires. If he wants to respond to someone else, he will do so. In the rare cases where there is no response, the subject will say when questioned that he merely didn't want to be bothered. He heard, but was too listless to pay attention.

44

CATALEPSY

This term is usually considered a matter of muscular rigidity which develops spontaneously under hypnosis. When this phenomenon is present, an arm or leg may be placed in some position, even an awkard one, and it will remain there. The position may be maintained for some time and an inhibition of fatigue in the muscles seems to accompany the catalepsy.

In fact catalepsy is not only muscular rigidity but includes the opposite condition, extreme flaccidity of the muscles similar to *cerea flexibilitas* or waxy flexibility. There is a change of muscular tonus but it may be either rigidity or flaccidity.

One of the usual "stunts" of stage hypnotists is to suggest complete body rigidity, then to lay the stiffened subject between two chairs, his head on one and his feet on the other. The hypnotist will then sit, or perhaps stand, on the subject's stomach. The weight will be borne with no apparent effort. This is spectacular but is not without danger. Back injuries and enlargement of hernias have occurred after such experiences.

One day while discussing catalepsy, one of the instructors with Hypnosis Symposiums who is able to enter a deep trance remarked that he thought this body rigidity might be artifical and that anyone laid across the chairs in this way could maintain the extra weight while not hypnotized. It was decided to try it. The instructor was slender and above average height. Stiffening himself as much as possible, he was placed across the chairs. He held this position, though with some grimacing and straining. When another person slowly eased himself down on the instructor's stomach, the position could not be maintained and he "caved in."

This was then repeated with the instructor hypnotized. He was able to hold the extra weight and gave no sign of straining. Afterwards he commented that the feeling was entirely different. He made no effort to maintain rigidity and the weight of the person sitting on him did not cause him to strain. This test proves the actuality of catalepsy in its rigid form, but it is not recommended for experimentation or demonstration.

MUSCULAR INHIBITIONS

A phenomenon sometimes resorted to in order to let a person realize that he is hypnotized is to suggest immobility of an arm or that it cannot be bent at the elbow. In the first instance it is suggested that the weight of the arm is so great that there is not enough strength to lift it. If suggesting it cannot be bent, the wording is that the arm is stiff and rigid like a bar and that it cannot be bent at the elbow no matter how hard you try, that the elbow is locked in place. It is most impressive to the subject when he fails on making an effort to lift or bend the arm. However, these are both challenges and in our practices we think it best, as a rule, to avoid challenges.

In carrying out these suggestions the subject may evidence much fruitless effort or he may accept the idea and feel too lethargic even to try. If he does make the attempt, the antagonistic muscles will be seen to oppose the movement.

There have been reports of suggestion under hypnosis greatly increasing bodily strength. Tests of strength of grip with a grip dynamometer show a considerable increase in the number of pounds squeezed by the hand, perhaps as much as 40 pounds. Undoubtedly the body has great reserves of strength, but strength tests have some element of danger.

Inhibition of fatigue through hypnotic suggestion seems to be possible to an extraordinary degree without being deleterious. This is also seen in catatonia. Since muscular fatigue is supposed to involve chemical changes in the tissues, it can be presumed that these changes are inhibited.

Old-time stage hypnotists used this phenomenon to attract customers to their performances. These hypnotists traveled from town to town. The day before a performance, a well-trained subject would appear in the town and enter the display window of a store. If the subject was a girl, she would sit down at a piano, place herself in hypnosis and play without stopping for 24 hours, not even attending to bowel or bladder elimination. If the subject was a young man, he would mount a bicycle with its rear wheel jacked up and would peddle it rapidly for the 24 hours. They were trained to do this and to inhibit fatigue and body functions of elimination while doing so.

HYPNOTIC ANESTHESIA

There will be a thorough discussion of anesthesia and analgesia in a later chapter where its use is described. It is something which the physician or dentist should be familiar with. It is of particular advantage in obstetrics, surgery and dentistry, although of course it has many other medical uses.

Theoretically there has been controversy as to whether hypnotic anesthesia is real, in the sense that pain is not felt, or is it felt but disregarded? Some research projects, such as by Sears and Dynes, have shown no changes in respiration, pulse, galvanic skin reflexes or in the pupils of the eyes when painful stimuli were applied. This would suggest that pain is not experienced.

On the other hand, some equally good subjects have shown these changes yet claimed they felt no pain. In one test, a subject was given suggestions for glove anesthesia. He was producing automatic writing at the same time. When pain stimulus was applied to his anesthetized hand, the other hand wrote automatically the word "ouch," although he reported that he felt no pain at all.

In all probability the difficulty in such research is that there is a difference in the subjects themselves in the way they accept suggestions for anesthesia. One may shut off all perception of pain and an organic change takes place, the nerve impulses from the stimulus not registering in the brain. Another subject subjectively does not feel pain but actually does, disregarding it, as is true when a lobotomy has been performed. Cheek has pointed out that pain may be perceived and indicated by idemotor signals when the subject is consciously unaware of pain.

AMNESIA

Following a deep trance a subject may awaken with a complete spontaneous amnesia for whatever occurred during the time he was hypnotized. Such an amnesia can also be suggested, or it can be prevented by suggestion. In our experience complete spontaneous amnesia is infrequent, although this may be because we are not too concerned about obtaining a very deep trance for most purposes. Total post-hypnotic amnesia usually requires a depth on the "yardstick" of 30 inches or more. A few subjects will produce it after having been in only a medium depth of trance.

A partial amnesia can frequently be established in a medium stage. This would be accomplished by suggesting amnesia for some particular occurrence during the trance or for some posthypnotic suggestion which has been made.

POSTHYPNOTIC SUGGESTIONS

If an acceptable suggestion is given for some action to be performed after awakening, it will be carried out compulsively. It is more likely to be carried out if there is also suggestion of amnesia for it, apparently because conscious reasoning is bypassed. Even some bizarre or very illogical behavior will be executed when there is amnesia for the suggestion. The subject usually rationalizes an explanation for such behavior.

LeCron gave a posthypnotic suggestion, with amnesia for it, to a young woman in a class demonstration. She was seated on a couch with a coffee table in front of her on which was a vase containing some flowers. It was suggested that, after awakening, she would take off one of her shoes and place it on the table. After she was awakened she fidgeted uneasily for a few moments, apparently trying to resist the compulsion to carry out the suggestion.

Finally she took off one of her shoes and placed it on the table. She then took some of the flowers from the vase and placed them in the shoe. When asked why she had done this, she explained that she had a vase at home shaped something like a shoe and she wished to try what kind of flower arrangement might be used in it! Thus she rationalized her unusual act. Herbert Spiegel has suggested that some forms of neurotic behavior may be initiated by suggestions picked up under circumstances of emotional stress.

Milton and Elizabeth Erickson have shown that the subject re-enters hypnosis spontaneously when carrying out a posthypnotic suggestion. They state that the act may be arrested and the subject will be found, when tested, to have reverted to the hypnotic state. This seems generally to be true. It is more likely to occur when there is amnesia for the posthypnotic suggestion.

Of course there may be unconscious refusal to accept a posthypnotic suggestion. For instance, if there is strong need for some psychosomatic symptom, any suggestion for its termination probably would be refused and it would persist. When the suggestion is acceptable the subject finds it very difficult to resist carrying it out. His thoughts continually revert to it, no matter how he tries to avoid it, and great anxiety may develop until it is performed. For this reason we urge that permission always be obtained by an ideomotor signal before suggesting posthypnotic activity.

A posthypnotic suggestion may wear off after a time, but with a good subject it may persist for years. Estabrooks writes of using a subject several times in demonstrations where the same suggestion had been carried out a number of times. This was in response to a signal made by Estabrooks. Twenty years later he met the man again and gave the signal to see if he would respond. When it was given, he did so.

LeCron once agreed with another member of our teaching panel to demonstrate hallucinations of the sense of smell. The panelist was told in deep hypnosis that he would smell only perfume. Then he was given perfume to smell. Next a bottle of 30 per cent ammonia was held to his nose. As he sniffed it he said it was very nice perfume and showed no reaction to the strong ammonia. Inadvertently LeCron neglected to remove the hallucination. Over a year later the instructor remarked that he seemed to have lost his sense of smell. He could only detect the odor of flowers. He had even quit smoking because he could no longer smell tobacco smoke. This is another example of the literalness of understanding during hypnosis. LeCron then remembered their demonstration and the hallucination of the panelist's sense of smell. The suggestion was removed and his sense of smell returned to normal.

At one of our symposiums a physician asked for help in stopping smoking while acting as a demonstration subject. He requested that he be given a suggestion that tobacco would taste like something most unpleasant. When questioned, he said he found the taste of castor oil as unpleasant as anything else. With his consent he was told under hypnosis that when he smoked he would find tobacco tasting like castor oil. Some months later this physician again attended a course. He was asked if he had stopped smoking. He replied that he had quit for a few days and then started again. "But you know," he added, "I've developed the most remarkable liking for the taste of castor oil!" Obviously his liking for cigarettes was greater than his motivation to give them up.

Posthypnotic suggestions can often be used to great advantage in hypnotherapy and hypnodontics. A caution here is that some termination to the suggestion should be set in order to avoid such an error as occurred unintentionally with the hallucination for "only perfume."

While a psychologist was treating a woman patient for alcoholism, she insisted that she be given suggestions of nausea if she took an alcoholic drink. Against his better judgment, the psychologist made this suggestion to her. When he saw her four days later she was pale and wan. She told him she had wondered if the suggestion would work and on returning home had drunk some whiskey. She had been violently nauseated and had continued to vomit frequently ever since, unable to keep anything on her stomach. The suggestion had not specified any time for its termination.

AGE REGRESSION

One of the most interesting of hypnotic phenomena, and the most valuable in hypnotherapy, is age regression. There are two forms of regression. There is also a variation which could be said to be a third form. Much research has proved the validity of age regression.

While it is never really complete, one form might be called *complete regression*. It has also been termed *revivification*. A deep trance is requisite for this type. By suggestion, the subject is told he is some certain age or is returned to some specific time or experience. Behavior then seems to be that of the suggested age. It seems as if time after that age has been blotted out.

The subject's voice becomes childlike if told he is six years old. His handwriting will be childish and he probably will print instead of writing. Intelligence and other tests given at various age levels during regression give results indicating the age level is nearly as young as suggested.

In infants before the age of about six months, there is normally a negative plantar reflex (positive Babinski). Regressed to three or four months old, a naive subject who knows nothing of this reflex will occasionally display the Babinski when the sole of the foot is stroked. Explanation for this phenomenon is that the subsequently learned grasping plantar reflex is eliminated during age regression to such an age.

The second form of regression might be called *partial*. Both types of regression are quite different from mere memory recall. The person relives an experience with all five of his senses functioning. He sees, hears, feels tactically, and if smell and taste were present they are re-experienced. In complete regression the subject is unaware of the identity of the operator who is then an anachronism to him. He may spontaneously assign some identity to the operator, or this may be suggested: "You know me, I'm just a friend." He is disoriented as to where he is. With regression to infancy he cannot speak.

With partial regression, on the other hand, the person is aware of where he is and knows the operator's identity. At the same time he relives the suggested time or experience. When taken back to a childhood incident, he is able to understand it with his adult viewpoint. He gains insight. With complete regression this is not true. Then insight is lacking as the viewpoint of the suggested age is retained. Therefore partial regression is much more valuable for therapeutic purposes. It is also more valuable because it can be obtained in only a very light state.

With either form of regression if an emotion was felt at the time there will be abreaction and discharge of the emotion: catharsis. Much feeling may be shown, which is desirable and just what the therapist seeks. Because some repressed experiences might possibly be overwhelming, regression should never be suggested without first inquiring with ideomotor answers if it is all right or safe for the patient to return to the experience. If the answer is affirmative, there is no danger of bad results. If negative, the regression should not be forced. Perhaps it can safely be carried out at a later time. It must always be remembered to return the person to the present before awakening him. In all probability this would occur spontaneously but one cannot be sure of this.

Regression even to a vague time or to a certain age should never be attempted without the precaution of asking if it *is safe*. The operator would not know what happened in a patient's life at some certain age. In a demonstration a patient was regressed to his third birthday without this precaution. He produced an actual asthma attack with difficult breathing and with actual rales. His face became red. Returned quickly to the present he soon recovered. Later the subject was asked if he would be willing to repeat this and agreed. This time he gave mild indications of breathing difficulty, but tests showed no real asthma. While he tried to cooperate, he obviously was only partially regressed and was protecting himself by showing only pseudosymptoms.

It is important to know how best to suggest age regression. To develop skill, complete regression should be induced for practice, selecting a very good hypnotic subject. Suggestions are aimed at causing disorientation. The principles of the confusion technique of induction are helpful here. They can be applied before resorting to the following methods.

One excellent way is to suggest that the patient is sitting or lying on a magic carpet. The carpet is described as floating in the air. He is instructed to look below him and there he will see a broad river. This is the "river of time." Downstream is the future and upstream is the past. Below him he is told to see a milestone representing the present year. Now the magic carpet begins to move upstream. Another milestone is seen approaching, the milestone of the previous year, which is stated. The carpet moves faster and faster. Other milestones are mentioned as being passed and the speed increases. Then the carpet stops at some designated year. Even the month and date can be stated. Perhaps Christmas or a birthday is selected, with the age mentioned.

Then the subject is asked how old he is. If regressed he will give the suggested age, putting it in the present tense. He can be encouraged to see some gift he has received at the time and to describe it. He can be told to see any other people present. Other detailed suggestions can be made so that the scene develops more clearly and vividly.

Another technique is to suggest that the subject is looking at a tall grandfather's clock. Below the face of the clock is a panel on which the present year is shown. Now, as he watches, the hands of the clock begin to reverse and speed up, whirling around. He sees the year on the panel change to the previous year. Then other previous years are seen in sequence, back to the desired date.

Still a different method is to suggest that the subject is looking at a large book, the book of time. It is opened at the present date, each page representing a month. He is told to begin to turn back the pages month by month, then to riffle them rapidly by years until the desired time is reached.

All of these methods depend on disorientation and the production of hallucinations, which requires a deep trance. When regression is to childhood, the operator should adopt the tone, words and manner he would use in speaking to a child of the suggested age.

It is far easier to obtain partial regression. Often no formal induction is necessary. The subject can merely be told to close his eyes. In regressing he will spontaneously enter hypnosis, perhaps only lightly, possibly going into a deep trance.

With a good subject, partial regression may be suggested directly to some particular incident in his life. This may be by saying you will count to three and the patient will then be at the suggested age, seeing the scene. This can be elaborated, stating that he will see it becoming clearer and will see the people present. He can be asked to describe the clothing worn by anyone present, with other minor details brought out which tends to develop the reliving of the experience further.

When a suggestion is given of returning to some event, it could be added that as soon as he has mentally regressed to it, the patient's right forefinger will lift up involuntarily as a signal. This tells the operator when his suggestions can be ended.

In teaching a patient how to regress satisfactorily, he can be told to go back to something which has recently taken place, something of no significance or importance. This might be to the time when he had breakfast that morning or to any recent meal when someone else was present. He is instructed to feel his position at the table, to see the food which he is eating. Then he is to taste and smell the food, perhaps a cup of coffee, and to hear the other person speak. This tends to develop perception by each sense. Details can be brought out, and the patient finds he is reliving the experience with all five senses functioning.

After such practice it is easier to take the person back to some event at a very early age or to one of importance. In therapy, sometimes traumas or happenings in infancy or even at birth may have importance. In psychoanalysis it is rare for a very early experience to be brought out.

The reader should be cautioned that experiences "relived" or recalled may either be actual or sometimes they will be found to be fantasies or misunderstood actual happenings. Freud has pointed out that fantasies may have as much importance as a real experience. It is always valuable to note the offerings of the subject but the therapist must use caution in their interpretations.

One interesting matter in partial regression to a very early age is that the subject will report what is being said by persons present. Perhaps this will be only fantasy but it seems possible that things said have been registered in the subconscious mind as sounds, as if a tape recording had been made. At an early age these sounds had no meaning but are interpreted when language is learned. They then may affect the individual. This fact will be considered further in chapters on hypnotherapy.

A third form of regression or a variation of the partial type of regression can be utilized. Instead of the patient re-experiencing the event, he is told he is to watch it as an observer and to see what happened. He watches rather than being the participant. This may be valuable if the experience was traumatic. The patient may then depersonalize it. He sees what is occurring, though not taking part. He may display emotion but it will be felt with much less intensity.

Sometimes it is best to use this form. The patient goes through the incident once or twice as an observer. Then he is told to return to it again but now as the participant. He can then discharge more of the emotion attached to the event. Unconscious resistance to regression can often be overcome by using this method. The subject may be willing to see the experience as an observer when it would be too disturbing to relive it as the participant.

When using regression in therapy, the purpose is to learn what has taken place and to discharge emotions tied up in it. Taking the patient through it once may bring out a great display of emotion. Going through it again discharges more emotion, but the display is milder. Further repetition finds less and less display of emotion and soon the patient is merely narrating the happenings. All emotion may be gone by the third trip through, or it may require a few more, but it should be continued until all emotion is vented. The importance of this is not always realized by therapists. Effects of the experience may linger unless all emotion has been discharged. Returning several times in this way can be conducted all in the same session.

A variation of the use of regression is to have the patient regress at an unconscious level. This type of regression allows review with nearly complete freedom from unpleasant abreaction. It permits the sorting of significant events in a minimum of time. He is told to go back to some significant experience *only at an unconscious level*. As soon as he is regressed to it, his "yes" finger is to lift. When he has gone through it, his "no" finger is to signal completion. The therapist thus knows when to suggest further review. The patient may have no conscious thought about it as he carries out this subconscious review. It is even possible to use *time distortion* (to be described) and have the patient go through an important experience in only a few seconds of world time.

It might be mentioned that age regression has been used successfully for the recovery of mislaid jewelry or important papers. It has also been used in police work to obtain forgotten information from witnesses of some crime, such as the license number of a car used by criminals.

HYPERMNESIA

It seems that everything that happens to us is stored in the memory in complete detail. Conscious recall is limited to a very tiny part of total memory. Regression under hypnosis can bring out completely forgotten memories. It is also possible to bring them out merely by suggesting that they will be recalled. In this situation the patient remembers but doesn't relive the event. Minor details which are unimportant will not be recalled. Recovery of memories in this way may bring out some emotion but it does not provide as much catharsis as does age regression.

HALLUCINATIONS

Hypnotically produced hallucinations may be either positive or negative. Something that isn't there may be seen, or objects or persons actually present may be blotted out. Both positive and negative hallucinations may be present at the same time as is seen in the following demonstration which is sometimes made.

With others present in the room, the subject in a deep trance is told that all the others have left the room. Only he and the operator remain. He is then asked to open his eyes. He will have a negative hallucination of the bodies of those actually still present. At the same time he experiences a positive hallucination of the chairs in which the people are actually sitting.

All five of the senses can be hallucinated. It is easiest to obtain those of taste and smell, more difficult with touch, and still more difficult to hallucinate the auditory sense. The visual one is hardest to induce. Auditory and visual ones usually require a deep state, the others frequently are obtainable in only a medium state. Some subjects can produce any of the five in only a medium state.

There has been much research into this phenomenon, which indicates that such hallucinations are actual. Complete blindness or deafness can be induced, even color-blindness, although indications are that deep subconscious correct awareness is always retained, though consciously the subject is blind or deaf. These distortions of the senses can also be suggested to be operative posthypnotically. As the Ericksons have mentioned, the subject probably relapses into hypnosis when hallucinating posthypnotically.

In a therapeutic situation, hallucinations may be valuable. One of the projective techniques to be discussed later involves having the subject hallucinate a TV or motion picture screen and see something happen on it. At times a dentist may find it valuable to distract his patient's attention by having him hallucinate a previously witnessed TV program while the dentist performs his work. Possibly anesthesia will also be suggested.

TIME DISTORTION

All hypnotic phenomena had been discovered by the middle part of the Nineteenth Century with the single exception of time distortion. The ability to distort time under hypnosis was a discovery of the late Lynn Cooper, M.D., of Washington, D.C. He presented his findings first in a paper, then in a chapter in LeCron's book *Experimental Hypnosis,* and later, with Erickson, wrote an entire book on the subject.

While in a deep trance, it is possible for a subject mentally to speed up time, disorting it so that involved mental processes can be accomplished in a remarkably short time. Cooper told his experimental subjects that they would hear a metronome beating at the rate of once a minute. He then assigned them a mental problem, perhaps a mathematical one, which would ordinarily take about ten minutes to solve. They were told they would have ten minutes (ten beats of the metronome) in which to solve it. Actually the metronome was set to beat once a second. The problem would be solved within the ten beats, thus speeding up time 60 times the normal rate.

To learn the use of time distortion it can be practiced best with children. It is easily established with most children ages 6 to 12. The child can be told he is to see again one of his favorite TV programs. He can be asked what he would like to see. He is then hypnotized and told to open his eyes and see a TV set in front of him. Then he is to turn it on, the wavy lines will appear and probably a commercial will be seen. Then the program will appear just as he saw it previously. The operator says he will count slowly to ten and the child will see the entire program while the count is made. Thus a half-hour or even an hour program can be seen in a few seconds. Counting should be slow. Questioned afterward, the child will describe in detail what he saw and heard.

A psychiatrist who attended one of our courses decided to practice induction with his ten-year-old son. He hypnotized the boy and told him he was to see a movie which they had attended a few days before, as a hallucination. He said he would awaken the boy in about ten minutes and he could then tell about it.

As the child sat hallucinating the movie, he suddenly began to lift his hand up to his face again and again, as fast as he could move it. The psychiatrist wondered what this meant but said nothing. The movement quickly stopped. After awakening his son at the end of ten minutes, he asked as to this arm movement. "Oh," said the boy, "I was eating popcorn." His father then realized that he had inadvertently produced time distortion in the boy. He had seen a two-hour movie in ten minutes.

Time may be distorted at either a conscious or unconscious level. It has been said that a drowning person may seem to relive periods of his life at the moment when he has almost drowned and will recall this when saved. This would seem to be the same phenomenon as hypnotic time distortion.

HYPNOTIC DREAM PRODUCTION

Suggested dreams have been mentioned previously. Probably at least a medium trance is required. The dream may be either like a vision, similar to daydreaming, or it may be of the type occurring during sleep. A posthypnotic suggestion of dreaming can be given, the dream to take place during the night. Even a definite hour for the dream to take place can be suggested. If the patient is told he will awaken at the end of the dream and is then to look at his watch or clock, he will find the dream probably occurred at the suggested hour.

Some subjects while under hypnosis have an ability to understand readily the meaning and symbolism of their own dreams or even the dreams of others. Dream interpretation is thus facilitated, though this also usually requires a deep state. Not many are able to develop this facility.

The production of dreams hypnotically is very advantageous. Much can be learned in this way. It is not necessary for the hypnotherapist to wait for the patient to bring him a dream. However, most physicians will hardly wish to study the interpretation of dreams and may not resort to suggesting dreams.

Another way of understanding dreams is to ask the patient while under hypnosis to redream a dream, changing the details and the characters but keeping the meaning. This can be repeated several times until the meaning is easily understood. This method is generally credited to Milton Erickson.

Cheek has found that physiological disturbances, such as bleeding from the pregnant uterus or the onset of premature labor, may be initiated by consciously unrecognized frightening dreams. Search for and correction of these dreams can reverse the reactions even during a telephone conversation at the time a patient reports the emergency. Ideomotor responses are used to localize the disturbing dreams. The patient automatically goes into hypnosis either because of the immediate fear or because she has been in hypnosis during previous office visits when ideomotor responses were being used.

HYPNOTIC CONTROL OF ORGANIC BODY FUNCTIONS

Apparently the subconscious mind has the ability to control body functions, working through the autonomic nervous system. There should be many possible medical applications of this ability. Strangely there has been little scientific research to verify these possibilities. Some such controls have been questioned. Perhaps this is due to the fact that one subject may produce a change, although others cannot do so, but, as the saying goes, it only takes one white crow to prove that all crows are not black.

Some of the bodily changes said to be capable of being made are speeding up or slowing down of the heartbeat, control of blood circulation as in bleeding, speeding up of the rate of healing of wounds and injuries, lowering or elevating body temperature and lowering of blood pressure. Proof of these possibilities is lacking.

Researchers in Europe, South America, Japan and the United States have reported control of other bodily functions such as digestion, metabolism, bleeding, skin reaction to allergens, etc. Not much is known of what glandular functions can be influenced by suggestion. Very little investigation has been carried out along these lines, probably because research centers are not usually manned by people interested in hypnosis. There is much room for productive research in these areas, for they would be valuable in medical practice.

REFERENCES

Cheek, D. B.: Some newer understandings of dreams in relation to abortion and premature labor. Pacif. Med. Surg. 73: 379-384, 1965.

————: Unconscious reactions and surgical risk. Western J. Surg. Obstet. Gynec. 69: 325-328, 1961.

Cooper, L. F., and Erickson, M. H.: Time distortion in hypnosis. In: Experimental Hypnosis (L. M. LeCron, Ed.). New York, Macmillan, 1952.

————, and ————: Time Distortion in Hypnosis. Baltimore, Williams and Wilkins, 1954.

Erickson, M. H., and Erickson, E. M.: The hypnotic induction of hallucinatory color vision followed by pseudo-negative afterimages. J. Exp. Psychol. 22: 581, 1938.

————: Breast development possibly influenced by hypnosis. Amer. J. Clin. Hypn. 2: 157-159, 1960.

Gorton, B.: The physiology of hypnosis. A review of the literature. Psychiat. Quart. 23: 317-343, 457-485, 1949.

Macfarlane, R. G., and Robb-Smith, A. H. T.: Functions of the Blood, New York, Academic Press, 1961, pp. 303-347.

Pattie, F.: The genuineness of some hypnotic phenomena. In: Hypnosis and Its Therapeutic Applications (R. M. Dorcus, Ed.). New York, McGraw-Hill Book Company, 1956, Chap. 6, pp. 1-18.

Ravitz, L. J.: Application of electrodynamic field theory in biology psychiatry, medicine and hypnosis. Amer, J. Clin. Hypn. 1: 135-150, 1959.

Schultz, J. H., and Luthe, W.: Autogenic Training. New York, Grune & Stratton, 1959.

Sears, R. R.: An experimental study of hypnotic anesthesia. J Exp. Psychol. 15: 1-22, 1932.

Spiegel, H.: Hypnosis and the psychotherapeutic process. Comp. Psychiat. 1: 174-185, 1960.

Chapter 7

The Principles of Suggestion

As HYPNOSIS and suggestion are closely related and results are largely dependent on proper suggestion, the therapist should know how best to apply it, and its laws. Everyone is suggestible to some degree, but we become hypersuggestible when we are in hypnosis or are unconscious. The deeper the trance, the greater the suggestibility. It is such an important factor in the art of medicine that research with drugs must eliminate the placebo effect or expectancy may produce the same effect as that of the drug.

TYPES OF SUGGESTION

Suggestion may be given in a commanding way or permissively. Most people resent being dominated, hence permissive ones are usually more acceptable. However, a permissive suggestion can be made in a forceful way for emphasis. If a suggestion is worded "You will," it is a command. "You can" is permissive. A command would be indicated when there is an unconscious need to be dominated, which the therapist may notice in a patient.

Another distinction between types of suggestion is positive or negative wording. A positive wording is much more forceful than negative suggestion. The words "not, don't, won't and can't" should be avoided as much as possible. All are negative. In mathematics, two negatives make a positive, but in medical or dental practice, "You will not feel any pain" means "He thinks I really will feel pain." Better wording would be "You will feel comfortable in every way" or "You may feel pressure or touch but will be free of pain." Negatives have negative effects with hypnotized patients, no matter how joined together.

A suggestion may be direct or indirect. The latter type may not consciously be noticed but can be very effective. Your manner, tone of

59

voice, dress, the way your office is maintained, the car you drive, all may
be indirect suggestions indicating that you are prosperous and a good
physician or dentist.

THE LAWS OF SUGGESTION

During the 1920s, Emil Coué in Nancy, France, conducted a clinic
where he taught the uses of autosuggestion. He was a pharmacist, but
he was a very successful therapist. Coué made a study of suggestion and
learned much about it and how to use it most effectively. Much of our
present knowledge of this subject stems from Coué's observation.

Repetition is one important factor in causing suggestion to produce results. Suggestions should be "rubbed in." Advertising is suggestion, and
a good example of how advertisers realize the need for repetition is seen
in TV commercials which are repeated again and again. Some TV advertisers make the mistake of overdoing repetition which may bring re-
vulsion and resistance to the listener. The effect of repetition is cumula-
tive up to a point. Hypnotic suggestions should ordinarily be repeated
three or four times.

Suggestions should be worded so that they are set in the immediate
future rather than the present, which allows time for them to be absorbed and to become effective. If suggestions were being used to remove a headache, instead of saying "Your headache is gone" (contrary
to fact, thus putting it in the present), the wording should be "Your head
will begin to clear and soon the ache will dwindle away and be gone."
Pain seems to disappear at a subconscious level long before the relief is
consciously recognized.

Establishing motivation for acceptance makes a suggestion more potent.
Desire for some condition to be ended is an excellent motive with
patients.

Visual imagery can be added to a suggestion. Repetition is just as important here as when the suggestion is given verbally. There is a tendency
on the part of the subconscious to carry out any prolonged and repeated
visual image.

To illustrate: in treating obesity in a woman, she can be told to obtain a photograph of herself taken when she was slender. If none is
available or if she has never been slender, she can cut out a picture from
a magazine of a slender girl in a bathing suit. If possible, the patient
should cut the head from a picture of herself and paste this over the
head of the girl in the picture. This picture is then to be fastened to her
mirror. Every time she looks in the mirror she should look at the picture

and think, "That is I." On going to bed at night she should close her eyes and visualize herself as being like this picture.

When giving suggestions, it is better not to plant too many ideas at the same time. This burdens the subconscious and diversifies results. No more than two or three should be given in one session when working with a patient.

Coué made a point of suggesting only the end result. Details of how it should be accomplished should be avoided. He believed a general, non-specific suggestion was best, avoiding telling the subconscious how to do it. His famous phrase, which he urged his patients to say to themselves several times a day was "Every day, in every way, I'm getting better and better." This was very specific as to end result but left the details of accomplishment to what he termed the "teleology of the unconscious."

THE LAW OF REVERSED EFFECT

Coué was the first to write about this law. It affects everyone at times. He said, "If one thinks 'I should like to do this but I can't' (a negative thought), the harder he tries, the less he is able." People troubled by insomnia often find this law acting to prevent them from going to sleep. Such a person goes to bed expecting to have difficulty in getting to sleep. He tries, and the harder he tries the wider awake he becomes. When tired out, he stops trying to sleep and then drops off.

Here is another example as given by Coué of how this rule operates. If a board a foot wide is placed on the floor and you try to walk its length, you need hardly glance at it as you do so. If placed between two chairs two feet from the floor, it is easily walked but with more care. "Put the board between the towers of a cathedral and you would assuredly fall," as Coué put it. Your doubts would either prevent you from trying to walk it, or you would likely fall if you tried.

THE LAW OF DOMINANT EFFECT

Another of Coué's contributions is this law: an idea always tends toward realization. A stronger emotion will always counteract and take precedence over a weaker one. If fear is stronger than anger in a situation, you will try to escape. If anger is stronger than fear, you attack. Coué said that the imagination will always win when the imagination and the will are in conflict. Actually this means that the subconscious will always win over the conscious mind when they are in conflict.

Negative and other detrimental suggestions affect everyone at times, although we may be unaware of them. A part of hypnotherapy is the locating and removal of these suggestions. They may act exactly like posthypnotic suggestions. Therapy is de-hypnotizing the patient of these ideas when they are present.

REFERENCES

Coué, E.: How to Practice Suggestion and Auto-suggestion. New York, Amer. Library Service, 1923.

Beecher, H. K.: The powerful placebo, JAMA, 159: 1602-1606, 1955.

Chapter 8

Self-Hypnosis

ESSENTIALLY all hypnosis is self-hypnosis. The operator is merely a guide and the subject produces the result in carrying out the ideas presented to him. The easiest way for one to learn to hypnotize himself is first to be inducted by someone else and be given posthypnotic suggestions for induction. There should be some definite formula to follow, stated in detail.

By going through this formula, the subject enters hypnosis. As it is a learning process, practice is usually necessary, although very good subjects may learn self-hypnosis in only one session and then be able to reach a deep state. Others will require two or three inductions by someone else, with further practice sessions.

While no statistics are available as to what percentage of people can learn self-hypnosis without being previously inducted, many have been able to accomplish this. A tape recording of an induction talk is helpful for this. Several are commercially available.

As with hetero-hypnosis, a deep stage is of little advantage for most purposes. The lethargy when deeply hypnotized may even be a disadvantage. A medium depth of about 20 to 24 inches on our yardstick is probably ideal for self-hypnosis. However, there are situations where greater depth is important, as when visiting a dentist, for childbirth, or if hypnotic anesthesia is to be used in any other way. Major surgery with hypnotic anesthesia can only be performed when the patient is deeply hypnotized. Depth is also important if the person's eyes are to be opened, as when using hypnosis for purposes of study.

There are many advantages in being able to hypnotize oneself. It is the best means of overcoming insomnia unless this condition is a deep-seated neurotic symptom. The relaxation attained in hypnosis helps one stay more relaxed and free of tension in his daily life. If some degree of self-anesthesia can be produced, there are often opportunities for its use, as when visiting a dentist. A student who can learn to study while hypnotized usually finds his concentration much better. Obstetricians who use hypnosis usually teach the woman patient self-hypnosis so that she can induce it on first entering the hospital.

Of course the elimination of pain must be handled with discretion. It would be a mistake to anesthetize a broken ankle and walk on it. Such relief would be beneficial with a sprained ankle. It could be dangerous to remove abdominal pain of appendicitis, but it might be a lifesaving maneuver if it were impossible to obtain the services of a competent surgeon or if a long trip to the hospital were necessary. People with painful terminal cancer have been taught auto-hypnosis and self-anesthesia and have been comfortable during the last days of their lives.

The student who can study under hypnosis finds his concentration greatly improved. Then there is better absorption and increased recall. Grades received are usually higher, and some have taken examinations and tests while self-hypnotized with greater recall.

A physician from another state planned to take the California state board examination. He had been in practice for several years and believed he had forgotten many things that might be asked. Taught self-hypnosis, he took the examination while in hypnosis and passed easily. He stated that he was able to recall the answers to some questions which had long been forgotten.

Practitioners will often wish to train a patient in self-hypnosis. After induction, a detailed formula to follow is suggested. This should include a key word or phrase which the subject is to say to himself with repetition. It should be added that this will have no effect unless the person intentionally uses it to hypnotize himself. Some movement, such as lifting one hand to the face, can be suggested as a deepening method. The imaginary escalator can also be used for deepening. The following wording is an example of suggestions given for self-hypnosis.

"When you wish to hypnotize yourself, you should take a comfortable position. It doesn't matter whether you are lying down or sitting up as long as you are comfortable. You need say nothing aloud, merely think your suggestions. Your eyes should be closed, and you can relax better if you take two or three deep breaths. Then think, 'Now I am going into hypnosis.' This is a suggestion. Then three times slowly repeat the phrase, 'Relax now.' As you repeat this, you will begin to slip into hypnosis.

"Then you will want to go deeper. Say to yourself, 'Now I am going deeper.' Use the imaginary escalator while you count backward from ten to zero, stepping on as you begin to count. Step off at the bottom when you reach zero.

"At any time you wish to go into a deeper stage, repeat this escalator technique. You can also go deeper at any time by merely lifting either hand until the fingers touch your face.

"When you are ready to awaken yourself, you should think, 'Now I am going to awaken.' Count slowly to three and you will then awaken, always feeling refreshed, relaxed and clear-headed on awakening."

After going through the suggested formula, the person should suggest greater relaxation, taking a few moments to let his entire body become more relaxed.

Self-induction should be practiced several times within the next few days after being given this formula. This will bring greater depth. When the operator has given these formula suggestions, it is best to awaken the subject and immediately have him go through the formula and hypnotize himself. Of course any other suitable formula may be suggested instead of this sample one.

Additional suggestions can be given as to whatever use of auto-hypnosis is intended. It is best for the patient to make no tests or try to produce any phenomena until he has practiced induction several times. He should take it for granted he is getting results and should not care as to the depth attained. After some practice he can make some of the tests, such as arm levitation, eye closure, or the handclasp test. He can also induce glove anesthesia, though only after the operator has shown him how this can be produced. After a few practice sessions, the depth he reaches can be learned with the use of the imaginary yardstick.

If a patient does not have good results in his practicing, he may do better if the operator will make a tape recording of an induction talk, adding to it the formula suggestions. After being inducted by the recording several times, the formula may be more effective.

Some practitioners believe it best to have the subject fix his eyes on something prior to going through his formula. This can be any object as described in the chapter on induction. It is not necessary to continue to gaze at the object for any great length of time. Two or three minutes should be sufficient. Hyperventilation by taking several short breaths at a very rapid rate can also be helpful. This should be continued until a slight dizziness is felt, then there should be as much relaxation as possible, followed by going through the formula.

With self-hypnosis there is some tendency to drift off into normal sleep. Usually this can be prevented by auto-suggestion that the person will remain in hypnosis until he is ready to awaken.

Time may seem to pass very quickly when in hypnosis. Thirty or 40 minutes may have passed and seemed like only ten. Self-suggestion can limit the time spent in hypnosis. It can be stated that one will awaken spontaneously at the end of 15 minutes, or any stated period, or at a certain hour.

DANGERS AND CONTRAINDICATIONS FOR SELF-HYPNOSIS

Our symposium instructors have taught thousands of patients and hundreds of professional men and women how to hypnotize themselves. We know of no one who has ever had a bad result or found any danger in self-hypnosis. Freedom from any possible danger should be emphasized to the patient who is learning it, because some psychiatrists have claimed that self-hypnosis is always dangerous (Rosen). We emphatically do not agree with this dictum.

A few psychiatrists have warned that a patient might form too many fantasies with self-hypnosis and tend to withdraw from reality. There have been no reports of this ever happening. Theory here is based on clinical experience with psychotic patients who can do this without any training. Such an argument fails to consider that daydreaming is self-hypnosis and that everyone is spontaneously self-hypnotized many times.

There are very few contraindications to the teaching of self-hypnosis. They are as to anyone who is retreating from reality, who is detached, or who tends too much toward introspection and daydreaming. Other contraindications are the same as for hypnosis in general, as will be considered in another chapter.

REFERENCES

LeCron, L. M.: Self Hypnotism, the Technique and Its Use in Daily Living. Englewood Cliffs, Prentice-Hall, 1964.
_____: Better Health Through Self-Hypnosis. New York, Delacorte, 1967.

Chapter 9

Is Hypnosis Dangerous?

WHAT DANGERS does hypnosis involve? Can it be used safely by the practitioner? These are pertinent questions. The answer is that there are some dangers. However, they are minimal and are readily avoided when their possibilities are understood and simple precautions are taken.

Many physicians and dentists who have considered attending courses or otherwise learning hypnotic technics have feared to do so after reading or hearing some psychiatric criticisms and statements about the great dangers they envision with hypnosis. It can be said emphatically that these are very greatly exaggerated. The title of psychiatrist does not qualify one as an authority on hypnosis in the absence of experience any more than the corner grocer can offer himself as an authority on nutrition.

Harold Rosen, a psychiatrist, has exaggerated the idea of hypnosis being dangerous. He has lectured throughout the country speaking to medical, dental and lay groups, warning that hypnosis should be used only by those who have had extensive training in psychiatry. If this were true, all physicians should also have such training before practicing medicine for much medical practice is concerned with psychosomatic, emotional illnesses. Fortunately psychiatrists with long experience using hypnosis disagree completely. Erickson, undoubtedly the greatest authority on this subject, has said that hypnosis itself is not dangerous in any way, although it can be misused. He feels that hypnotherapists can learn much psychiatry from their patients as long as they respect the needs of these patients and refrain from coercing them in hypnosis.

The best indication that dangers are minimal is the fact that thousands of lay hypnotists and many stage hypnotists who know little about hypnosis other than how to induce it use it indiscriminately, yet bad results are rarely reported.

Another important point is that the professional man is fully covered by malpractice insurance carriers when using hypnosis in the field of work for which he is qualified. No insurance company writing malpractice insurance has had any claims because of the use of hypnosis by physicians or dentists. This was reported at a meeting of the Professional Liability Underwriters. No company knew of any difficulties having developed and no company plans restrictions on the use of hypnosis.

WHAT ARE THE ALLEGED DANGERS?

A very common idea is that if a symptom is removed by hypnotic suggestion another will form, possibly a worse one. The compulsive drinker might turn to narcotics if his need to drink were to be inhibited. This idea is based on a Freudian concept that behind a symptom there is a force seeking an outlet, the symptom providing the outlet. If the outlet is blocked by removal of the symptom, the force will seek another outlet. It is surprising how prevalent has been the acceptance of this theory which has no basis in fact. Just what is this mysterious force? It cannot be demonstrated in any way.

It is true that there may be a strong need for a symptom and it may serve some purpose, such as being a defense mechanism. It is very doubtful if a greatly needed symptom could ever be removed by suggestion. Suggestions are only effective if they are acceptable.

In actual practice, symptom removal by hypnotic suggestion is seldom attempted. In the old days of hypnosis, that was the only method of psychotherapy known, yet it was very rare for a new symptom to form, and the method was often successful. When a situation calls for an attempt at symptom removal by suggestion, there is a safeguard which would prevent any danger: that is to make the suggestions permissive rather than commanding. If there is a strong need for the symptom, the suggestion would not be carried out and no possible harm would result.

Another safeguard should also be applied. With the questioning technique it should be asked of the patient, "Is it all right for you to lose this symptom?" If the answer given by the subconscious mind is affirmative, there is not the slightest danger. If negative, no attempt at removal should be made at that time.

Strangely, this idea of danger in symptom removal is applied only to the use of suggestion. Psychiatric critics prescribe tranquilizers by the millions for depression and for other conditions. This is symptom removal by drugs. If it is by drugs it is considered safe, but if by suggestion it is dangerous. Of course this is nonsense and ridiculous. It is well recognized that loss of resistance to infection may be psychogenic. Use then of an antibiotic would be "dangerous" removal of a symptom.

Dorcus, in a paper given at a meeting on hypnosis at the University of Kansas, called attention to this and emphasized that in the rare cases where a symptom was removed by suggestion and another appeared, there was no reason to believe it was because of any mysterious force seeking another outlet. The new symptom might have no relationship to the former one, or it might have been present but consciously unobserved because of the dominant symptom.

As a matter of fact, a very large part of medical treatment is nothing but symptom removal. Usually it is by means of drugs, but even surgery can be symptom removal. If a gallbladder is removed, the cause of the illness is not being treated, although surgery may remedy the condition. With the Freudian idea of a force seeking an outlet, some other illness should develop following such surgery. Treatment of migraine or other headaches with drugs is symptom removal. Does some other ailment then occur? Headaches are frequently psychosomatic. If you take an aspirin and relieve it, do you develop some other symptom? These are merely examples pointing out that symptom removal by hypnotic suggestion is no more dangerous than any other treatment that does not eliminate the causes.

OTHER POSSIBLE DANGERS

Psychoanalysts state that a patient undergoing hypnotherapy becomes extremely dependent on the therapist, with a greater transference developing. It is true that there may be a great dependence initially, but this is of advantage to both the patient and the therapist. As progress is made and the illness or condition responds to treatment, dependence dwindles away. A large part of hypnotherapy is the building of ego strength in the patient. Hypnosis facilitates this and then dependency needs are ended or modified.

It could be pointed out that anyone continuing in analysis for three or four years with little progress certainly is displaying great dependence on the analyst.

As to transference, in brief therapy it seldom is of any importance and usually is disregarded or does not even develop. Ordinarily it can be handled easily through hypnosis.

Still another criticism by some psychiatrists is that if hypnosis is used with a person on the verge of psychosis, he could be thrown into a psychotic break. This is a possibility, but it would be from the misuse of hypnosis and not from the mere fact of being hypnotized. A skilled therapist might even use hypnosis with such a patient to prevent a psychotic break. In itself, being hypnotized never caused anyone to become psychotic. Undoubtedly misuse can do so. Any form of treatment can be misused through ignorance or inadvertence and promote such a result.

CONTRAINDICATIONS

One of the contraindications for the non-psychiatrist in the use of hypnosis is to avoid it with anyone who is extremely disturbed, greatly depressed, suicidal, or who the therapist might think is pre-psychotic. The pre-psychotic is difficult to recognize. If there is a question in the mind of the therapist as to any such possibilities, no attempt should be made to use hypnosis. Of course this is also true of anyone who is obviously psychotic. In all conditions mentioned, referral to a psychotherapist is advisable.

It should be realized that a psychosomatic symptom such as insomnia or an illness such as severe headaches may be masking great depression with the patient consciously unaware of being depressed. Whether or not this is so can be ascertained with the questioning technique.

WHEN DE-HYPNOTIZING IS DIFFICULT

In rare occasions there may be difficulty in awakening a subject. This can be annoying and embarrassing but would only be dangerous if the operator is not prepared to handle it properly. It should be emphasized that many practitioners who have hypnotized hundreds of patients have never had this happen. It is indeed rare but can occur. The danger here is that the hypnotist might become alarmed and transmit his fears to the subject, with panic and hysterics then resulting.

If a patient does not awaken at once when it is suggested, there is always some reason for it. The operator should find out why this has happened. With knowledge of the cause, the subject is almost sure to awaken readily. The ideomotor questioning method can usually locate the reason. It may not consciously be known by the subject, but his inner mind knows.

If time does not permit questioning, wiping the patient's face with a cold, wet towel, at the same time blowing on his eyelids is almost sure to awaken him. To prevent shock or resentment, he should first be told this is to be done.

When there is failure to awaken, the operator must reassure his patient. He should be told there is no danger; that there is some definite cause which can be learned and he will then awaken. The best reassurance is to suggest that it might be well for him to go even deeper into hypnosis. Thus he will be more comfortable and it will be easier to find the reasons for the difficulty.

No one has ever stayed in hypnosis for any long period of time. If nothing at all was done to facilitate awakening, the person probably would soon drop off into normal sleep and eventually would awaken.

In this situation some tricky methods have been successful. One patient visiting a dentist did not awaken at once. When told by the dentist that another patient was waiting to use the dental chair but that the first patient could continue to occupy it if she were willing to pay the fee for the time, she quickly awoke.

A psychiatrist who had difficulty awakening a patient used another technique. He asked if the man would mind walking out into the waiting room and returning in the same way as he had when he first came into the office. Returning, he awoke, for he had been awake on first entering the office.

To show possible reasons preventing awakening, some actual cases can be cited. After a demonstration when this happened it was learned that the subject had been a battle fatigue victim during World War II. He had then been treated with sodium amytol. Unconsciously he associated hypnosis with the state he had been in with this treatment. It had taken some time for the effect of the drug to wear off. Therefore he expected the same thing to happen with hypnosis. Explanation that the states were not the same enabled him to awaken thereafter.

In a course where student physicians were practicing induction, a woman physician acting as a subject failed to awaken. The class had had instruction in handling this situation. The colleague who had hypnotized her therefore was not alarmed but reported it to one of the instructors. She was reassured, told to go even deeper and asked to come to the head of the class so the other students could witness the handling of the situation. She sat down in a comfortable chair and the instructor then noticed that she spasmodically stiffened herself at very frequent intervals. He believed this had some meaning. Questioning with ideomotor replies revealed that she was relating her hypnotic state to some past experience. This was narrowed down and located as that morning. She had witnessed the showing of a motion picture on hypnotic childbirth. A month before, her only son had died suddenly. All day after seeing the movie, she had thought of her own delivery of the boy. When hypnotized, she had spontaneously regressed to her delivery. The spasmodic movements represented her uterine contractions. She did not want to awaken because she would then continue to think of her dead son. Brought back from the regression and given posthypnotic suggestions of being interested in other things and thinking no more at the time of her son, she quickly roused.

DANGER TO THE HYPNOTIST

In hypnosis there is a possible danger to the operator rather than to the patient. Women patients have sometimes fantasied a sexual assault by the therapist. This can happen also without hypnosis. While it is not feasible for a psychotherapist to have someone else present, others should take the precaution when dealing with a woman patient of at least having the door of the room open and someone nearby.

A dentist was visited by a new woman patient who was accompanied by her husband. Hypnosis for her dental work was suggested and the couple agreed to it. She was then hypnotized. Her husband was present throughout the interview and the hypnotic session. Another appointment was made for her work but the next day the husband phoned to cancel this appointment. Asked why, he said that his wife claimed the dentist had made sexual advances to her while she was in hypnosis. The husband apologized profusely, saying he knew this was not true as the dentist had never been alone with his wife, but he said his wife refused to return. It was most fortunate for the dentist that he had not seen the woman alone. Such an incident is made less likely by setting up ideomotor responses and asking first if it would be all right for the subject to be hypnotized.

Another precaution for the therapist is to make sure that the hypnotic patient is fully awake before dismissal. Most people awaken within a moment or two, but following a deep trance several minutes are sometimes needed for complete arousal.

Before awakening a patient, any suggestions other than those intended to be posthypnotic in effect should be removed. For example, if anesthesia had been produced, it is important to terminate it.

UNEXPECTED PATIENT REACTIONS

A beginner with hypnosis might become very alarmed if a hypnotized patient reacted in some unexpected, perhaps hysterical manner. His first thought might be to awaken the subject. Since much better control is possible with the patient hypnotized, reassurance should be given and the patient told to *go even deeper.*

It is not unusual for a subject to display sudden emotion on entering hypnosis. A woman may burst into tears. Hypnosis seems to remove some inhibitions and to allow the subject to display emotions which have been bottled up. Properly handled, this is an advantage. It is helpful to the patient to be able to vent these emotions and to talk about what is disturbing. Encouraged to ventilate and verbalize what is bothering her, the patient will soon quiet down and feel relief. Sometimes the patient may not consciously know why she has become so emotional. Ideomotor answers to questions can usually uncover the reasons.

In rare instances, a patient has been known to regress spontaneously when hypnotized. Usually it is to some childhood experience, and the regression becomes apparent from the patient's behavior and the way he talks. If this is suspected by the operator, the question might be asked suddenly, "How old are you?" The answer would then show what has happened.

During the first hypnotic session with a 40-year-old male alcoholic, LeCron saw the man begin to sniffle, to squirm in his chair and to show regressive signs. Asked how old he was, he replied, "Six." Encouraged to talk and asked what was disturbing him, he said, "It's my birthday. Dad bought me a goat as a present, but Mom won't let me bring it into the house. She's so mean to me! She says it stinks." Just why he regressed to such an incident wasn't apparent, but further investigation showed that he hated his mother and needed to bring this feeling out and resolve it.

It is always well for the therapist to remember that the subconscious takes everything literally and to be careful to say what he means when giving suggestions. A rather strange unexpected reaction to hypnotic suggestion took place in the following case.

A senior dental student attending a course on hypnotic techniques in dentistry undertook to practice induction with his girl friend. She came from Pasadena but was attending a university and living in a sorority house. Before awakening the girl, the dental student gave her what he thought was a helpful suggestion. He told her "You will go home, and tonight you will get a very good night's sleep." This was actually two suggestions.

The girl returned to the sorority house and slept very well, but the next morning she demanded that someone take her to her home in Pasadena. As it was a school day, no one could do so. She became hysterical. A sorority sister who had been present when she was hypnotized the night before phoned the dental student. He re-hypnotized the girl and found out the trouble. He had told her to go home. Home was Pasadena, not the sorority house. She felt compelled to go home as had been suggested posthypnotically. This suggestion was removed, and she calmed down and was all right again.

Most professional men have had little or no training in psychodynamics or much instruction in treating psychosomatic illnesses other than with drugs. Most physicians in general practice or specializing do not wish to become psychotherapists. With the methods given in Part II of this book, much can be accomplished with such patients without extensive knowledge of psychotherapy. This can be safely carried out with this information and with the safeguards given here. Dangers are so minimal that they can be disregarded. Of course some knowledge of psychotherapeutic methods is to any physician's advantage, but this need not be extensive if basic principles are followed.

Part II

The Clinical Applications of Hypnosis

Chapter 10

Orientation to Hypnosis

WE HAVE SEEN that hypnosis can be induced spontaneously by lulling stimuli, in driving an automobile, that it can occur spontaneously during times of great emotional or physical stress and that it can be produced by disorientation in space and by confusion in thoughts. We have learned that the state of hypnosis is characterized by restriction of attention through any of the five senses, by dimunition of physical and mental wastage of effort and by literalness of understanding of words. We have seen that the hypnotized subject may relate the present state of hypnosis to a previously experienced traumatic event even when the means of induction are very different. We have found that movements are slow and that speech is more difficult as depth of hypnosis is increased.

There is a great speed of thought in relating meaningful events at a deep subconscious level. Ideomotor signals may show that such events may take many repetitions of the subconsciously remembered experience before they are recognized consciously. Let us take note of these matters and come back to them presently, for they are of great importance if we are to use hypnosis meaningfully in our research and in the healing arts.

Animals, plants and saprophytes from the most primitive to the most complex seem to share a tendency to go into resting states when living conditions are unfavorable. Spore formation, hibernation, sleep and hypnosis share the common factor of diminished need for oxygen and nutrition. Sleep overtakes the unfortunates who are freezing to death before they die, but if they are lucky enough to be partially insulated by air while buried under snow, they will fall asleep during a blizzard and awaken a few days later, wondering about the passage of time and the fact that they have not needed to eat or to excrete urine or feces. Such is the pseudo-hibernation of human beings and some of their domestic animals. If the temperature goes too low and their insulation is insufficient, they will freeze to death.

In some mammals, however, there have developed further protective features of resting states. If the surrounding temperature drops too low, there will be an arousal response that first increases the metabolism and circulation in the forepart of the body and finally causes awakening and bodily activity. The effect is like that of a thermostat in a furnace.

Some of the living fossils, Dipnoid fishes in Africa, South America and Australia, are able to survive long periods of drought by digging into the mud and sleeping for months at a time in the absence of water and air. Some species of swallows will enter a hibernation-like state when deprived of insects necessary for their food. Anatol Melichnin has given us an interesting account of his experience with starvation in a Nazi prison camp in Russia in 1941. He has pointed out the improvement in suggestibility of Pavlov's dogs when they were starved before testing their ability to conform to expected patterns of conditioning.

It has been pointed out by students of hibernation that pain tolerance is very high in some hibernating mammals such as the ground hog but that they will awaken during otherwise painless surgery if they hear a human sneeze. Such sounds do not normally occur where these animals are hibernating. They are phylogenetically alerted by potentially threatening sounds but have had no conditioning for the effects of a sharp scalpel or gentle handling in preparation for surgery. Perhaps some of these features of animal behavior will make sense when we consider some of the other characteristics of behavior under stress and characteristics of learning process.

An opossum caught in its natural environment by a dog will struggle awhile and then suddenly appear to be long dead. Its skin temperature drops to that of its surroundings, its eyes glaze over, and it loses all reflexes except that of its prehensile tail. The effect of this sudden change is to shock the dog and cause it possibly to drop this disturbing cold thing and go looking for the real opossum that seemed to have escaped. Though seemingly insensate, the opossum knows when the dog has gone far enough away for it to escape into the forest or up a tree. Curiously, this all-out effect of danger does not occur when the opossum has been kept a few days in captivity. Instead there may occur a sort of catalepsy, a rigid immobility. The body temperature may be only slightly diminished during the time of accommodation and apparent discovery that chance for survival is good. In the interim the animal will not eat and there is no elimination from bladder or bowel. Explanation for the sudden drop in temperature and assumption of a seemingly dead appearance probably resides with the apparent occurrence of massive intravascular coagulation which is later corrected by massive production of fibrinolytic enzymes. These enzymes dissolve the intravascular clots and allow resumption of circulation.

This mechanism is not restricted to marsupials such as the opossum. McKay et al. have suggested that human shock, the findings in eclampsia, placental separation and the generalized Schwartman-Sanarelli phenomenon are related. John Hunter, shortly before his death from coronary occlusion, a possibly related phenomenon, reported on the interesting fact that human beings killed suddenly, when they might be expected to be initially frightened, will have fluid blood in their vessels and that this blood does not coagulate when removed from the body. His report on "The Blood and Gunshot Wounds" was delayed in being published in 1794 after his death, because the Royal Society objected to Hunter's seeming belief that the blood really was able to think for itself. Later it was learned that Hunter was the first to discover the fact that the fluidity of cadaver blood after sudden death resulted from fibrinolytic enzyme activity. This phenomenon was put to use by Yudine in Russia in 1930 as he developed methods of using human cadaver blood for massive blood replacement after hemorrhage. The phenomenon occurs only when death has been sudden and associated with greatly increased epinephrine secretion.

With consideration of these apparently widely separated observations on resting states, limitation of motion, high pain tolerance, massive intravascular coagulation and rebound fibrinolysis, we may wonder a bit about threatening situations present with human beings during sleep, anesthesia, surgery and pregnancy. We can well wonder why some cancer patients will go into shock during surgery, look dead for a time and then rally only to start bleeding from every possible source. We can wonder why perfectly healthy men and women may go into cardiac arrest or may show the shock-massive-bleeding phenomenon during surgery or while being suddenly jolted in positioning them after induction of anesthesia. We have been gathering evidence since 1957 to show that unconscious human beings are thinking and listening under general anesthesia, though at an unconscious level. They may believe they have cancer even when they have been told the contrary by their doctors. They may have such a pessimistic frame of reference or masochistic need for self-punishment that they misunderstand normally innocuous statements by the operating room team.

Why should inflammatory reactions to trauma and infection be the same in organs incapable of transmitting painful messages to the brain as they are in organs well supplied with pain-transmitting nerve pathways? Is it possible that the human mind is kept aware of tissue damage even though consciously unable to recognize any painful stimuli? This seems indeed to be the case. We can find improvement in joint mobility and decrease in muscle guarding and edema when a hypnotized patient has accepted *subconscious* relief from *consciously unrecognized pain,* indicated only by appropriate movement of a finger. We can now more sensibly consider the possibility that a patient can be oblivious to pain during an operation under anesthesia but may be so alarmed by conversation in the operating room that his brain is intensely "zeroed in" on all painful stimuli from the operative area on awakening as seems to be the case with the hyperawareness of causalgia or reflex-sympathetic-dystrophy occurring after injuries coupled with great emotional upheaval.

LEARNING

There are four major types of learning: (1) genetic, through the DNA and RNA, (2) imprinting (single impact learning), (3) mimicry (observation of parent animal) and (4) repetition (commonly recognized type in schooling).

The first of these is beyond our grasp at the moment. Imprinting has only been recognized during the past century, and for the most part our understanding of it has been limited to observation of birds and some lower mammals. That imprinting of some sort plays a major role in human learning has received only vague attention. Breuer recognized that traumatic events could produce a state akin to hypnosis which he termed "hypnoid." Bernheim observed that catalepsy and a sort of hypnotic behavior occurred in some patients seriously ill with typhoid fever. Breuer noted that the induction of hypnosis often reminded the patient of a traumatic episode and would evoke responses appropriate to the traumatic event being relived. We have noted the great tendency of the human mind in hypnosis to revert to a frightening experience when a request has been made for recall of a pleasant experience. Perhaps there is a logical reason for this phenomenon if we consider the possibility that one of the brain's functions should be the storage of salutary impressions and appropriate reactions associated with escape from danger and the maintenance of these "package deal" reactions in readiness in case of a similar experience. It would be helpful for the animal to waste no time in trying to decide whether to climb a tree or run from a threatening animal. There could be no possible value in storing up for immediate action the memories of pleasant happenings.

Two medical students opened their eyes and refused to go on with a group induction of hypnosis which Cheek was demonstrating to the class. Separately these two boys asked the demonstrator why they had felt alarmed and could smell ether while Cheek had been talking about relaxing in the sunshine in a mountain meadow. They each discovered with ideomotor questioning that they had previously entered a state something like the hypnosis they were experiencing in the lecture. The previous state occurred in association with a frightening induction of anesthesia. Both entered hypnosis rapidly and comfortably after deciding that they need not be so reminded again.

Lorenz has pointed out that a single exposure of mallard ducklings to a moving piece of wood shaped like a mother duck could cause a fixed and permanent memory. The ducklings exposed once to this decoy in the absence of their real mother would thereafter go to the decoy in preference to their real mother. Similar observations have been made by D. A. Spaulding with chicks in 1873. It seems clear now that emotionally weighted experiences at critical stress periods during human existence are able to evoke more or less permanent responses for which there may be conscious amnesia. These responses caused by a single experience may be very much like the effects of classical posthypnotic suggestions. Herbert Spiegel has drawn a comparison between imprinting and posthypnotic suggestion with its amnesia for the original suggestion, the compulsion to carry out the suggested act, and a rationalization for the act to be completed.

It is beginning to appear likely that experiences or misunderstandings of experiences at birth, at times of great stress and during periods of unconsciousness may be single-impact producers of patterned behavior. These may be harmful to the individual. With the tools of communication with deep subconscious memories furnished by Milton Erickson and Leslie LeCron with better understanding of ideomotor activity, we seem to be approaching sources of learning which are identical with or very similar to the imprinting of Lorenz. We are learning how to communicate better and are opening wide horizons for research into the physiological and psychological meanings of natural sleep. We are learning from patients how best to communicate hope and what mechanisms and uses of words can destroy hope and crush the will to live.

The feature of mimicry as a learning process is seen in all birds and mammals that care for their young. At times of danger we see that the young become silent and immobile. They turn to the parent and mimic the behavior of the parent or remain immobile while the parent either attacks or leads the enemy away. These facets of restricted attention, immobility, silence and mimicry for animals in danger are classical features of hypnotic behavior.

Every mammal mother licks her young at birth and with each feeding. It is mere speculation but it is a possibility that the mesmeric passes of Europeans healers and the blowing on the face and stroking the body as done by the medicine men of Assam are just variations of the natural process whereby mother mammals reduce the requirements for oxygen in their young at birth and lull them to sleep after nursing. Strength is given this speculation by discovery that the electrical field potentials are altered by stroking the body and that similar changes are effected during natural sleep and chemoanesthesia.

We are still groping for a better understanding of the meanings of hypnosis for better concepts of its values and limitations. Perhaps we can make better use of hypnosis if we consider it a phenomenon of natural selection enabling animals in trouble to survive, that it is far more than a man-made contrivance allowing one person to suggest behavior to an uncritical and obedient receptor for suggestions. Perhaps we can better understand why hypnotizability can be well categorized for volunteer student subjects but lose all meaning when a sincere and highly motivated doctor works with a sick and frightened patient. The subjective, literal willingness to accept sincerely given hopeful suggestions is ever present when a human being is in danger. We have only to recognize the potential in order to use it for the benefit of our patients. We can better understand why fears of causing trouble with hypnosis can create the trouble we fear.

We can better understand why victims of assault may confuse a would-be hypnotherapist with the person who once assaulted them. We can understand better why the review of traumatic experiences in life occurs so quickly during a hypnotic interview and when the review is carried out at a level of awareness reflected by ideomotor responses and unrecognized at a verbal level of awareness. We can better understand the spontaneous elimination of conscious pain, for conscious pain serves no good purpose at a time of danger. Subconscious awareness of tissue damage is another matter. It takes a deep hypnotic trance to eliminate subconscious pain. When we think of the hypnotic state as a generally protective one with a long phylogenetic history, we can begin to understand that no single group of intellectuals should decide whether this thing should or should not be studied in our medical and dental schools. This channel of understanding the patterns of conditioning in a threatening environment should be carefully studied from many angles. We are just beginning to learn about it.

REFERENCES

McKay, D.: Disseminated Intravascular Coagulation. New York, Hoeber, 1965.
Melichnin, A.: The Pavlovian syndrome: A trance state developing in starvation victims. Amer. J. Clin. Hypn. 4: 162-168, 1962.

Chapter 11

Uncovering Techniques

METHODS of treating psychosomatic illness, neurosis and other emotionally caused conditions are by no means standardized nor can they be claimed to be as successful as therapists would wish. For many years, ever since the beginning of this century, Freudian concepts have been the accepted ones in English-speaking countries. More recently some of Freud's ideas have been modified and some discarded. Many therapists do not believe as Freud did that everything is based on childhood conditioning, with emphasis on sex, and they look more to present happenings as the genesis of many conditions. For psychotherapy to be more successful we need to know much more than we do about the subconscious mind and how it functions, for these troubles as a rule are centered in the inner mind.

Psychoanalysts still follow Freud rigidly. In fact, Freudian analysis has become a cult with set rituals. The patient must lie on a couch with the analyst sitting at its head where he is not seen. This ritual is only because Freud worked in this way, by his own admission being somewhat shy and uncomfortable if his patient could watch him.

To become an analyst there are the years of medical school, psychiatric and analytic training with at least 300 hours of training analysis. Then the analyst practices. A complete analysis requires about 300 to 600 hours. If the analyst works a 40-hour week for 50 weeks of the year he puts in 2,000 hours. Thus he would presumably deal with five patients a year if the average analysis consumed 400 hours. Of course many patients do not complete their analysis and he would see more patients, but to us it seems that this is the worst possible waste of a medical education, with only the wealthy able to afford lengthy analysis.

The United States remains the only country where Freud has great acceptance, although the British Commonwealth countries still lend him much credence. Elsewhere in the world, psychotherapists follow the teachings of Pavlov, seeking conditioned reflexes which are regarded as the basic causes of emotional illnesses. It is difficult to assess the results of psychotherapy. Some Pavlovians claim results as 80 per cent successful (Wolpe and Russian texts). Most effectively administered placebos give 70–80 per cent improvement.

It should be said that hypnosis is more commonly used in some other countries than it is in the United States; in others is little known. It is used extensively in Russia where the highest claims are made.

Regardless of method, hypnosis seems to improve results and accelerate the course of therapy. The general practitioner or specialist cannot spend as many hours with a patient as a psychiatrist does. Hypnotherapy for psychosomatic illnesses may require only a few minutes in a single session, more likely a few hours, but seldom more than 15 or 20 sessions at the most.

ANALYTIC PROCEDURES

The main tools in analysis are free association and dream interpretation. Free association consists of having the patient try to verbalize every thought that enters his mind during the analytic hour. No matter how embarrassing his thoughts, he must say what comes to mind. This is difficult for anyone. Some patients learn to do it well, though it may take some time, time largely wasted. Some spend hours talking of inconsequential things while repressing important data. Others find it impossible to talk so freely. Eventually, repressed ideas or memories may come out or the patient may resolve the repressed problem without ever knowing consciously why improvement has occurred.

Dream interpretation also aims at bringing "insight." An analyst may become adept at seeing the inner meaning of dreams and the sources of problems can be reached through the patient's dreams. For the non-psychiatrist or non-analyst, this is not very practical unless the physician is willing to make a study of dreams and their interpretation. Even the trained psychotherapist may encounter dreams he is not able to interpret, and, unfortunately, his interpretations may not always be correct. Recent studies (Cheek) indicate that the most cogent dreams are mostly repressed.

These methods require long-time therapy, much of it unproductive. The therapist who uses hypnosis and resorts to dream interpretation does not wait for dreams to be presented by the patient. He can have his patient dream while under hypnosis or can suggest a dream to occur during the night. Many dreams have no bearing on the patient's problems, but hypnotic suggestion can cause dreams about some specific problem. Even the symbols to be used in the dream can be suggested, thus making understanding the dream easy. If it is difficult to see the meaning of a particular dream, suggestion can cause the same dream to be produced again but with a different set of symbols or "cast of characters." This can be carried out again and again until the inner meaning becomes obvious. Furthermore, interpretation of a dream can be checked for accuracy by asking questions with ideomotor signals made in reply. Repetition of repressed dreams at an unconscious level of awareness makes them more accessible for verbal reporting.

The other analytic tool, free association, is much easier and freer if the patient is in hypnosis. In fact, patients who associate best often will slip spontaneously into hypnosis, although the analyst may not realize this if he is not familiar with the behavior of hypnotized people. For the non-psychotherapist, these methods can be disregarded, for there are far better ways of delving into subconscious thought processes.

AUTOMATIC WRITING

Probably the ideal way of gaining information from the subconscious and thus uncovering the causes and motives for any condition being treated is by means of automatic writing. This is a most interesting phenomenon. It consists of placing a ball-point pen or soft pencil in the hand of a subject. Then his mind is diverted from the hand, allowing his subconscious mind to take control of the hand. In automatic writing, the subject may not consciously know what is being written until he reads it later. He may read something while the hand busily writes. A few "automators" have been so good at it that they can read with the conscious mind and have both hands write at the same time, each writing on a different subject. Thus three mental activities can be carried on at the same time.

Automatic writing may be very rapid with the hand racing across the paper, or it may be very slow. The handwriting never looks like the person's normal writing. Rarely are words separated. They will be run together. This makes the writing difficult to read. Sometimes the letters are not clearly formed.

In writing automatically, the subconscious mind takes shortcuts and may write cryptically. The word "before" might be written B4; a figure 2 or the word "to" may appear for any of its three meanings. Why take the trouble to add extra letters? The writing may be performed in a normal way from left to right or might be upside down, backward, mirror writing, or a combination of all these styles. Sometimes the subconscious seems to take delight in punning, though otherwise it will show little humor.

The late Anita Mühl, a psychiatrist, was the leading authority on automatic writing and used it continually in her therapy. She claimed to be able to teach it successfully to 80 per cent of her patients, though this might require 20 or 30 hours of practice. Others have not had such good results. It is easiest developed with the patient under hypnosis. Most deep trance subjects will be able to write automatically.

In learning to write automatically, it is best to use a bread board or lap board of some kind, as the arm can move more freely when at a lower level than it would be at a desk. For paper, a roll of wide shelf paper spread over the board is ideal. More can be unrolled then as required. The pen should write a broad line, or a soft pencil should be used. It should be held upright between the thumb and forefinger instead of in the usual writing position.

Automatic writing is a very valuable technique if it can be developed without too much time required. With it the subconscious can express itself freely, bringing out any information it wishes to disclose. It can write out the answers to questions. Unfortunately it is not always co-operative. If resistance is encountered in therapy, it may refuse to write at all or may avoid repressed material. The technique which follows is only a variation of automatic writing; signals take the place of writing. The Ouija board is another variation.

USE OF IDEOMOTOR MOVEMENTS IN OBTAINING ANSWERS TO QUESTIONS

We regard this as the most valuable of all uncovering methods. In one session more information can be learned than in many hours of free association, unless there is strong resistance. The technique consists of wording questions so they can be answered affirmatively or negatively. This sets up a code of signals which the inner mind utilizes in replying. These signals are unconsciously controlled movements of some object or the patient's fingers. Ideomotor signaling can be carried out effectively while the person is awake as well as while in hypnosis.

A light object such as a finger ring, an iron washer, a nut or any other light weight can be used in one method. To this is tied a thread about eight or ten inches long. Holding the thread between the thumb and forefinger, the object is allowed to dangle freely, the elbow being rested on the arm of the chair or on the subject's knee. A kind of pendulum is thus formed. The subject holds this in his right hand (or left hand if left-handed).

Four basic movements of the pendulum are possible. It may swing in a clockwise circle, or counterclockwise, straight back and forth across in front of the person, or in and out away from him. Each of these motions can then have a meaning. One can mean "Yes," another "No," a third can signify "I don't know," and the fourth can mean "I don't want to answer the question." This last may be important at times. These signals then form a code allowing direct communication with the subconscious mind.

The therapist may assign a particular meaning to each of these answers. However, it is more interesting to the subject and there is better coopera-tion from the inner mind if it is allowed to make its own decisions as .to which signal to use for each of the four answers. It also proves definitely to the subject that his subconscious thinks and reasons when it makes its own decisions.

The subject is shown the four motions and is told what the four replies are to be. While he holds the pendulum so that it dangles, the subcon-scious is asked to select one of the four motions which is then to represent "yes." When the pendulum has swung in reply to this request, the sub-conscious is then asked to select a motion to mean "no," then for "I don't know." The remaining one is to mean refusal to answer.

It is better for the subject to watch the pendulum, although it will move even if the eyes are closed. He should be instructed to try to hold the pendulum motionless and not to think how he wants it to move. He should let his inner mind control the movements and make its own decisions as to which one it is to use for each reply.

This technique is very impressive to the subject. When the pendulum moves involuntarily, it invariably brings exclamations of surprise. The reader should certainly try this technique himself. He will find his re-sponses can readily be established. It is not necessary for the questions to be verbalized in doing it yourself. You merely think them.

Usually the pendulum will begin to move almost at once when the subconscious is asked to select one of the four movements. Sometimes there is a lag of two or three moments. In our own experience and that of several hundred of those who have attended our classes and learned the technic, the pendulum will work with about 95 per cent of those who try it.

It is well for the therapist to explain to his patient that the inner part of the mind controls many muscular movements, thus avoiding any thought that it is magical. Breathing is an example, as is walking. It is much easier for the subconscious to control the movements of the fingers which causes the pendulum to swing than to coordinate and regulate all the muscles involved in walking, or even in breathing.

A similar code of communication can be established by movements of the fingers. Any four of the ten fingers can be utilized for the replies. However, we have found it best to designate certain fingers on one hand because it is easier for the therapist to watch only one hand. Also, if the same code is used with all patients it is easily remembered without taking notes. The dominant hand should be selected. The fingers are specified instead of allowing the subconscious to select. The forefinger could signify "yes," the middle finger "no," the little finger for doubt and the thumb for refusal to answer.

We are somewhat at variance in the use of this technique. Usually Cheek prefers the finger movements either in the waking state or with the patient under hypnosis. LeCron uses the pendulum when the patient is awake, the fingers if he is in hypnosis. It really makes little difference except that the hypnotized person's eyes will probably be closed and he cannot see the pendulum if it is used. Sometimes it will be found that finger movements cannot be established, but the pendulum will move readily. Sometimes the opposite is true, and rarely neither will operate.

During questioning of a patient, sometimes something interesting and unusual occurs. Instead of the pendulum moving in one of the four basic directions, it will swing diagonally. With finger movements the ring finger may lift instead of one of the other four. This indicates that the subconscious is trying to offer information. It cannot answer the questions properly. This signal may mean "perhaps" or "maybe," or it could mean that the question is not understood. Perhaps it cannot be answered affirmatively or negatively. It may have been ambiguous or improperly worded. Further questions can determine the meaning of this undesignated response. It is further proof of the reasoning power of the subconscious mind.

What questions to ask and their wording requires some skill, and future chapters will teach this in describing the treatment of illustrative cases. A question must be clear as to meaning. Here we get into semantics. Often we do not say what we mean. A commonly used expression is "That makes me mad." We mean we are angry but we actually say we are insane. The inner mind invariably takes everything literally. As an example, if the question is asked "Will you tell me where you were born?", a person in hypnosis (perhaps not if in only a light state) will reply with a nod or will say "yes." If awake he will invariably name the place where he was born, interpreting the question. The literal answer is "yes." More examples of the literalness of the subconscious will be given later.

With this questioning technique, how accurate are the answers to the questions? From our experience the subconscious rarely offers false information in answering. It seems to prefer to refuse to reply rather than to lie. This might not always be true, particularly if the patient is a pathological liar, but we have found that false information is rarely given.

Often it is obvious that the reply is correct. Sometimes it is well to take the answer with a grain of salt until verification is possible.

In trying to be cooperative, a patient may lift a finger or move the pendulum voluntarily. Close observation will quickly detect this. When the pendulum swings, the movement of the fingers or hand in swinging it is not noticeable. With a consciously controlled movement, such a motion can be seen. With finger signals, the finger will almost invariably tremble slightly as it comes up and the movement is very slow. With a very few people the lifting is more rapid and the finger may jerk. If it is suspected that the patient has consciously controlled a response, he can be questioned and told to let the finger or pendulum move of its own accord.

Some patients will lose track of their hands during finger movements, dissociating the hand. They are not aware of the finger moving although it may be quite pronounced. Therefore the therapist should always announce the result so the patient knows what information has been received.

HANDLING RESISTANCE DURING THERAPY

During questioning, resistance may be encountered with refusal to answer by a signal. This situation calls for careful handling. Resistance can be broken and information gained, but it would be dangerous sometimes to force this too strongly because the patient might not be able to tolerate the knowledge. A safeguard here is to ask if it is all right for him to bring out a suspected conflict or trauma. If the answer is affirmative it is safe to do so, but if negative the matter should be dropped for the time being.

Resistance may be due to reluctance to bring out some unpleasant memory, some idea may be too unacceptable to entertain, or there may be a conflict which cannot be faced. Resistance is an indication that the subconscious does not want something exposed. Steps can be taken so it may become available at some later time.

During questioning, if a reply is not made, the hypnotized patient can be instructed to imagine a blackboard in front of him, his eyes being closed. Then he is told to see an imaginary hand write words, a phrase or a sentence on the blackboard in white chalk. Sometimes this will appear, perhaps only a word which will offer a clue.

When the subconscious blocks in answering a question, another technique may bring results. This is one utilized by Freud in his early work when he was using hypnosis, although he learned it from Bernheim. He would say that he was about to squeeze the patient's head between his hands and that this would press a thought into the patient's conscious mind, which he could then verbalize. Often an important idea would then pop into the person's mind. A variation of this method is merely to make the suggestion "I am going to count to three and a sudden thought about this matter will come to you." Snapping a finger or tapping a desk seems to crystallize nebulous thoughts and make them accessible for verbal reporting.

A patient may remark that the answer to a question is certainly "no" (or "yes") while the ideomotor reply is contradicting the spoken statement or some head movement. This is very impressive to the patient, and it usually represents the more correct answer.

Aside from gaining valuable information and insight, the questioning technique has another benefit. When the therapist makes interpretations and explanations, the patient may doubt if they are correct. When information comes from his own inner mind through these responses, he accepts it. The therapist is not telling him; he is telling the therapist. In psychotherapy it is known that insight from within is preferable to that derived from a therapist's explanations. More than concious understanding is needed. There must also be a kind of digestion of the knowledge. These replies from within aid in the "digestive process."

The patient suffering from a psychosomatic illness is likely to believe his condition to be entirely a physical one. He may continue to be skeptical after the physician has explained how the mind can affect the body and cause illness. An excellent way to bring realization to him that this is true in his own case is through the questioning technique. The physician might handle it in this manner: "Perhaps there's some emotional or psychological cause for your condition, or possibly it's entirely a physical matter. Your inner mind knows which is true. Let's see what it will tell us about this." Then the question is asked "Is there some psychological or emotional reason for this condition?"

When the answer is affirmative, as it is sure to be if the condition is psychosomatic, the patient accepts the idea without qualification. His subconscious has said there is such a cause; the therapist has not said it. A good therapeutic relationship has then been established. Sometimes a physician will say to a patient, "It's all in your mind," a statement often resented and probably disbelieved.

OUR MENTAL MAKEUP

In dealing with the subconscious in the ways we have described, it may seem as though there is another person inside us. This is a wrong conception, for the subconscious is merely one part of the total mind. It does think and reason, though in a different way than we do consciously. It has been said that the subconscious reasons only deductively while consciously we can also reason inductively.

Unfortunately we know little about the actual makeup of the mind. Strangely enough there has been little further investigation to learn more about it since the days of Freud. We know something of the way it works but not nearly enough.

Today the most usual conception of the mind's makeup is that advanced by Freud. He considered the mind as consisting of the id, which contains our basic instincts and drives, the preconscious, the ego or self, and the super-ego. The super-ego is mainly our conscience, according to the Freudian concept. Freud thought awareness present only in the ego and apparently believed the id incapable of reasoning.

There have been other theories about our mental makeup advanced before the days of Freud. Such men as Janet, Prince, Myers and James credited knowledge, reason and awareness to the subconscious. Anyone dealing directly with the inner mind through hypnosis certainly must revise the Freudian concept. The hypnotherapist quickly learns to respect the extraordinary amount of knowledge accumulated in the subconscious and its ability to control bodily processes. Everything that ever happened to us is stored in the memory in complete detail, and hypnosis can bring out forgotten memories even back to infancy.

While it is a very difficult matter to prove scientifically, even memories of birth seem to be stored in memory. They can be brought to consciousness through hypnotic age regression. LeCron wrote a paper on this subject: when memory actually does begin. Nandor Fodor attempted to prove through the interpretation of dreams that there are not only actual memeroies of birth but even prenatal memories.

Any good hypnotic subject can readily produce fantasies, and an apparent birth memory might only be a fantasy. Nevertheless it is a possibility that such memories are retained in the subconscious memory bank. Our own opinion is that such recall may be a valid one. This same opinion is shared by a number of psychiatrists and others who have had patients apparently regress to birth, sometimes spontaneously. Cheek believes that birth experiences may be similar to imprinting which makes a permanent behavior characteristic with one stimulus.

Some case histories will be cited later where such a memory seemed to have an effect later in life, as in asthma and in cases of chronic headache. Freud, Rank and others have termed birth a trauma, possibly having such effects, which would indicate that there must be a memory of birth or no such effects would occur.

Using automatic writing, Mühl has reported being able to contact seven different layers or levels of the subconscious, each of which would identify itself. She claimed that these ranged from the equivalent of Freud's basic id, which would call itself the Old Nick or the Devil in us, to what seemed to be Jung's Super-conscious. Jung felt that this is much more than the conscience and is something having a connection with a collective subconscious or perhaps with God. Mühl worked with some 50 subjects in her research on this matter and claimed all 50 brought out these seven segments. It is possible that her own ideas as to this might have been impressed on her subjects and they then responded as she expected them to do. Her claims certainly warrant more investigation.

Although Freud greatly furthered our knowledge of the inner part of the mind, it is interesting to know that such a part of the mind was recognized by the ancient Greek and Roman physicians as well as by many later psychologists and psychiatrists who proceded Freud, such as Janet, James and others.

OTHER PROJECTIVE TECHNIQUES

Still other projective techniques are possible in hypnotherapy. The patient may be instructed to imagine that he is looking at a stage or a motion picture or TV screen. A scene is to develop there and he is to relate what he sees appear on the stage or screen. The illusion or fantasy is to be about some problem and what he describes will afford interpretation and insight.

Sometimes a posthypnotic suggestion can bring a bit of insight with a problem. The patient is told that sometime within the next day or two, the time being left indefinite, a sudden thought or idea or memory will come to him which will clarify the problem. This is not always successful if there is much resistance, but often insight is gained when the thought appears.

While any light object which will dangle freely makes a satisfactory pendulum, "professional models" are obtainable. For example, such a model available from the Wilshire Book Company, Dept. K, 8721 Sunset Blvd., Hollywood, California 90069, is a clear plastic ball just over an inch in diameter attached to an 8-inch chain.

For induction of hypnosis this pendulum also makes an excellent object for eye fixation. In fact the therapist will often notice that his patient has slipped spontaneously into hypnosis as he gazes at the pendulum during questioning. This is a good induction method, for then the operator merely deepens the resulting trance. This occurs at least half the time with use of the pendulum and often while finger movements are being obtained.

REFERENCES

Fodor, N.: Search for the Beloved. New York, Hermitage Press, 1949.

LeCron, L. M.: A hypnotic technique for uncovering unconscious material. J. Clin. Exp. Hypn. 2: 1, 1954.

Mühl, A.: Automatic writing and hypnosis. *In:* Experimental Hypnosis (L. M. LeCron, Ed.). New York, Macmillan, 1952.

Platonov, K.: The Word (Russian publication in English). San Francisco Book Imports, 1955.

Wolpe, J.: Psychotherapy by Reciprocal Inhibition. Stanford, Stanford University Press, 1958.

Chapter 12

The Hypnotherapy of Psychosomatic Illnesses

THE GENERAL PRACTITIONER encounters a wide variety of illnesses which have behind them tension and stress, and in many there will be emotional and psychological factors as causes. These diseases will also be treated by the specialists in whose field they fall. It will be impossible in one book to cover all of these, and we will deal with only a few of the more common ones. However, the general principles involved will apply to any of these conditions with similar factors in their causation. Treatment would be similar in many ways for all of them.

While this is not a text on psychotherapy, if the physician will look for certain causes which may be present in any of these illnesses and apply the hypnotherapeutic methods given here, he will be successful in helping many patients, far more than drugs can cure. With some conditions, medical treatment may also be indicated.

Ideomotor answers to questions can locate the causes present in any particular case, no matter what its type, and will eliminate other possibilities. There are seven causative factors which we might term keys to the genesis of these conditions. They are also involved in those more serious mental disturbances which would be dealt with by referral to psychiatrists or psychologists. With these seven keys the door to the understanding of these ailments can be opened and insight gained by both patient and the physician. They can be treated in the way we will describe.

THE SEVEN KEYS

CONFLICT

A simple definition of conflict could be that it is a situation where we want something or want to do something but are prevented by our moral code or the taboos of society. It might be stated even more simply as *I want* colliding with *you can't.* Soon after birth an infant encounters life's prohibitions: *no, don't, you mustn't,* etc., and he is frustrated by not having his desires fulfilled.

There are many sources of conflict. One of the most common concerns sex. Conflict may be a source of strong guilt feelings, particularly if the person acts against moral codes. A conflict may originally be at a conscious level but later may be repressed and the person then is consciously unaware of it. Often there is no repression and the conflict is consciously recognized but is not resolved. While in hypnosis a patient can more easily talk of his conflicts and problems. He can more easily bring to consciousness a repressed conflict.

Every therapist must be objective but must have empathy with his patient for a good relationship to be established. He does not judge; he listens and encourages reorientation of attitude on the patient's part, giving him reassurance and clarifying harmful viewpoints and ideas. He serves as a "wailing wall."

Hypnotherapy is active and dynamic rather than passive, as in orthodox analysis. It deals in a direct way with the subconscious part of the mind. To some extent it is forceful, although the therapist should not be too forceful and often must proceed with caution in order not to bring out something which might be threatening to the patient if too rapidly raised to conscious awareness. Safeguards as to this will be pointed out. The therapist is more thoughtfully directive than is the analyst.

As a result, hypnotherapy usually is brief and results may come very rapidly. Resistances and repressions can occur and can defy the therapist as is the case with other forms of therapy. The difficulty in these conditions is centered in the subconscious part of the mind, not in consciousness.

A case of persistent conflict was shown by a young man who visited LeCron because he suffered much anxiety whenever he was with a group of people or even with individuals. He was a successful salesman in spite of this. At a meeting of any kind he always had to sit in the rear of the room near a door so he could leave if his anxiety became too great. He hated to shake hands with anyone and avoided it when he could.

Ideomotor answers to questions with the pendulum quickly revealed a conflict as the cause of his anxiety. The reason came out in his third session. While he knew of the conflict consciously, he had never connected it with his symptoms. In hypnosis he told of his boyhood masturbation. He was unmarried and had continued to masturbate. He had heard the usual false ideas about masturbation, including the statement that the hands of anyone who masturbated would be moist and would perspire. This was his reason for not liking to shake hands.

His anxiety was based on a fear that his associates or others to whom he talked would know of his masturbation, that it would be evident to them. To overcome this, he was asked if he could tell by his observation of others if they masturbated. He admitted that he couldn't and saw his fear as illogical. He was also straightened out as to his mistaken beliefs, and some of his guilt feelings were assuaged. Hypnotic suggestion was employed to help him digest the insight he had gained. After a fourth session his anxiety around people had disappeared.

MOTIVATION

Does an illness or symptom serve some purpose? Here there can be much variance. A simple motive would be if the ailment or symptom gained sympathy and attention. This would be immature behavior but might be entirely at an unconscious level. Most of us have immaturities along some lines.

A motive in hysterical blindness could be that the condition prevents the person from seeing something unpleasant or could serve as punishment for having seen something about which he feels guilty. As an unconscious means of escaping from hated housework, a woman might develop an allergy to detergents. These are merely possible motivations, the condition thus serving some purpose.

The motive behind a symptom or illness frequently is defensive, the condition acting as a protection. An example would be migraine headaches which are used as a defense against unacceptable feelings of hostility and aggression, emotions which almost invariably are found in migraine patients.

Motivations are sometimes deeply hidden but much more often can quickly be located through the questioning technic. Often insight alone is enough to overcome the condition.

IDENTIFICATION

Anyone who has children in the family has noticed how a child tends to copy the parents and at times tries to be like them. In early childhood we all identify with those close to us, and this can be carried over into adult life. Identification means dramatization. It may be difficult to know whether some trait or even illness is inherited or is merely a result of identification. If a mother, or perhaps the father, is greatly overweight, the children probably will tend to be fat. There may be some hereditary tendency for obesity, but certainly identification plays a role.

Children identify with parents or other loved ones for several reasons. Love for the person is a strong motive but even a hated parent may be the object of identification. Then the child wishes to be like that parent because he wants to be big and strong and powerful, as the parent seems to be. He has a will to power. Such a parent tells the child what he can or cannot do and may punish transgressions. A child may be told repeatedly he is just like one of the parents, that he takes after that side of the family, this acting as a suggestion. Another factor in identification with the father is where a boy has the same name, such as John Jones, Jr. Calling a boy "Junior" is psychologically poor practice, for it can promote feelings of inferiority. Identification tends to come and go, at one time it is with one person, at other times with another.

LeCron encountered what seemed to be a very strange identification in one patient. She was the wife of a very prominent author. Her nose was long and beak-like. She definitely resembled a bird. Everyone who knew her remarked on how bird-like she looked and acted. During her therapy she happened to tell of a very traumatic childhood experience. For some years she had had a pet crow which she loved dearly. It had been accidentally killed. When questioned as to whether her love for the bird might have caused her to identify with it, her finger response was affirmative. If true, it certainly was a peculiar identification.

MASOCHISM

Self-punishment due to strong guilt feelings is a very common form of unconsciously damaging behavior. Most of us will exhibit masochism at times in minor ways, but it may be so exaggerated that it includes self-destruction. Menninger wrote a book on this subject entitled *Man Against Himself*.

Some people have such an overgrown conscience that they will punish themselves severely over the most minor transgressions or unacceptable thoughts. Strangely, sometimes one part of the subconscious will compel a person to behave in an unacceptable way, another part then demanding punishment for the offense.

Extreme masochism can bring suicide or fatal illness. The alcoholic frequently uses his drinking as a means of self-destruction. While there is an instinctive need for self-preservation, sometimes the will to die overcomes it.

A 38-year-old man came for help through hypnosis in order to stop cigarette smoking. He smoked three packs a day and suffered from

Buerger's disease. Both feet had already been amputated and his hands were affected. He claimed he had tried to stop smoking but with no effect.

At the end of four sessions with hypnosis he was smoking four packs a day instead of three. Suggestions and the technique described by LeCron in *How to Stop Smoking with Self-Hypnosis* had been unsuccessful. In discussing the situation it was found that the patient had not carried out any of the methods recommended. Pendulum questioning brought replies that he would not stop smoking and would eventually lose his hands from the illness. He did not want to get well and refused therapy. No follow-up was made as he was not seen again.

In factories with large numbers of employees, it has been shown that 80 per cent of the accidents occur to 20 per cent of the personnel. Obviously many accidents are therefore unconsciously self-induced and are intentional. The housewife who often cuts or burns herself is undoubtedly punishing herself. In painful psychosomatic diseases, masochism frequently will be a factor in their genesis. It can often be uncovered by questioning in such conditions as migraine, chronic headache of other types, in arthritis and bursitis, slipped disc, dysmenorrhea, neuralgias, and other painful conditions.

When self-punishment is located as a cause, insight is seldom enough to end the symptom. The reasons for guilt feelings should be explored. These often center on sex, though many other reasons for guilt can be present. The therapist needs to reassure the patient and have him understand that his feelings of guilt are probably unwarranted. No one wears a halo and everyone does things he regrets and has thoughts which are not acceptable.

It should also be pointed out that self-punishment not only harms the person who is punishing himself, but that he also punishes everyone in his family at the same time. His illness worries and upsets his family and may be expensive, causing family hardship, which is unfair to innocent people.

We might cite here a case of very painful bursitis which had self-punishment as one causative factor and also motivation in that it served as a defense in two different ways. The patient was a dentist who practiced in California and was attending one of our symposiums in Honolulu. We returned by ship and Cheek attempted to help the dentist. Dr. Jones, as we will call him, could not lift his right arm. In fact it was even painful to move it at all. He had been forced to stop his practice and had taken the trip in the hope of recuperating.

In one session of less than an hour, with ideomotor replies to questions, the dentist brought out plausible reasons for the condition in this case.

Dr. Jones had a very busy practice and worked long hours. His physician had warned him to ease up as he had a slight heart condition. He did not follow this advice. One cause for the bursitis was an attempt on the part of his subconscious mind to permit him an excuse for a long needed rest. If he couldn't use his right arm, he couldn't practice. Thus bursitis was a defense.

Dr. Jones had a daughter married to an alcoholic who weighed over 200 pounds and beat her up frequently. Jones weighed only 150 pounds. This man had threatened to murder the daughter if she tried to leave him. She was living in constant fear of him. Jones intervened once and had been slapped down by his over-sized son-in-law. He longed to clobber the man. Due to his bursitis he couldn't, the symptom apparently serving again as a defense in keeping him out of trouble. He considered shooting the son-in-law and thought seriously about it. This was unconsciously an unacceptable thought as Dr. Jones was a good Christian. The bursitis may have been acting as a punishment for such a desire.

It was suggested that Dr. Jones have his daughter go to the police, see a lawyer and get a restraining order against her husband. Dr. Jones agreed to do this. Using the finger signals, he was asked if the bursitis could be ended with the insight gained as to its causes. The reply was affirmative. The patient was then awakened and Dr. Jones found to his surprise that all pain had left his shoulder. He could move it freely when he cautiously tested it. He had only slight further trouble with it. X rays showed the calcium deposit still present, but it hurt only at times when he recognized a cause for tension. The symptom served as a reminder for him to ease up and relax.

IMPRINTS

Psychotherapists unfamiliar with hypnosis and the effects of suggestion are rarely aware of single impact imprints which often seem to explain the cause of a problem. An imprinted experience may seem consciously trivial yet they are often of great importance. An imprint can be said to be an idea which has become fixed in the subconscious part of the mind and then is carried out in exactly the same way as a posthypnotic suggestion is carried out. Spiegel has pointed out that many neuroses may be of this origin with compulsion to act out behavior for which the causative stimulus is forgotten.

Estabrooks has said that when a person is under an emotion he becomes very suggestible. Something said at the time may register in the subconscious and it is as though a post-hypnotic suggestion has been given. Apparently when one is under an emotion we slip spontaneously into hypnosis. Thought processes become childlike and literal just as in hypnosis. There is no doubt that everyone is unconsciously affected by emotionally charged imprints or "engrams." Depending on their wording, they can be very beneficial, but at other times they are extremely detrimental. They can affect behavior, cause illnesses, and some types of imprint or "prestige suggestions" may prevent recovery from disease or prevent the loss of some symptom.

The authors have encountered such damaging imprints many times. Here we are in the field of semantics. These "command statements" are worded something like this: "You'll never get over this," "You'll have to learn to live with this condition," "Nothing does any good," "It can't be helped." If such an idea is set up, therapy will be unsuccessful until the imprint is removed. Of course such phrases would have no effect if the person were not under an emotion when it is said. At the time a discouraged or frustrated physician makes such a statement the patient is very likely to be frightened or discouraged enough to be hypersuggestible. The physician speaks with prestige or superior knowledge and years of experience.

An interesting case was that of a middle-aged woman with a cough which had plagued her as long as she could remember. Every few moments she would have a bout of coughing. She said no treatment had ever helped her. Some explanations were made as to imprints, identifications, and other possible factors which might be present as causes. Then questions were asked, using the pendulum.

Q. Is there some emotional or psychological reason why you have this cough?

A. Yes (with the pendulum).

Q. Does the cough serve some purpose? Is there some benefit from the cough?

A. No.

Q. Are you identifying with someone who in your childhood had a similar cough?

A. No.

Q. Is organ language involved? Are you trying to cough up something, some idea or memory which is unpleasant, trying to get something out of your system?

A. No.

Q. Is there a fixed idea working in your inner mind that makes you cough?

A. Yes.

Q. Is there more than one idea involved?

A. No.

Q. Is that the only reason why you cough?

A. Yes.

Q. An imprint or idea has to have an origin. Is there some past experience where this fixed idea developed?
A. Yes.
Q. Is there more than one such incident?
A. No.
Q. Let's find out when it happened. You've had the cough for many years, ever since you can remember. Did this past experience take place before you were ten years old?
A. Yes.
Q. Was it before five years old?
A. Yes.
Q. Was it before three?
A. No.
Q. Was it when you were three?
A. No.
Q. When you were four?
A. Yes. (Finding the time within a year is usually close enough.)
Q. Is the cough associated with some illness?
A. Yes. (The patient then verbally volunteered that she had had a bad case of whooping cough at that age and had nearly died from complications.)
Q. Was this whooping cough the experience we are trying to locate?
A. Yes.
Q. Did someone say something at that time that set up this imprint or fixed idea?
A. Yes.
Q. Was it one of your parents?
A. No.
Q. Was it a doctor?
A. Yes.
Q. What was the doctor's name? Answer verbally.
A. I don't know.
Q. Does your inner mind know his name?
A. Yes (pendulum).

During the questioning as the patient watched the swing of the pendulum, she had gradually slipped spontaneously into hypnosis. This was deepened and she was then regressed to four years old to the time when she was ill with the whooping cough. She related that she was in bed and her mother and father were standing by the bed. The physician was also there and she now recalled his name. Her mother was crying and the physician was saying to them, "She'll never get over this." She heard and was frightened.

Here was her imprint. The physician represented authority. While still in hypnosis it was pointed out to her that she had recovered from the illness but the cough was a major part of it. With this imprint in force her inner mind had carried out the idea, causing her to retain the cough. She was then questioned further.

Q.   Now that you see why you have continued to cough and since you really did get over the illness, do you think that this false idea the doctor planted need continue to affect you?

A.   No. (finger signal).

Q.   Can you now be free of the cough permanently?

A.   Yes.

It was rather significant that the patient had stopped coughing during the pendulum questioning as soon as she began to slip into hypnosis. A checkup with her some weeks later showed that she had not coughed again after this one session.

The steps taken with this case were: explanation of the possible causes, search with the questioning technique, spontaneous development of hypnosis, age regression to the experience, reorientation and "mopping up" by establishing that the symptom could be terminated.

An imprint is somewhat similar to a conditioned reflex. A Pavlovian method of eradicating a conditioned reflex is first to locate it, then to erase it through insight and the use of hypnotic suggestion combined with explanations and rationalizations. Knowledge of the wording of an imprint, with regression to the time when it was originally established, then taking the patient through that experience several times, can wipe it out. Insight and explanations usually occur during this process.

In the coughing case, going through the experience once was sufficient to permit it being eradicated. If the patient had answered negatively to the question as to the cough continuing, she would have been taken back over the incident until an affirmative was given. If this was not obtained after three more times of going through it, a question would have been asked as to whether something was blocking her from now losing the symptom. If so, this would have been investigated.

When it would seem that a goal has been reached it is wise to try to obtain a commitment from the subconscious by asking in this way if the patient can now be rid of the imprint. An affirmative answer usually but not always means that the outlook for relief is probable.

ORGAN LANGUAGE

An interesting source of physical difficulty at times is what has been termed "organ language" in psychology. Often we speak of something unpleasant, saying "That's a headache to me," "That makes me sick at my stomach," "I can't swallow that," "It's a pain in the neck to me," "That gives me a pain," and various other phrases. The actual physical condition mentioned may develop from such an idea. Many a chronic headache, nausea, pains, etc., seem to arise from organ language. This can be seen sometimes in cases of dermatitis, the person "itching" to do something. A breaking out of the skin can appear because something is "irritating," the skin being one's outside.

As part of the causes in a strange case of torticollis, two organ language phrases were implicated. The patient was a man whose head was turned far to the left with the muscles so taut that it could not be straightened. The condition had persisted for about three months and his physician thought hypnosis might help in relaxing the muscles.

Ralph, as we will call him, had a responsible position and was married, with four children of whom he was very fond. He was a heavy drinker, usually getting drunk on Saturday night, recovering over Sunday, and staying sober the rest of the week. He was a good hypnotic subject.

During the second visit, questioning was used to locate the reasons for the condition. First he was asked if there was any psychological cause for his wry neck and the answer was affirmative. Further inquiries eliminated identification and imprints. Involved were conflict, self-punishment, past experiences, motivation and organ language. It seemed rather complicated for there to be five of our seven keys involved. Further questions were as follows:

Q. Is your conflict over sex?
A. Yes (finger movement).
Q. Are you punishing yourself because of this?
A. Yes.
Q. Is there more than one past experience connected to this condition?
A. Yes.
Q. More than two?
A. Yes.
Q. A series of experiences?
A. Yes.
Q. Self-punishment is one motivation. Is there any other motive or reason for your wry neck?
A. (A movement of the ring finger.)
Q. Does that lifting of the ring finger signify "perhaps?"
A. Yes.

Ralph was then hypnotized, and further questioning located the past experiences. He was then able to verbalize the situation. Nothing was repressed, but he had not associated his torticollis with what had happened. Organ language had not been explained to him, though it was described later when he used the phrases in his speech.

Ralph had fallen in love with his secretary, whose desk in his office was to his left and slightly to the rear of his own desk. She had returned his regard but both were Catholics and divorce was impossible, nor did he want to be separated from his family, and hence there was conflict. After a time they decided that the situation could not continue. They agreed not to see each other any more and she left his employment. His drinking had then become worse and torticollis developed.

In telling of this affair Ralph remarked that the girl had "turned his head." A little later he said he was "looking back" at the experience with regret. Here was the organ language, his head being turned in the direction where the girl had sat. Replies to more questions confirmed this. Masochism was due to his strong guilt feelings about the affair, although he had not had sexual relations with the girl.

When awakened after this second session, the tension was gone from Ralph's neck and he could hold his head straight with no discomfort. A few days later he returned with the head again to one side. Strong reassurance and suggestion enabled him again to lose the symptom. A week later it had returned. He said he had been all right until Sunday morning of this week, and the same was true of the week before. Sundays he had awakened with his head twisted once more.

Further questions determined that he now was punishing himself for his Saturday night drinking bouts. The answer was given that he would be free of the torticollis the last four days of the week but if he continued to drink in this way it would then return for the first three days of the week. Ralph doggedly refused to stop drinking and the last known of the case was that it persisted in this way, three days of wry neck and four days without.

PAST EXPERIENCES

Experiences of the past may be involved with some of the other of our seven keys. In Ralph's case, the past experiences with his secretary were a part of his conflict and the motivation for the symptom. When an imprint is established, a past experience was involved. Guilt feelings and unacceptable ideas originate in the past.

A different type of experience is one which was traumatic. A great fright may be responsible for the development of a phobia or may produce many other effects. In two stutterers it was found that a sexual trauma combined with verbal suggestions was one cause of the speech difficulty, both cases being almost identical in this respect. As a child the stutterers had been sexually molested by an adult and had been told, "If you ever tell, I'll kill you," which was the command statement. The molester in each case meant he would kill the boy if he told of the attack but literally "If you ever tell" means about anything; if you speak at all. With the subconscious carrying out this idea, if he talks he will die. It doesn't matter if the threat was made years ago and there is no present danger, the threat hangs over him like the sword of Damocles. The subconscious does not view this logically. A need to talk collided with the fear of being killed if he talked, so there is blocking and stuttering.

Of course there can be many other reasons for stuttering, but these two stutterers quickly found they could speak normally after the trauma had been brought out and the imprint removed. Strangely most stutterers are good hypnotic subjects and most do not stutter if they talk while in hypnosis. When awakened the speech difficulty returns. This fact is of help in the therapy of stuttering. Some other command statements may also be active with a stutterer. One is where a stern parent has repeatedly told a child to "shut up" or "be quiet" "shut your mouth" or some similar exclamation.

Difficulties may develop from other kinds of traumas. When a past experience is located, the patient can be age regressed to the time and the effects removed. Much emotion may be tied up in the experience. The first time the patient is returned to it he may show the emotion strongly. Going back over it again it may still be rather strong, a third time reduces the emotion greatly, and by a fourth or fifth time all emotion will probably have disappeared. The object of such a regression is not only to gain insight but to discharge the pent-up emotions tied to the experience. The patient should be taken back through it again and again until a finger response says all emotion has been discharged. This may be done in a single session.

The patient should never be regressed to a traumatic event without first obtaining an affirmative answer to the question "Is it all right for you to return to this event?"

The causes of many psychosomatic illnesses will be found to be very superficial and easily remedied, though other cases may be very complicated, so deep-seated that special consultations may be necessary. In our courses we always demonstrate the treatment of such cases as may be available, usually finding some among the physicians and others who attend, or sometimes having patients brought in. Frequently we can only make a start at helping the patient, giving him some insight through the questioning technique. But it is surprising how often in one demonstration perhaps lasting only 30 or 40 minutes we can uncover the apparent roots of the matter and witness a rapid clearance of symptoms. A later check often shows that permanent benefit resulted. In such cases the causes must have only been superficial. Long suffering usually crystallizes many constellations of triggering causes for distress. It takes longer to effect cure and one may have to settle for mitigation of distress.

The cases we have cited here are typical in showing how ideomotor answers to questions can bring out apparent causes for psychosomatic ailments. Almost any such illness can be handled in the same general way. In our experience a large percentage of psychosomatic illnesses can be cleared up in a very few sessions, indicating the superficiality of the case. These can usually be handled readily by the non-psychotherapist. Others may take much longer, and there will be failures with some. Resistances and repressions can prolong treatment.

REFERENCES

Estabrooks, G. H.: Hypnotism. New York, Dutton, 1943.

LeCron, L. M.: Technoques of Hypnotherapy. New York, Julian Press, 1961.

_____: How to Stop Smoking with Self-Hypnosis. Englewood Cliffs, Prentice-Hall, 1964.

Menninger, K.: Man Against Himself. New York, Harcourt Brace, 1938.

Chapter 13

Hypnosis in Gynecology: Frigidity

IN THE PRIVATE PRACTICE of gynecology, the major problems are not what we saw during our residency. The most common source of trouble begins at birth and reaches its peak of unfavorable conditioning during the first three years of life. Its influence is made less tractable because it occurs before the first glimmerings of conscious awareness, development of reasoning power or the learnings by repetition. Adult understanding of anatomy and normal sexual drives come later. None of these, unaided, can adequately overthrow the imprinting and preconscious conditionings for the majority of women in the "civilized" world. Their problem is genital taboo, learned in the cradle and often carried unaltered to the grave.

It is normal for babies to put things in their mouths. It would be dangerous if there were no sucking instinct. Parents recognize this yet they become embarrassed and improve the habits of their babies by gently denying them use of thumbs, toes, movable objects and "security blankets." Babies need stimulation of their skins in order to develop normal patterns of bladder and rectal elimination. Many premature babies are denied this stimulus.

Parents have a way of mocking babies for soiling their diapers, giving babies names of pseudo-endearment such as "Poopsie," "Droopy-drawers," and "Stinky," which might interfere with normal eliminative needs of babies. Multiple studies in age regression with patients who have suffered from colitis and repeated urinary tract infections have brought out similar early impressions of parents looking disgusted and making angry sounds while changing diapers or cleaning up the "messes" in cribs, behind sofas in the living room or in clothing after "accidents." The information on this matter was not suggested to adult patients in hypnosis. It has been a repeated spontaneous offering of patients with intestinal and urinary complaints on orienting to some important experience relating to the origin of troubles with bowel and bladder.

Mammal young will die of ureteral and intestinal obstruction due to inadequate peristaltic action if they are denied the instinctive licking given them by the mother at delivery and after each nursing period. This lesson was learned by keepers of zoos and the early experimenters raising mammals in germ-free states. LeCron has mentioned the importance of an empty bladder for the successful induction of hypnosis. Normally there has been a long period of association between feelings of anxiety with the stretching of the bladder and the rectosigmoid and peaceful relaxation after feeding, elimination and comfortable reclothing. Feeding, elimination and the drowsy comfort of warm, dry clothing are usually followed by sleep in secure contact with the mother and siblings for most mammals. Let us study parental methods in our advanced Western Culture. We laugh at "Stinky" making grunting noises after feeding. We cannot remember the feelings of humiliation we had at the same period of life with the mocking noises of our own parents. We plunk the infant on a frighteningly high place in the most defenseless position. We make wry expressions as we hold our breath or make comments about the odor and quality of the excrement. We hurriedly wash, oil, dust and rewrap. Then we either take the "little monster" to tire it out in the living room or we eliminate it from civilization and bodily warmth directly in its "very own" room. It does not take long for the toddler to learn that the living room bit is the prologue to physical elimination from the family. No wonder the child cries in the night!

Next in the course of unfavorable conditioning is discovery that digital exploration of the nose, mouth, ears and umbilicus is acceptable but exploration of the genital area and rectum evokes sounds of objection, restraining action or even a slapped hand. The process of learning that stimulation of the clitoris, vulva and perineum can be pleasurable would normally include unconscious rubbing against a bunched-up blanket in sleep, but mothers have a habit of "looking in" on babies at this stage of development in order to make sure they are covered. They snatch away such blankets incorrectly used. The child will have no conscious knowledge that there is something bad about rubbing against a bunched-up blanket, but this child as a frigid adult will report in hypnotic age-regression that this sleepy experience has been a powerful one in teaching her that pleasurable sensations around the clitoris are frowned upon by mother.

The same can be said for the pleasures of "riding a cock horse to Danbury Cross" on daddy's shoe. Sliding down the bannisters too often or climbing poles may also call for correction from parents or grandparents. One 30-year-old frigid patient remembered the admonition of her grandmother after too many gleeful trips down the bannisters: "There are nerve endings there between your legs. If you rub them too many times you'll go crazy. Now run along and play in the yard."

Punishment for being curious about what is under the little neighbor boy's pants, admonition against accepting candy from men or riding in strange automobiles are probably all necessary to protect growing girls from trouble. These more mature learnings would probably not cause too much trouble if there were no prior taboos and imprinted fears.

Eczema and the rashes of measles and chicken pox feel good to scratch, and the havoc caused by scratching receives concerned and loving attention from parents in an atmosphere of acceptance. There is no such acceptance when a child develops a vulvar itching although it feels good to squirm and scratch. Habit patterns of acceptable skin-scratching often supplant non-acceptable masturbatory activities.

Children in private or parochial schools are usually kept in the dark about the reasons group activities in communal bathrooms or behind locked doors are matters of concern for their adult guardians of sanctity. Their usually innocent desires for privacy and exclusion of adults are somehow made into unsavory urges by the way they are treated.

What are some of the problems the gynecologist sees in private practice, away from the funnelling concentration into teaching hospitals of tumors, torsions, hemorrhage, congenital anomalies and venereal disease? First on the list would probably be vaginitis associated with trichomonas, monilia, herpes simplex, cocci, mixed infection or chemical irritation from too much douching. Conditioning processes, guilt feelings and self-punitive drives seem to play a large part in the anxieties capable of making the vaginal mucosa more vulnerable to normally non-painful stimuli.

Hyperventilation during anxiety may play an important part in producing trichomonas vaginitis. Hypnosis in the treatment of vaginitis is of value for helping the patient pinpoint the first moment at which symptoms or discharge began. Patients may recognize the relationships between symptom and sexual experiences or fantasies about which they feel uncomfortable. Continuation of the problem in spite of the usual treatments may allow the therapist a chance to point out that her body is reacting badly to the anxiety of a hopeless affair, that she should break off an association where mutual respect and interests have been sacrificed.

As with all psychosomatic complaints involving a target organ, it is helpful to demonstrate the effects of postural suggestion, the power of the challenge and the word "try," show the difference in tissue reaction with a painful scratch on a sensitive arm as compared with the same injury to the opposite numb area when it has been made analgesic. The patient in light hypnosis can "orient back to the first time" something was happening that had something to do with her problem.

One patient who had never had an orgasm developed an acute trichomonas vaginitis 12 years after her marriage when she began having orgasms in her sleep, dreaming about a sexually attractive, married associate in her teaching job. She consulted a woman gynecologist who said that this infection could eventuate in cancer if it were not cleared up. A strict ritual of vaginal salves and douching was maintained for two years. In the meantime there was no intercourse with husband or anyone else.

The dreams stopped and a painful relief from subconscious sin continued with vaginitis until the patient was able to talk about her problem with another doctor. She was told to stop douching and let her vagina have a chance to heal. The unintentional misunderstanding about cancer was corrected and reinforced by subsequent vaginal smears. Within 48 hours the foul discharge, pelvic pain and tissue edema had gone. The patient was congratulated on learning at this late date that the subconscious mind almost never offers gratifying sexual dreams about a husband when she has never had an orgasm with him. Fantasies about other males occur normally until the learning process, which should have occurred in sleep many years before marriage, has taught that orgasm is a mental process and depends upon recognition that sexual feelings are normal. Then and only then can she have dreams about her husband if she is sexually attracted to him and is not using sexual rejection to punish him. It was added that real intercourse could be much more satisfying than dreams.

DYSMENORRHEA

The common history for this second most frequent gynecological complaint is that there are several painless menstrual periods until ovulation occurs. Men of science have decided that ovulation is the cause of dysmenorrhea and there is some justification for this conclusion because dysmenorrhea may stop when a woman with regular ovulation is shifted into anovulatory menstrual cycles with estrogen therapy.

Some people have wondered about the factors responsible for stimulation of ovulation and the instinctive physiological weeping that occurs when pregnancy has not followed ovulation. These questions may be worthy of consideration. There have been approximately thirty major approaches to the problem of dysmenorrhea through the years including successful use of various aromatic spices and cocainization of the "genital areas" in the nasal passages, described by Fliess.

Radiologists before World War I were irradiating the ovaries and pituitary glands with token doses of X-ray. Presacral neurectomies made popular by the Frenchman Cotte only temporarily removed sympathetic innervation but often permanently cured dysmenorrhea. These all seem to share the more or less costly and traumatic quality of implying to the suffering young woman that this way lies cure. Some young women are more suggestible than others, but many develop a need for pain to escape from sexual guilt feelings, punish themselves or manipulate associates. These are the people who are finally subjected to hysterectomy or may, in desperation, ask for psychological help.

Another common factor arises from the expectation of having cramps and pain at the time of a period. This expectation comes from repeatedly hearing from mother, sisters and friends about the discomforts they have experienced. These suggestions can act to produce dysmenorrhea.

Therapy does not depend solely on hypnosis. Treatment of the patient must include recognition that unconscious forces cannot always be directly reasoned with or corrected by mechanical means. The patient must be absolved from the feeling that she is being difficult. Therapy can be accelerated by setting up ideomotor signals and asking if it would be all right for her to know how to menstruate comfortably and learn the control of pain in preparation for letting her future pregnancies be exciting and pleasurable experiences instead of painful ones. In the search for factors which might first have made the pelvic organs vulnerable to pain, we have had case upon case reporting that their birth caused mother much pain, that this is a way of making it up to mother. Naturally this impression is immediately recognized as ridiculous. It remains the most powerful force militating against the painless labor ideal of "natural childbirth." When it is brought up by the patient, it is helpful to ask the questions referred to in the chapter on obstetrics.

Some patients have discovered that dysmenorrhea began shortly after they had experimented in mutual masturbation with a girl friend or followed fears that petting or being kissed might make them pregnant. Whatever the subjectively significant assumed causes chosen during orientation back to "an important" reason for the pain, it is usually rather easy to let the patient decide whether or not it is worthwhile to continue with the misunderstanding.

Since the advent of the contraceptive pill, it has been Cheek's custom to put the patient on "the pill" for two months with the consent of the parents. This allows time to evaluate the importance of ovulation versus conditionings for pain. It allows time to know more about the problems of the young lady before directly approaching the subject of dysmenorrhea as a purely psychological problem. Hypnosis is mentioned at the second visit as an adjunct in speeding up the cure. The patient is told that she can raise her tolerance for pain by learning how to relax and how to shift awareness. Motivation is added by pointing out the value of knowing how to review material she is studying in school and how to use brief rest periods several times a day. It is mentioned that the girl who learns to stop the pain of menstruation will have an easy time delivering babies.

Emotional causes for dysmenorrhea are far more common than the organic ones of adenomyosis, endometriosis, myomata and salpingitis. Most gynecologists now agree that retroposition of the uterus has little to do with causing menstrual cramps. It is worthwhile to expose the patient with organic possible factors to the same treatment as the patients with purely psychogenic factors to assure success of time-honored treatments.

Treatment is usually broken up into three sessions of thirty minutes each: (1) exposure to relaxation induction and selecting ideomotor signals. Attempt to run down factors subjectively believed important in making the first painful menstrual period. (2) Have the patient develop slightly deeper trance state and relive the feelings of the first painful menstruation. Ask her to turn off the pain at a subconscious level and have an ideomotor signal indicate completion and have her report verbally when she feels comfortable. (3) Place the patient in hypnosis with dropping of a pencil as the indicator of reaching a level deep enough to permit helpful use of hypnosis. She is asked if it will be all right for her now to menstruate scantily, perhaps one pad a day, three days each month, and with complete comfort to do any of the things she would like to do when she is not menstruating. This is a means of giving helpful suggestions in the form of a question. It reveals resistance due to unresolved self-punitive attitudes.

If a painful menstrual period occurs after acceptance of this suggestion, the therapist must look for previously undiscovered organic and emotional factors. These steps take only a few moments of the third session. The rest of the time is spent having the patient rehearse autohypnosis as discussed in the chapter on obstetrics.

During the course of therapy for dysmenorrhea, the patient is told that there will be times when dysmenorrhea may occur again during an illness or a time of depression or stress. At such times she must think of this "slip-back" as a reminder to ask herself about and learn the factors responsible. It can remind her how to turn off pain and the practice can be helpful.

LOW BACK PAIN, MUSCLE SPASM, MITTELSCHMERZ, PERITONITIS

Many factors play a part in producing these painful conditions. We are the only primates who spend most of our waking hours walking on two legs or sitting. There are, therefore, gravitational forces at work on the viscera of the abdomen and on the pelvic girdle muscles for which our bodies were not primarily constructed. Continued hypertonicity of the back and pelvic muscles will cause pain because of interference with oxygen supply. Pain increases muscle tone in the area and we have a vicious circle. The peritoneum lining the pelvis and covering the intestine, bladder, uterus, tubes and ovaries is sensitive to proteolytic enzymes released on contact with some virulent organisms, with blood containing fibrinolysins, with bile, stomach contents and the groumous material contained in dermoid cysts. In addition there may be a genuine chemical reaction of a painful nature when turpentinue, potassium permanganate or soaps are injected into the uterine cavity and out through the tubes to the abdominal cavity during abortion attempts.

Pelvic pain may then be produced slowly because of continued tonicity of back and pelvic muscles in response to external stresses or it may have an acute onset with a primal insult that sets up a pattern of increased sensitivity to moderate stimuli. We have learned that freedom from conscious pain does not mean that the central nervous system is not receiving slightly painful or subconscious messages of discomfort.

In the therapy for these conditions it is again important to know something about the emotional factors associated with whatever organic cause there was in the beginning. It is important to know what emotional as well as physical factors are active in continuing the pain. For general principles, refer to the chapter on pain.

AMENORRHEA

This also is a condition with many possible causes, most prominent of which are pregnancy, great emotional stress and great physical disability. Before subjecting such patients to extensive hormonal assay and exploratory laparotomy, it is wise to do a quick scanning of attitude about menstruation if menstruation has never occurred, and it is helpful to orient the patient back to the last normal period and come forward to something responsible for a change of reaction if there has been an unexplained cessation of menses. Menstruation is not a necessity for cleansing the body or soul. The patient can be congratulated on her ability to do something that most women cannot do. She is told that efforts will be made only to find out that she is free of problems and that she will be made to bleed only if she thinks it is necessary to do so.

Having searched for factors she is asked if she can now menstruate regularly with three days of light bleeding. If the answer is "yes," she is asked to select the time for her next period. This does not always work on the first effort but repetition of the suggestion will usually eventuate in regular menses.

It should be mentioned here that primary consultation with an endocrinologist at the first concern over secondary amenorrhea may complicate matters. The emotional background and the frames of reference of endocrinologists, like those of many neurosurgeons, neurologists and orthopedists, make them uncomfortable when dealing with psychosomatic illness. They are highly competent in diagnosing trouble but have a tendency to stress rather frightening possibilities of grave genetic abnormalities and various types of endocrine-producing tumors in the course of their examinations. Fortunately these are rarely found but once considered are rarely removed as sources of fear for the patient exposed to them. Unconscious fears and identifications may be compounded by these added fears of the unknown.

Warning. Please remember that consciously unrecognized self-punitive attitudes may make men and women with serious organic disease believe consciously *and unconsciously* that their problems are trivial. They may jump at the opportunity of having their underlying disease go undiagnosed. Amenorrhea may be caused by brain tumors, hyper- and hypothyroidism, panhypopituitarism after massive blood loss (Sheehan's syndrome), ovarian tumors, adrenal tumors and any far advanced disease including tuberculosis and bilateral renal calculi. We must be more alert for serious disease when amenorrhea follows previously regular menses than when there has been no onset of menstrual cycles (primary amenorrhea). Remember, however, that primary amenorrhea may result from occlusion or non-formation of the cervical canal. Failure to discover this fact during the first few cycles may leave permanent damage to the tubes and ovaries. Never forget that pregnancy occurs at any age from 8 to 56 whether females are married or unmarried. We have seen women who have been totally unable to accept the fact of their pregnancy even though witnessing their delivery and being shown the child.

MENORRHAGIA

Visible bleeding is not essential in the course of being a normal fertile woman. One woman at Johns Hopkins Hospital established this fact with 11 normal children delivered at appropriate intervals during 15 years of amenorrhea.

An acceptable amount of bleeding, intended to keep women from worrying about themselves, is ideally that amount which will require changing a pad or vaginal tampon three times during a 24-hour time and terminating at the end of three days.

Bleeding after intercourse and bleeding at irregular intervals between menstrual periods must always be considered due to organic pathology in the vagina, cervix, uterus, uterine tubes or ovary. It should never be assumed to be emotional in origin or due to endocrine therapy until repeated examinations of the pelvic organs, vaginal smears and uterine curettings have been done. Intermenstrual bleeding often occurs with young women using contraceptive hormone pills. Such women are also likely to be troubled by fluid retention, tender breasts and pelvic discomfort. In the author's experience, these complaints are rare with women who are free of worry about their reasons for using "the pill." Religious and other conditioned guilt feelings play a large part in these evidences of aldosterone activity, but it is still necessary to rule out potentially dangerous pelvic pathology. Cervical cancer has been reported in newborn infants and is being found fairly often in women less than 20 years old.

Spotting between periods and postcoital bleeding are diagnosed as metrorrhagia, but when disease processes of an organic nature have been excluded, the approach to their correction is the same as for heavy bleeding. That scant intermenstrual bleeding can be psychogenic is clearly seen during physical examination of women who have become alarmed over the chance that they may have cancer or some other serious malady. Approximately 10 per cent of the authors' patients in this category will be seen to have a trace of blood in the cervical canal during speculum examination. Absence of blood in the vaginal secretions and on the vaginal walls indicate that bleeding began as they got on the table for examination. This minimal bleeding seems to occur without respect for time in the menstrual cycle and is probably comparable to the capillary bleeding witnessed by Markee within a few seconds of fright or injection of epinephrine intravenously. In his classic studies of endometrial implants in the anterior chamber of the eyes of rhesus monkeys, Markee was able to see that this type of bleeding terminated with clot formation, whereas menstrual bleeding did not lead to clot formation. Stieve has reported this type of bleeding in amenorrheic women within a few minutes of learning the time of their execution.

Profuse bleeding which gushes around pads and requires frequent changes during the night occurs about as frequently in women who have no demonstrable gynecologic abnormality as it does with endometrial hyperplasia, polyps, submucous myomata and cancer. True menorrhagia may well relate to hormonal disturbance due to emotional or physical stresses. We must keep the organic factors in mind, but we should always ask the patient about emotional stresses at the first interview, whether it be on the telephone or in the office. The question allows the patient great relief from the primal worry over some dire disease. She knows the question would not have been asked unless emotional problems were known to cause hemorrhage. Profuse bleeding may occur after great personal loss, after great disappointment or coincident with suppressed rage. Menorrhagia associated with emotional causes is well recognized, and there are abundant references to it in the world literature.

Psychogenic uterine hemorrhage will sometimes stop within a few minutes when a physician indicates possibility that emotion can cause bleeding. Women seem to recognize this fact subliminally if not consciously. They need to know, however, that a qualified physician is willing to recognize it also and is willing to listen. Epsilon-amino-caproic acid (Amicar, Lederle) is a valuable adjunct for slowing down uterine hemorrhage until emotional possibilities can be assessed. An initial dose of 2 Gm. (four tablets) followed by two tablets per hour for no more than three hours will usually prevent the need for emergency hospitalization and curettage. It is never safe to use general anesthesia under circumstances where a patient is alarmed. This drug apparently inactivates fibrinolysins or their precursors and is a valuable addition to a physician's office medications and handbag.

STEPS OF PSYCHOTHERAPY FOR ABNORMAL BLEEDING

1. Set up ideomotor responses.
2. Orient to the moment just before heavy bleeding starts and ask for a "yes" finger to lift at that moment.
3. Advance from this moment to some thought or feeling that might have something to do with starting the trouble. The "no" finger is to lift at this time, and she is instructed to bring this thought up for conscious recognition.
4. Ask "In light of what you have discovered, do you think it might be possible to stop this heavy bleeding and return to a normal type of menstruation?"
5. At this point, and no sooner, it is helpful to ask the following very important questions: (a) "Does the deep part of your mind feel that you

have a serious or dangerous disease?" (b) "Have you identified yourself with any other person who has had bleeding like this?" These questions are placed here to diminish chances of the patient thinking the therapist believes a serious condition exists.

6. A very helpful addition recently has been a scan of thoughts and dreams during the night before trouble began. Dreams may give significant clues which may escape notice if questioning is limited to daytime.

Warning. Cessation of bleeding on discovery of emotional factors does not exclude possibility that emotional bleeding has been superimposed on an underlying dangerous disease process. The author has seen one clinic patient and two private patients whose early uterine cancers were discovered because of the lucky accident that they were emotionally disturbed enough to bleed from their normal endometrium and require diagnostic studies. Vaginal cytology and uterine curetting should be examined in each instance after the emergency is over.

FRIGIDITY

The term "frigidity" is used here in a general sense to cover the problems of men and women whose fears, misunderstandings and guilt feelings have interfered with maturation of sexual attitudes. The problems are in general related to sexual behavior but cannot be restricted to this area, because sexual feelings of inadequacy, fear and guilt certainly influence general behavior in all spheres of activity. Since homosexuality does not occur among any animals that are not tampered with by human beings, it is a logical conclusion that the problems of homosexuality must be conditioned by disturbing experiences in early life and their solution, if desired, could be found in reconditioning by psychotherapeutic methods. The treatment of homosexuality will be omitted here because it is a complex psychiatric problem. Its treatment should be restricted to the province of psychiatrists who are comfortable in this type of work.

Considerations will be limited to those areas in which physicians and psychologists can be helpful without risk of uncovering information too stressful to be handled by the patient.

Some women ask for help because they recognize their physical attraction to a sexual partner but are unable to reach a climax during intercourse. Some feel happy with their responsiveness even though there has never been an orgasm but ask for help because their sexual partner has complained of inadequacy according to his values. Some men ask help because they have had sexual dreams with ejaculation but are unable to ejaculate during intercourse. Some men eventually seek help at the request of their sexual partner because they ejaculate before or immediately after entrance into the vagina or they lose an erection before or during the act of entering the vagina.

Basically women and men meeting these criteria for frigidity, premature ejaculation and impotence have similar backgrounds of disturbed sexual learnings. They can be helped, providing they love and respect their sexual partner and can be motivated toward more satisfactory behavior for the benefit of their sexual partner. Human beings may love and respect each other at one plane of awareness but continue to use sexual maladjustments as punitive or manipulative tools. Such perversities may tax the skills of the most expert therapists.

The task is much more difficult when sexual fears and misunderstandings are so great that men or women will not permit themselves to engage in a healthy, loyal relationship with a member of the opposite sex. In this category we find the boastful "confirmed bachelor," the young girl in a triangle, some homosexuals, and women who work for companies supplying temporary office help. Some people extend their fears of commitment into their work. There are great variations in capacity for sexual response among individuals in this second category, but fundamentally they avoid any great strength of emotion.

Group 1 are willing to be helped; they are *sexually* frigid. Group 2, afraid of commitments, are *emotionally* frigid and should be cared for by psychiatrists who themselves are comfortable in discussing sexual difficulties.

There are many men and women in the first group who will not primarily come under the care of a physician for sexual help. Attention should be drawn to the classes of problems so often associated with sexual difficulties that sexual factors should at least be excluded before attacking the visible trouble.

In women:
  Psoriasis, neurodermatitis and recurrent genital Herpes
  Adolescent acne of face and upper trunk
  Dysmenorrhea
  Endometriosis
  Myomata uteri
  Pruritis vulvae
  Repeated vaginitis due to trichomonads or monilia
  Recurrent urinary tract infection in absence of obstruction
  Unexplained infertility
  Habitual abortion and repeated premature delivery

In men:
 Psoriasis, neurodermatitis and recurrent genital Herpes
 Migraine headaches
 Meniere's syndrome
 Recurrent urinary tract infection in absence of obstruction
 Prostatis

By no means do the authors express or mean to imply that these problems are always linked with sexual inhibitions, guilt feelings and fear. We suggest that the target organs are somehow made more vulnerable to infection, disturbances of endocrine balance and the influence of catechol amines. Among the factors responsible may be found problems arising from conflicts of a sexual nature.

STEPS OF THERAPY

It seems important during history-taking to note the parent whose age is used from which to compute the age of the other. This is not an absolute means of knowing which parent is most influential but it is helpful. Note carefully when an American girl carries a name suggesting that her parents had planned on a boy, when a girl is the first-born, the only child or the only surviving child. She may have very confused understandings of her importance as a female in the family. Watch for a history of parental death, serious illness or separation of parents before your patient has reached the age of five years. Every child is capable of misdeeds evoking signs of displeasure in parents. Propinquity of such acts and death, illness or divorce may fill a youngster with consciously unrecognized guilt feelings capable of injuring all future happiness. It is helpful to ask married women whether intercourse is painful or not and whether or not they feel they respond adequately. Their statement of satisfactory responses should be followed by an estimate of how frequently, in percentage, they achieve an orgasm. Less than 80 per cent call for further study because it is probably an overstatement.

The above history can be taken during the first interview and without the aid of hypnosis. If there is an expressed feeling that sexual patterns are in need of improvement, it is wise to discuss these at another time after the patient has had a chance to think over her reactions to you and decide whether or not she could comfortably embark on a course of therapy. If she satisfies the requirements of having a good relationship with her sexual partner in other areas and does not use her difficulties for punishment or manipulation, she can be told that therapy should take no more than a total of two hours. This may be broken into three visits of one hour the first time and a half hour each of the remaining times. It would be foolish to hazard a guess with unmarried women asking for help or women who give the impression of carrying hostilities for their sexual partner. There are too many variables to permit more commitment than the willingness to evaluate the problem during a one-hour interview with the help of hypnosis.

At the second visit, the patient is asked if she has had sexual dreams culminating in orgasm and whether or not she has had something like an orgasm with petting. At least 10 per cent of all women are consciously unaware of ever having had an orgasm. It may be necessary to search their dreams on this matter with the help of ideomotor responses and light hypnosis. This might be a helpful way of inducing hypnosis while clearing up a historical point.

Results and methods of attack vary according to which of four major groups a woman belongs:

F.   Has never had an orgasm when awake or asleep, does not know what an orgasm should feel like, has never masturbated knowingly.

F-1.   Has had orgasm in dreams, with masturbation or with petting but never during coitus.

F-2.   Has had orgasm with coitus at one time but not anymore.

RF.   Relative frigidity estimated on percentage basis in relation to times of coitus. Classify with number as RF 20 (per cent) at beginning of therapy.

The first group (F) have no basis on which to judge experience but remember every sexually normal woman was that way in childhood. Class F women often come from broken homes or homes where indications of affection were never given. It would be a speculation, but they have probably had little skin stimulation during infancy. Their development stages of sexual learning have been blocked at every turn. Fortunately, the Creator seems to have given all women a genetic capacity for sexual responsiveness at birth. It is usually necessary to place these Class F patients in deep hypnosis, check for misunderstandings at birth, and have them hallucinate the necessary steps of learning that have had no chance to occur. This includes being fondled and hugged by mother and father, discovering that it feels good to have the genital area cleaned and dusted with powder, that it feels good and is all right to slide down bannisters, that it is normal to explore the pleasurable feelings of masturbation. A search must be made for traumatic experiences with male relatives, old and young, and guilt feelings removed.

They must be told that sexual learning is the only one which is consistently excluded in parent-child relationships except when it is made important by obvious avoidance or expressed dismay. All other learnings are associated with expected mistakes, and encouragement is given by parents to persist until the task is learned.

The second visit can be terminated by asking for visual hallucination of Christmas tree lights in various parts of the body representing the sensory awareness in these parts. These can be recognized at an ideomotor level and then elevated to a speaking level and reported in the following order:

	Right	Center	Left	Date
Head		yellow		2/10/62
Arms	green		green	(7/15/62)
Legs	brown		gray	
Breasts	"nothing" (pink)		black (pink)	
Abdomen		yellow		
Genital		red (pink-white)		

The patient is then asked to let a thought come to her of what the color should be for her breasts to be exquisitely sensitive to caressing and what the color for the genital area should be for her to be able to reach climax 8 or 10 times with intercourse. These are marked down inside brackets and the patient is asked to hallucinate forward to the time when these changes will have occurred after she has removed all the guilt feelings and fears that have interfered with the capabilities she was born with. This hallucinated date is put in parentheses beneath the date of the first evaluation. Failure to select a date indicates resistance to therapy and must be discovered; immediate selection of a date is a helpful signs of willingness to learn.

The third visit can be started with a review of dreams and events since the last time she was in the office, to see if there have been any moments when sensations in her body were something like the chosen ideals. She is then asked to orient back to about 13 years of age and pick up the normal type of dream of being fondled and of noticing pleasurable sensations in her breasts and clitoral area. It is difficult to describe an orgasm to one who has never experienced it, but it should be remembered that the normal child of that age has not yet been taught what an orgasm is. She is asked to have an ideomotor signal if and whenever she has a subconscious feeling that approximates what she believes an orgasm might feel like.

The course of therapy from here on would depend on information as presented. In general it is wise to make clear to your patient that there are conscious feelings she will have at an appropriate time with the real experiences, but that you are asking now only for *subconscious* feelings which act rather like blueprints for the total feelings when the situation calls for these. This approach protects the patient from embarrassment and keeps her from defeating herself in trying too hard.

Patients in the other three groups offer much less of a problem and can be handled in the same general way: (1) Is there subconscious willingness to be helped with this problem? (2) Is there any real or imagined cause for the difficulty as it is now presented? (3) Subconscious rehearsals of helpful dreams and real experiences with successive increasing loss of fears and inhibitions until there is ideomotor indication that orgasm can be reached with kissing, caressing of the breasts, entrance of the penis into the vagina, continued alternate contracting and relaxation of the vagina around the penis and at any time there is an awareness of pulsating enlargement of the penis with ejaculation. Relatively few women will be able to achieve these goals in reality, but subconscious repetition of the possibilities teaches them that orgasm is a mental process that does not need any specific stimulation to a target organ.

It should be stressed that orgasm is a mental process or it could not occur with dreams or with hallucinated experience. Arnold Kegel, in an experiment with developing the pubococcygeus muscles of women suffering from urinary stress incontinence, accidentally discovered that patients using the intravaginal instrument according to his directions found they were no longer frigid during intercourse. He concluded that development of the vaginal muscles is essential for curing frigidity. In his writings he shows no indication of realizing that frigid women have usually been prevented from even thinking of putting something in the vagina. He was giving them permission to do this and an acceptable excuse to pay attention to awareness from that part of their anatomy.

In 1950 one of us performed a radical vulvectomy, inguinal and femoral gland dissection, hysterectomy and removal of the rectum in an effort to salvage the life of a 27-year-old woman who was soon to marry again. She was sexually responsive before this radical surgery for advanced cancer of the vulva. Much time was spent during her recovery period adjusting her emotionally to her colostomy, loss of her vulva, clitoris, and half her vagina. Ten years later she stopped in the office to report her good health and announce that she was as responsive now as she had ever been. Perhaps this example explains why the authors do not recommend circumcision or hormones in the treatment of sexual frigidity in women.

Therapy for male impotence, premature ejaculation, and inability to ejaculate during intercourse should be considered from the same viewpoint as similar problems in women. There should be search for key or imprint-like experiences in childhood and inhibiting factors should be searched out and removed before rehearsal of experiences as they should be.

We should always keep in mind with the treatment of frigidity in women that their sexual partner may be the cause of trouble and may need help. Occasionally it may be possible to help even the male who refuses to come in for help. It is a common fact that males will make excessive demands for intercourse when their sexual partner seems unresponsive. The effect of this is to make the female even more frigid. In one instance, a woman who had never had an orgasm begged for help because she was being raped several times a day by her troubled husband. She was willing to try the experiment of reaching a climax "at least ten times" with his next advance. It worked. His demands fell to a happier level of twice a week.

Conversely, a frigid wife may search for an increasing number of ways to justify her unwillingness to have intercourse. These will include excessive fatigue, disgust over her husband's drinking, not wanting to muss her hairdo and having a child not feeling well. Always suspect the possibility of serious sexual inhibitions when a woman states her father "is an alcoholic." One drink can make an alcoholic in the eyes of an insecure, frigid wife, and a real alcoholic father can be the target of so much resentment and disgust that a child of that family may be hypercritical of the man she marries.

REFERENCES

Cheek, D. B.: Some newer understanding of dreams in relation to threatened abortion and premature labor. Pacif. Med. Surg. 73: 379-384, 1965.

Dunbar, F.: Emotions and Bodily Changes. New York, Columbia University Press, 1954.

Chapter 14

Hypnosis in Obstetrics

FORMS OF HYPNOSIS have been used for centuries to diminish labor pain. We must consider the pain relief in labor because the beginner needs to know the primal advantages and limitations in this area before he is able to accept hypnosis in the very much more valuable role of affording a means of discovering and correcting consciously unrecognized fears and guilt feelings of obstetrical patients.

A century ago there were many reasons for pregnant women to fear childbirth. Now we have been largely freed from concern about infection. The duration of labor for primigravid women has been shortened from 18 to 14 hours. Perfected techniques of giving continuous caudal anesthesia by highly trained specialists in anesthesiology has made childbearing an easy experience in hospitals where the facilities are available.

All in all, it seems that the honest and perfectly understandable fears of pregnant women a century ago have been removed by the progress of civilization. It is now no longer socially acceptable for pregnant women to admit fear of labor. They suppress their feelings and relegate their fears to areas of awareness troubled by dreams and disturbed biological adaptations.

There continue to be problems. Habitual abortion and premature labor are among these. Toxemia of pregnancy, placental separation and the problems of diabetes and erythroblastosis go on. Perhaps the greater part of the problem rests in the inability of physicians to communicate with the unconscious disturbing attitudes of their patients that can damage the course of pregnancy and threaten the life of unborn babies.

Hypnosis becomes a tool of lifesaving value in the presence of pyramiding fears due to prolonged labor, toxemia, hemorrhage, premature labor and overwhelming infection when medical attendants have become discouraged and frustrated with their failure to cure. With hypnosis we have a means to reestablish hope, diminish pain, stop fibrinolytic hemorrhage, reverse some of the effects of toxemia and improve resistance to infection.

CLASSIFICATION OF PATIENTS: THOSE WHO NEED HYPNOSIS AND THE OTHERS

It is possible to use some rather simple criteria in deciding which patients will require little more than routine examinations and answering of questions of everyday obstetrical practice. Chances of spontaneous abortion in Good Risk patients are less than 5 per cent, of toxemia less than 5 per cent, of premature labor less than 4 per cent, of serious hemorrhage less than 1 per cent. For this group with a neonatal mortality, less than 1 per cent hypnosis could be a luxury to be used only if the patient is interested and would like to experiment to diminish the need for analgesic drugs during labor. True that hypnosis could be valuable to speed the onset of lactation and accelerate recovery from discomfort of the episiotomy. It could be used for rest with each period of nursing after discharge from the hospital, but it is not a necessity.

GOOD RISK PATIENTS

Patients belong here when they are free of problems to be considered for classification in category A or B of the Poor Risk group. Generally speaking, they are found on history-taking to have: (1) a planned pregnancy with both patient and husband happy, (2) a happy marriage and history of uncomplicated previous pregnancy, and (3) freedom from factors considered for Poor Risk classifications.

POOR RISK PATIENTS

A. Top priority (one or more of the following):
   1. Serious illness or death of mother or father before the patient is ten years old.
   2. Serious illness of mother during pregnancy or at time of delivering the patient.
   3. Separation of parents or divorce before the patient is five years old.
   4. Serious illness of patient during childhood.
   5. Patient has had gynecological operation or appendectomy through midline incision before reaching maturity.
   6. Four or more years of unexplained sterility before this pregnancy.
   7. History of abortion, stillbirth, premature or abnormal baby for the patient, her mother or her sister.
   8. History of serious complication during pregnancy.

The first three of these criteria have been chosen because of the intensity of guilt feelings assumed by children under these circumstances. Normal children will assume that they caused the difficulties. Reason for this is that normal children are scolded by one or both parents for misdeeds. If illness, death or disappearance of a parent follows such an event the child will almost invariably believe she has caused the tragic aftermath.

One woman presenting herself for help with frigidity and ten years of sterility after a fulminating toxemia and death of a baby, burst into tears in hypnosis, announcing that she could not have babies because she had killed her daddy. The patient, then seven years old, had refused to eat her oatmeal at breakfast. She had argued with her mother. Her father scolded them both over this and stamped off to work. He died that afternoon from a coronary occlusion at the age of 37. When the news arrived, her mother made the unfortunate comment that he might still be living if they had not troubled him with their argument.

It would be logical to assume that conscious reasoning would exclude possibility for such ridiculous origins to continue their harmful effect. Reason and conscious logic, however, do not have a chance to correct imprinted learnings fixed by emotional or physical stress.

Serious illness such as rheumatic fever and polio in childhood seem to make women afraid they will have abnormal babies. Similarly, a gynecological operation creates doubts about normalcy that cannot be wiped out by conscious reassurance. Appendectomies with midline or a Pfannenstiel incision are usually performed with recognition that gynecological abnormalities can cause identical symptoms and physical findings. The question alarms the patient subconsciously even when the appendix has been found diseased and the pelvic organs normal. Criteria numbers 6, 7 and 8 are selected because of the unfavorable identifications and the tendency for growing superstitions during pregnancy.

B. Secondary priority (two or more of the following):
1. Firstborn child bearing feminized boy's name (e.g., Carla).
2. Only child or sole surviving child.
3. History of acne during adolescence.
4. Tall and thin or short and fat during teens.
5. History of debilitating dysmenorrhea.
6. History suggesting frigid and over-protective mother.
7. Patient has been divorced at request of former husband.
8. Pregnancy preceded marriage, father of child resentful.

These criteria have been found important but not as important as those in the A priority. They relate mainly to factors which would make a woman unsure of herself as a mother, diffident as a wife or unconsciously hostile toward males. Curiously, hostility toward a father, brothers, or the father of the child leads to unconscious rejection of the conceptus. We have seen several instances where women have recognized that subconscious rejection of the unborn child began after an argument with a father, brother or husband. One young lady, illegitimately pregnant, developed a fulminating pre-eclampsia within an hour of learning that her father would be arriving for dinner at the home of her brother with whom she was staying. She did not want her father to know about her condition and felt betrayed by her brother.

Cause-and-effect relationships of this type appear worthy of consideration only when patients select them during hypnoanalysis and when the information can be put to work helpfully with other patients at critical times when the life of the baby is in jeopardy.

LABOR

Patients are told that our prime concern is to have them deliver a baby in the best possible frame of mind and with minimal obstruction going through the birth canal. We intend to keep mothers comfortable to insure this goal and plan to use any methods necessary to do so. Notes are made of any strong feelings expressed by the patient regarding choices of drugs or methods of producing anesthesia.

It is further explained that we intend to help her accomplish the job of delivering a happy baby. She is not to feel like a failure if her doctor decides that she needs some help with analgesic drugs or local anesthetics should the speed and intensity of her contractions increase to the point that unfair pressure is being put on her baby. It is explained that the baby picks up the stimulating effect of epinephrine from a mother suffering a painful labor. Continued stress on the baby's system from epinephrine combined with obstruction caused by tight pelvic muscles is more harmful than any drugs that might be used to relieve these pressures. There are some ways of diminishing attention to pain with the help of hypnosis if she is interested in learning about them, but it will probably not be necessary to use them.

In case she might be interested, it is pointed out that hypnosis is *a use of familiar experiences* and is really nothing more than all children use very well up to the age of five or six when they go to school. With it she can learn to recall the effects of previous anesthesia to block the soreness of an episiotomy incision, speed up lactation or turn it off, rest during nursing and feel refreshed when her husband comes home at night. Mention is made that some patients get so interested in what they can do with hypnosis that they go through an entire labor without need of drugs or anesthetic agents.

Experienced nursery attendants immediately recognize differences in behavior of babies to be placed for adoption as compared with those to be kept by their parents. Babies are usually taken out of the delivery room immediately to spare the mother anguish. A ten-year study as to keen awareness of babies at birth was made by Cheek with 18 women and three men who knew their adoption history. Their reports were compared with those of people reared by their natural parents. Those in both groups who thought their origins were traumatic were asked to hallucinate their birth and early experiences as they should have been to make them most happy. Results can be summarized as follows:

1. Babies need to hear the mother talking kindly about them immediately after delivery. Heavy sedation or general anesthesia denies them this opportunity as does hurried removal to the nursery.

2. Four heard their mothers weeping during or immediately after delivery. One believed this due to the pain of labor and felt guilty for causing such distress. The others, with judgment based on mature experience as adults reviewing in age-regression, smiled in happiness at this discovery, feeling that the mother had strong feelings for her and that circumstances rather than rejection had led to adoption.

3. All, adopted and unadopted, expressed feelings of acceptance and of being among friends in the nursery. Perhaps some sort of communication goes on among babies kept together. At least half of these subjects recalled kind words and gentle care at the hands of nurses. We feel that babies for adoption should be kept in the main nursery rather than in isolation.

4. Those taken from the hospital to foster homes before final adoption have much resentment for adopting parents as compared with babies taken by adopting parents directly from the hospital within the first week of life. The reason for this seems to be the double adjustment from natural mother to foster parents to adopting parents.

We previously held the bias that newborn babies have insufficient development of their nervous system to allow storage of visual and auditory perceptions from the first moments of life. Their initial experiences pointing to the possibility of keen awareness at birth were thought to be accidental. When volunteer information accumulated we then learned how to search for information included in these reports. Subsequently we became convinced that there is a definite memory of birth in the subconscious portion of the mind which can be recalled with hypnotic age-regression, as has been previously mentioned.

NURSING

Continuing study of subjective impressions of grown-up, former babies about feeding has convinced us that every mother should go through the motions of nursing her baby during the hospital stay, if not longer. Holding the baby while offering it a bottle is no substitute for the physical contact of nursing.

In order to motivate mothers toward nursing, it is helpful to have them go over their own birth and feeding history. Those who have been nursed recognize how much it meant to them. Bottle-fed babies will need no urging as mothers in giving their baby what was denied them. Curiously, all adults who were bottle-fed babies have expressed strong feelings of disappointment during age-regression, almost as though there were a genetically learned expectancy for breast feeding.

POST-DELIVERY MATTERS

A woman who has had mild sedation and hypnosis during labor and delivery can get off the delivery table and walk back to her room. She can do this even if she has had a pudendal block for the episiotomy and repair. It is not possible for this to occur if she has had caudal anesthesia or a saddle-block spinal anesthetic.

Walking patients are immediately aware that they are free of complications. They know the obstetrician does not expect complications and they know the nurses are surprised at their achievement. These emotional dividends are added to the accelerated healing of the episiotomy and involution of the uterus attributable to immediate ambulation. The choice of walking out of the delivery room, however, should be left to the patient. She knows how she feels and she knows her husband. One patient said, "Lordy, if my husband saw me walking back to the room, I'd *never* get him to help me with anything at home!"

With immediate ambulation there is seldom the need for the use of ergotrate-like drugs. These have been used in less than 1 per cent of Cheek's cases since 1952.

Subcuticular sutures of 000 chromic catgut on an atroloc needle should cause very little pain when the episiotomy is kept in the midline with slight "hockey-stick" angulation to avoid extension into the rectum. Perineal heat lamps are very comfortable during their application, but they increase tissue edema and cause maceration of the skin. When the heat is gone, the patient is more aware of this area than when heat is not applied. Patients should be told of this before denying them the pelvic "barbecue," because they will feel left out if others in a ward are getting it.

Patients are taught to make the perineum feel cool and numb during prenatal visits. To this is added memory for the chemical anesthetic of a pudendal block or caudal anesthetic. They learn to achieve these hallucinated results at an ideomotor level and are asked to check from time to time by asking for a finger-signal answer to the question, "Do I have any subconscious soreness or pain now?" It is explained in advance that there can be unconscious guarding and interference with healing with soreness that is not consciously recognized. They are asked to ask for complete comfort for stipulated periods of six hours and have their "yes" finger lift when they know they will maintain the comfort for that length of time.

LACTATION: HORMONES OR HYPNOSIS

Onset of breast engorgement and lactation has advanced from the time-honored period of 4–5 days to 2 or 3 days. It is a safe speculation that greater freedom from fear, fatigue and pain have been responsible for this advance. Kroger and August feel that suggestions of increased feeling and circulation will accelerate the onset of lactation. We believe this can be accomplished within the first 48 hours with women who are motivated to nurse. Certainly the effects of suggestion are far better in suppressing lactation and breast congestion than the commonly used hormones.

A Japanese woman decided to stop nursing her child approximately two weeks after she had become pregnant again. She called to report massive engorgement of the left breast with accompanying great pain and a temperature of 101°. This breast was double the size of the right one. There were red lines of apparent lymphangitis running from the areola toward the axilla. The skin was shiny and transparent. Cheek felt unsure of this being infectious in origin. The breast was so engorged that antibiotics would have had difficulty reaching the site of infection.

Cheek asked the patient to enter hypnosis and turn off the pain. After a few minutes her finger lifted to indicate this had been accomplished. Two minutes later her finger again lifted to indicate acceptance of continued freedom from pain for 24 hours. She aroused from hypnosis saying that she felt much better and could now move her arm more easily.

Next morning she reported having slept well, but the breast was still swollen and her temperature still elevated. She was asked to have a finger lift when she knew what had interfered with cure of her trouble.

After a few seconds the finger lifted and she laughingly reported that her mother-in-law had been home when she arrived yesterday and had expressed distress that no shots had been given. This raised some doubts about the sanity of her physician. The patient became unsure that she was doing the right thing to rely entirely on hypnosis rather than drugs. Cheek's prestige was now improved by her seeing that something had troubled the results. Now the patient accepted the same suggestions of the previous day and within two hours called to report normal temperature and normal size of her left breast.

Uterine atony and hemorrhage at the time of delivery seems attributable to the influences of continued pain and associated fear. Bleeding after the first 24 hours is much more commonly caused by depression or hurt feelings. It is Cheek's custom to tell all obstetrical patients that they might bleed at some time when a mother seems critical of their baby care or a husband has disappointed them in some way. They are to ask themselves about these possibilities before picking up the phone to report.

The possibility of retained placental tissue always comes up in discussions of postpartum bleeding. Mentioning the possibility is comparable to telling a woman that she will not miscarry if her baby is normal. It is better to ask the patient to shut her eyes and orient her thoughts to what was happening just before bleeding commenced. She is told to have her "yes" finger lift when she is there and to report what comes to her mind.

This was done with a patient who was hemorrhaging two weeks after delivery. She had been nursing her baby when her daughter, aged two, came into the room and wanted to climb on her lap. The child's forlorn look reminded the patient of her own lost feeling on seeing her own mother nurse the little sister. This patient believed bleeding started with the thought, "I wonder if I will have enough love for both children?" She laughed at the association of ideas but 30 minutes later called back to report that hemorrhage had stopped completely.

LABOR AND DELIVERY

Ralph August, William Kroger and Leon Chertok have very adequately discussed various methods of hypnotic preparation for labor and delivery. Occasional experiences suggest possibility that extensive training is really not essential. A screaming, frightened patient can shift within seconds to a bemused, quiet discussion of events on an automobile ride while strong uterine contractions continue. The human mind is quite willing to shift its response to match input data associated with peace and comfort providing the doctor recognizes and uses this willingness at critical times.

Generally it is easy to work with patients in a hospital attentive to the values of hypnosis. It is nearly impossible in one where nurses and colleagues are apathetic, suspicious or hostile. There are still some hospitals where hypnosis is banned by attending staff leaders and non-medical trustees. Some doctors are allowed to use hypnosis but with the stipulation that a permit must be signed by the patient and her husband absolving the rest of the staff and the hospital of all responsibility for damage done by hypnosis.

It is comforting to know that all methods offering hope of relief are helpful in labor. Patients motivated toward having an easy time for the sake of their baby will do well with any form of chemical or psychological analgesia. Those who carry guilt feelings over real or imagined events will invariably do poorly. Those who have suffered much from dysmenorrhea or painful childhood illness will require more attention than others who have grown up without distress.

METHODS USED BY THE AUTHOR

The effects of postural suggestion are demonstrated with imagined weight on one arm. A challenge is given to try opposing this downward pull. Attention is drawn to the fact that an established suggestion (or imprinted learning) takes precedence over later suggestions that oppose it. It is pointed out that we succeed better when we conceive a new suggestion like "removing the weight and having a number of balloons attached to the wrist instead."

The second step of training involves establishing ideomotor signals as answers to questions in light hypnosis.

Next it is helpful to check on possible fears that might interfere with pain control in labor. To ask about fear directly is to suggest our expectation that pregnant women should be afraid. Indirectly we can discover consciously unrecognized fear by one of two methods.

Women who are happy with their pregnancy and unafraid will give definite ideomotor responses regarding the sex of the unborn child. They are often correct but this is not as important as the fact that their attitude is a healthy one when they commit themselves on whether they will have a boy or a girl. Those who answer "I don't know" or "I don't want to answer" are afraid and should have their fear uncovered. This can be done with the patient in a light stage of hypnosis by asking her to orient her thoughts to reasons for her answer. She is asked, "Are you afraid either for yourself or your baby?" The answer will be "yes." After learning the target for fear, she is asked to go back to the moment when this fear started and to bring that memory up to where it can be put into words.

The source of the fear is usually some ridiculous identification originating in reading material, moving pictures, television or conversations with well-meaning friends or relatives. After checking for other sources of fear, it is usually quite easy to ask questions in such a way as to resolve the problem. Commitment can then be obtained by restating the question about the sex of the baby.

The other approach for discovering consciously unrecognized fear can also be used as a training rehearsal for an easy labor. Under hypnosis the patient is asked to project forward to the time of her delivery and signal the moment she hears her baby crying. During the preliminary induction and deepening she is given the following suggestions aimed at promoting the projection:

1. You have had a very comfortable pregnancy. You have learned to put yourself in and out of hypnosis very quickly. You have controlled your absorption of food and are right at the best weight. Your sleep has been restful and your dreams happy.

2. Your labor has been going on a little at a time during the past couple of weeks to soften the cervix and get it ready to dilate and let your baby be delivered in the easiest possible way. At last you are ready for real labor. The contractions have just been mild feelings of tightness in your back and upper abdomen occurring five minutes apart and lasting 20 to 30 seconds.

3. You have come into the hospital and have been given an enema to empty the bowel. This allows you to let the contractions bring the baby down through the birth canal without making you worried about soiling the bed. Otherwise you would unconsciously have tightened the muscles around the rectum to hold back with each push.

4. Your contractions became a little stronger. You found you were getting sleepier and more relaxed as the efficiency of these contractions improved. You became too sleepy to bother about anything but you knew when you were ready to deliver and told us.

5. We took you to the delivery room and put your legs up in the stirrups. At this moment you became increasingly numb from the waist down. You pushed a couple of times and there was the baby.

6. (Shifting from past to present tense) Your "yes" finger can lift as you hear your baby cry for the first time. It's a good-looking, healthy baby. You can look over there to the right and on a blackboard see the

nurse write up the sex of the baby, its weight, the date, and the length of labor. I think it will only be 4 or 5 hours because you have relaxed so well. As soon as you see this at a subconscious level, your "yes" finger will lift again. Tell me what you see.

By watching the facial expression of the patient it can be noticed if the suggestions are being accepted.

Results before and after use of ideomotor questioning methods

	Deliveries	Premature	Stillborn	Mortality
Before 1946–1955 Chico	527	34 (6.5%)	4 (.8%)	15%
After 1956–1966 San Francisco	231	6 (2.6%)	5 (2.1%)	0%

GOOD RISK AND POOR RISK PATIENTS

During the years 1946–1955, Cheek tried to refer all patients who had delivered normally in previous pregnancies. Patients with history of successive abortions, complications of pregnancy and Caesarean section were accepted, as were most of the primigravida. Statistics for that period do not include emergency deliveries in consultation with other doctors. All patients were followed personally during their prenatal period although 11 were delivered by colleagues during Cheek's temporary absence.

The significance of prior history and the importance of unconscious ideation becomes clear during the period of 1956–1966 when all patients were accepted but were classified according to criteria presented at the beginning of this chapter.

Class	Total	Misc.	Stillborn	Premature	Mortality
Good Risk	169	3 (1.8%)	0	4 (2.3%)	0
Poor Risk	62	8 (13%)	5	2 (3.2%)	0

All three miscarriages in the Good Risk group occurred in pregnancies that were undesirable and unplanned although no efforts at abortion were made by the patients. On the other hand, no effort to salvage the pregnancy was made when abortion threatened. Two immature twins weighing less than two pounds each are included under miscarriage in the Poor Risk group. Placental separation destroyed one twin and forced labor for the other. The remaining six spontaneous abortions occurred too quickly to permit salvage efforts.

It seems significant that all stillbirths occurred in the Poor Risk group. They were all unwanted pregnancies and all the mothers were under great emotional stress at the time of fetal demise before onset of labor. Only one of these mothers was married and she was subconsciously convinced that the pregnancy was a threat to her life. She had lived several weeks in fear after delivery of her first child. Intraepithelial carcinoma had been diagnosed on routine postpartum examination. Later it was decided to revise the diagnosis to hyperplasia after conization of the cervix, but the fear was subconsciously very strong. Fetal death was due to abruptio at the end of the second trimester before the author had a chance to talk with her.

There were four premature babies in the Good Risk group. These were all over 4 pounds 2 ounces and all survived. There were two premature babies in the Poor Risk. These also were over four pounds and both survived. The number of cases reported here is much too small for statistical evaluation. They are submitted because the author has had adequate time to study the attitudes of all these patients during routine examinations and during times of emergency.

RESULTS WITH PATIENTS PRESENTING THREATS TO THEIR PREGNANCY

The significance of unconscious ideation was dramatic when it came to analysis of factors leading to threatened abortion, abruptio of the placenta, toxemia, third trimester bleeding, and premature labor.

Threat of hemorrhage or premature labor

	Total	Serious threat	Living baby
Good Risk	6 (3.5%)	3	6
Poor Risk	37 (60%)	11	37

Threats were considered serious when hemorrhage exceeded 100 cc. at one time or when bleeding and uterine contractions occurred two or more times during pregnancy. One patient in the Good Risk group required 1000 cc. of blood replacement but delivered a normal child. One patient in the Poor Risk group lost an estimated 1200 cc. of blood and required three suturings of her incompetent cervix before delivering a 4-pound, 2-ounce normal child at 38 weeks. Convincing is the fact that seemingly impossible situations can be corrected by patients when they are treated with respect for their needs and faith in their capabilities.

DANGERS OF FRIGHTENING DREAMS

The author has found that 54 per cent of hemorrhages in the first trimester occur while the patient is asleep. Less than 10 per cent of women threatening abortion or premature labor because of frightening dreams will know on awakening that they have had such dreams. This has been the reason we have gone so long in ignorance of the very strong physiological disturbances which can result from uncorrected, very real dreams. The apparent threats in dreams are intensely real until we can recognize on awakening that we have only been dreaming. Very threatening dreams are shut off from conscious awareness by the well-recognized method of suppression.

One patient had complete amnesia for a disturbing dream which occurred within a few minutes of falling asleep. She had identified herself with a friend whose child was severely retarded. The patient awakened with strong two-minute contractions at 36 weeks. The author made a house call at once and placed the patient in hypnosis in an effort to postpone labor. The contractions were expulsive, lasting 30 seconds but they stopped within five minutes of having the patient review her sleep and discover the foolishness of her dream about having an abnormal baby. She comfortably delivered a term-sized child two weeks later.

There is much room for constructive research into the role of thoughts and dreams in producing complications of pregnancy. We should always look for disturbed sleep with the following:

    Nausea and vomiting of pregnancy
    Severe headaches
    Sudden weight gain from fluid retention
    Nocturnal leg cramps due to unconscious hyperventilation
    Sudden onset of moniliasis of the vagina
    Urinary tract infection
    Repeated "colds" and "sinusitis"
    Asthma
    Hemorrhage or premature uterine contractions
    Indications of pregnancy toxemia.

A commonly voiced objection to the concept of dreams causing disease is that the disease causes the dreams. We have great respect for the strength of faith or the "power of the placebo," as it has been termed by Henry Beecher. It is easy to prove that a command to stop bleeding may permit this to happen. With experience now extending over a ten-year period, the authors feel sure that most obstetrical complications result from misunderstandings, guilt feelings and fears which have their strongest influence during times when conscious understanding and the reasoning processes of conscious thought are blocked off by sleep or the unconsciousness of trauma and chemo-anesthesia.

Contrary to the beliefs of armchair skeptics, honest observers consider alternatives also in carrying out investigation. It would be very difficult to prove beyond a reasonable doubt that all disease occurring at night is caused by disturbed thoughts during sleep. On the other hand, the evidence is strong that diseases mentioned in this chapter can be and often are caused in this way. Results with vomiting of pregnancy, fluid retention, urinary tract infections, hemorrhage and premature labor have improved tremendously since we have considered and searched the dangers of dreaming. Patients are the best teachers. Ask them about their complications. Argue with them about possible explanations other than the ones they offer. After doing that you can comfortably challenge the opinions of colleagues in the medical arts.

REFERENCES

August, R.: Hypnosis in Obstetrics. New York, McGraw-Hill, 1961.

Bradley, R.: Husband-coached Childbirth. New York, Harper & Row, 1965.

Caldeyro-Barcia, H., Alvarez, H., and Poseiro, J. J.: Normal and abnormal uterine contractility in labor. Triangle 2: 41-52, 1955.

Cheek, D. B.: Effectiveness of incentive in clinical hypnosis, Obstet. Gynec. 9: 720-724, 1957.

————: Value of ideomotor sex-determination technique of LeCron for uncovering fear in obstetric patients. Int. J. Clin. Exp. Hypn. 9: 249-258, 1961.

————: Some newer understandings of dreams in relation to threatened abortion and premature labor. Pacif. Med. Surg. 8: 379-384, 1965.

Chertok, L.: Psychosomatic Methods in Painless Childbirth. New York, Pergamon Press, 1959.

Coulton, D.: Prenatal and·postpartum uses of hypnosis. Amer. J. Clin. Hypn. 8: 192-197, 1966.

Dick-Read, G.: Childbirth Without Fear, New York, Harper Bros., 1953.

Hartman, W., and Rawlins, C. M.: Hypnosis in management of a case of abruptio placenta. Int. J. Clin. Exp. Hypn. 8: 103-107, 1960.

Kroger, W. S.: Childbirth With Hypnosis (J. Steinberg, Ed.). New York, Doubleday, 1961.

————: Psychosomatic Obstetrics. Gynecology and Endrocrinology, Springfield, Charles C Thomas, 1962.

LeCron, L. M.: Uncovering of early memories by ideomotor responses to questions. Int. J. Clin. Exp. Hypn. 11: 137-142, 1963.

Lindner, R. M.: Rebel Without a Cause. New York, Grune & Stratton, 1944.

Montagu, A.: Prenatal Influences. Springfield, Charles C Thomas, 1962.

Rank, O.: The Trauma of Birth. New York, Harcourt Brace, 1929.

Schwartz, M.: The cessation of labor using hypnotic techniques. Amer. J. Clin. Hypn. 5: 211-213, 1963.

Sonntag, L.: Effect of maternal emotions on fetal development. In: Childbirth With Hypnosis (J. Steinberg, Ed.). New York, Doubleday, 1961, pp. 8-13.

Chapter 15

Sleep and Its Relationship to Pain and Disease

WE SPEND a third of our life sleeping, but it has been recognized only within the past ten years that a number of disabling illnesses may have their origin in distressing dreams and thought processes during natural sleep. Dreams are very real, and our responses to threatening dreams may greatly disturb health if we cannot expose them to the softening effect of conscious reason.

Investigations pioneered by the psychiatrist William Dement of Stanford into the effects of sleep deprivation suggest that rapid-eye-movement (REM) phases of natural sleep are very important in maintaining the individual's balance with threatening daytime stresses. Alcohol, barbiturates and central nervous stimulants will all tend to diminish the REM periods of sleep. The continued deprivation of REM dreaming periods causes severe neurotic behavior in vulnerable people. There is some evidence that REM dreaming is decreased by depression and by the drugs used in the treatment for depression. New areas for productive research into the causes of psychosis, severe depression and pathological paranoid behavior are thus opening up for those competent to use hypnoanalytic and hypnotherapeutic methods now available.

For a time it was believed that dreaming occurred only during the ascending phase of EEG stage 1 sleep but it now appears that important ideation goes on at all levels of sleep, that we have only lacked the tools to obtain information from sleepers who cannot consciously remember what has been going on just before they were awakened.

It may come about that the prolonged rest periods of hypnotic sleep used by Wetterstrand at the end of the Nineteenth Century in Sweden will be used again. Cheek has found that patients who are trained to stay in deep hypnosis for part of each night indicate having regular intervals of "hypnotic sleep" interspersed with ordinary sleep rather than spending the entire period of hypnotic sleep in a continuous stretch.

We do not know why all mammals require regular alternating phases of sleep ranging from great depth to the nearly awake type associated with rapid-eye-movements. The study of all psychosomatic complaints should include a careful evaluation of night-time ideation with the technique described in the chapter on obstetrics to be sure the daytime therapy is not being sabotaged by unfavorable thought processes at night.

Cheek has found that 50 per cent of spontaneous abortions are initiated by bleeding that commences while the patients are asleep. Scanning the night time of sleep prior to the onset of obstetrical and surgical complications makes it increasingly clear that such exploration is a necessary part of diagnosis.

Patients with peptic ulcer are finding that acid production occurs with repetitive dreams unknown to them on awakening with pain, and that correction of sleeping habits with substitution of peaceful thoughts can diminish symptoms. Obstetrical patients are teaching us that toxemia with hypertension, fluid retention and albuminuria begins after four or five successive nights of worrisome dreams about abnormal babies or complications of pregnancy.

Recognition of the dreams is impossible with ordinary interview techniques because the troublesome ideation occurs apparently at deep levels of sleep, deeper than dreaming. While reviewing these periods of troubled sleep it will usually be noted that the patient in hypnosis will show no movements of the eyeballs. When asked if the thoughts are like ordinary dreams, these patients will say it is a different sort of experience, much more real than dreaming, yet they seem somehow detached from the scene. Hypnosis and ideomotor responses to questioning permit exploration of these dreams and other mental processes occurring during sleep.

Depressed patients have difficulty sleeping and usually ask for sleeping pills from their physicians followed by amphetamine-like drugs to stimulate them into feeling better in the daytime. The influence of various drugs are still being investigated, but it already seems probable that barbiturates for sleep and amphetamines for pep both interfere with REM phases of sleep.

METHOD OF SEARCHING SLEEP IDEATION

After setting up ideomotor signals, the patient is asked to orient back to the moment of falling asleep on the evening to be studied, to have a "yes" finger lift at that point. The "no" finger is asked to lift each time the patient is dreaming and the "I don't know" finger is to lift at the end of the night of sleep. Time distortion or skipping over periods of time will take place during this review.

People often awaken during the night. It is not necessary to ask for a signal on this because the patient will usually lift the going-to-sleep signal on going back to sleep. It will soon be observed that signals of "dreaming" coincide with roving eye movements such as are seen during age regression in hypnosis. It is seldom possible to see the very rapid convergent movements typical of dreaming. These need electronic monitoring unless the light is just right on the eyelashes of the patient. Signals of dreaming occur at evenly spaced intervals and compare fairly well with the 90-minute peaks four to five times during a night of sleep.

When another signal indicates the appearance of a disturbing thought or something that might have a relationship to the onset of symptoms, it is found that these may occur at any time of night, but there is an increased concentration of troublesome, causative thoughts within the first four hours after falling asleep. No definite statement can be made at this time regarding position of troublesome thoughts in relation to EEG staging, but it can be said that less than 10 per cent of dreams causing complications of pregnancy are remembered consciously on awakening. They are deeply repressed and can be discovered only by the process of nighttime scanning as described here. Sometimes it is necessary, as was found true of surgical anesthesia experiences, to go over the troublesome segment of sleep a number of times, signalling the beginning and ending, before the patient can tell what the thoughts or dreams have been about.

Again it is a speculation, based only on studies of the complications of pregnancy and surgery, but it is our feeling that problems relating to heart disease, respiratory disease, digestive disease, orthopedic pain and cancer may have their origins in, or owe their continuation to, conscously unrecognized disturbances of sleep.

CASE EXAMPLE

A 38-year-old Negro woman on the clinic service was moaning and in tears on awakening the first day after Caesarean delivery of her healthy second child. The attending staff consultant happened to pass her door at this time. It was learned that her previous Caesarean for cephalopelvic disproportion had been complicated by great distention, vomiting and a prolonged hospitalization under the presumptive diagnosis of a bowel obstruction. The consultant had been present at the recent delivery and could tell the patient that no adhesions had been visible. It was pointed out to her that she was swallowing air and that distention of the intestines with air causes pain. Furthermore it was possible to hear peristaltic action of her bowel, and this meant she had recovered from the irritation of her surgery in record time.

Because she was still frightened, it was decided to put her into hypnosis on the possibility that cause for her pain could not be corrected by simple reassurance if it had occurred in her sleep. Finger signals were quickly set up, and she was asked to close her eyes and orient back to the beginning of her sleep last night and then come up through her night of sleep until she arrived at the time when pain began. She was told to have one finger lift if she ran across any disturbing dreams and to have another lift when she knew the pain was beginning.

It took approximately two minutes for her to discover that she had had a dream that the baby was dead. It had occurred about 6 a.m. and preceded her first pain by about five minutes. She volunteered that this was the same dream she had had after her first surgery. At that time they had explained that surgery was necessary "to make sure the baby would be all right." This normal explanation had suggested that they thought the baby would not be all right. The patient was asked to give an ideomotor signal when she turned off all the pain. This took about 80 seconds. She was then asked to maintain that freedom from pain as long as she wanted to and to give another unconscious signal when she knew this would be possible. It took another three minutes before that signal was given.

In the meantime, suggestions were made that she would feel very hungry in order to move gas along in her bowel and permit absorption of some of the gas. She was awakened and helped out of bed to sit in a chair and eat her breakfast. One hour later she was seen again. The distention was gone. She was laughing and talking with one of the nurses.

Discovery of the dream and its relation to her first operation made it unnecessary for the consultant to search for organic sources of pain and distention. Rapid resolution of the symptoms seemed to justify the speculation that the symptoms were psychogenic.

RECOMMENDED EXERCISE

Place the subject in light hypnosis and ask for a review of the previous night's sleep, signaling going to sleep, dreaming, and final awakening. Notice the time intervals between dream signals, the number of signals and the relation between dream signals and movements of the eyes under the closed lids. Ask if there have been any disturbing dreams or thoughts. Ask permission to know more about these, but do not follow it if the patient indicates reluctance to communicate.

REFERENCES

Dement, W., and Kleitman, N.: Incidence of eye motility during sleep in relation to varying EEG pattern. Fed. Proc. 14: 216, 1955.

_____: The effect of dream deprivation. Science 131: 1705-1707, 1960.

Snyder, F.: The new biology of dreaming. Arch. Gen. Psychiat. 8: 381-391, 1963.

_____: Progress in the new biology of dreaming. Amer. J. Psychiat. 122: 377-391, 1965.

Wolport, E. A.: Studies in psychophysiology of dreams: an electromyographic study of dreaming, Arch. Gen. Psychiat. 2: 231-241, 1960.

Wolstenholme, G. E. W., and O'Connor, M.: The Nature of Sleep. Ciba Foundation Symposium. Boston, Little, Brown, 1950.

Chapter 16

Pain: Its Meaning and Treatment

By DEFINITION, pain must be a consciously perceived, uncomfortable awareness. There is no word to describe subconscious perception of inflammation or any of the defense mechanisms initiated by trauma, infection or antigens. The expression "subconscious pain" will be used here to refer to the very large area of discomfort that is not noticed at conscious levels of awareness.

We can understand that all learned processes of adaptation may be shifted from consciousness into subconscious levels of awareness. The beginner has to concentrate with effort on each step of driving a car. A few months later he can talk and look at scenery while letting his unconscious mind make all the appropriate decisions.

We also know that consciously perceived, unpleasant experiences may be suppressed or pushed out of conscious awareness. They are not eliminated by this mechanism. They are pushed into unconscious horizons of thought where they can dictate unreasonable reactions to real or imagined threats in the future. We are learning that ideation during natural sleep may be injurious to the dreamer, but the experiences are too disturbing for conscious recognition on awakening. They are repressed at a subconscious level and may continue their harmful effect on subsequent nights of sleep or even on successive cycles of sleep during the same night.

The minds of experimental animals and of humans may not only repress a particularly unpleasant experience but go on to repress conscious knowledge of events preceding the moment of trauma, as though trying to forget everything leading up to the experience as well. We have for years assumed that retrograde amnesia is caused by actual brain damage. Now we know how to break this form of amnesia with repetitive subconscious review. We are learning that retrograde amnesia is merely suppressed or repressed memory. It is not obliterated memory.

It seems naive to exclude all the possible ramifications of consciously unrecognized discomfort and limit our thoughts about pain to the zone dictated by definition. This is comparable to considering only the part of an iceberg that is above water. If we so restrict our thoughts on pain, we miss the whole phylogenetic meaning of pain. Our patients suffering from sterile fractures, bruises and surgical incisions are therefore forced to recover as best they can with methods originally designed to make animals survive dirty and infected wounds. They have the same muscle spasm, the same stasis of circulation, the same deposition of collagen, exudation of fluid and mass migrations of inflammatory cells.

We must be very rigid in our thinking to believe that a central nervous system is going to ignore messages from traumatized or infected tissue just because conscious attention is absorbed in fighting off another animal or in looking for a safe place to hide during recovery. The same gross and microscopic changes occur in liver, brain and skin abscesses, yet those in liver and brain are often "painless."

When we question a person suffering from rheumatoid arthritis, we find that several joints are consciously painful and some with visible pathologic changes are not painful. There may be muscle guarding and limitation of motion in the nonpainful joints. Now set up ideomotor symbol responses to questions and ask the patient about pain. He may shake his head and answer "no" verbally while his finger is lifting to say "yes, there is pain" in the joints which he thought were comfortable. If we go a step farther and evoke an unconscious signal that all "subconscious pain, soreness or discomfort" has been removed, we will begin to observe relaxation of the neighboring muscles. With relief from subconscious pain protracted over a period of 24 hours, there will be increasing mobility and a decrease in local edema.

Ask a person with a three-day-old blister if the blister is painful and you will learn that it is not consciously painful. An ideomotor response will show that it is not subconsciously comfortable. Obtain a signal for acceptance of numbness and coolness for six hours. The blister fluid will reabsorb within the first two hours if the subject is willing to go along with the suggestions.

Response in a simple sprain of the ankle, without fracture, is dramatic when both conscious and unconscious components of pain have been removed. But here we must move carefully, because another factor in pain and tissue reaction must be considered. We are not always at liberty to order freedom from pain. An injured person has a tendency to feel guilty about the factors leading to the injury and we must clear his attitudes first.

SEQUENCE OF EVENTS WITH BLOCKADE OF SUBCONSCIOUS PAIN

1. Appearance of ideomotor signal that pain has been blocked at a subconscious level. Facial expression continues to reflect conscious discomfort. (Interval before finger response: 1–5 minutes.)

2. Facial expression changes to indicate spread of subconscious relief to preconscious recognition. (Interval between this and finger response: 1–10 minutes, depending on severity of pain.)

3. Regional muscles begin relaxing around painful area. (Interval: approximately two minutes after #2.)

4. Conscious movement of regional muscles to verify reality of the feeling of comfort. Verbal acknowledging relief. (Within 60 seconds of #3.)

5. Diminishing signs of inflammation after two or more hours from #1.

HYPNOSIS, INFLAMMATION, HEALING

In 1845 James Esdaile discovered that repetitive, lulling, mesmeric passes not only permitted patients to undergo painless surgery but diminished the signs of inflammation and dropped his surgical mortality from 50 per cent to 5 per cent. Nothing was then known about bacteria. Surgical mortality throughout the world was close to 40 per cent. Surgery was limited to drainage of abscesses, removal of visible tumors and amputation of limbs. Amputation was the most common surgery because all compound fractures became infected. Operations were occasionally done within the abdominal cavity, but only those who could be operated upon at home survived.

This was the period of "laudable pus" indicating better resistance to infection and better chance for survival. Surgeons made their hospital rounds carrying a bucket of water and a sponge. The intern swabbed away pus to expose the wound for inspection before dropping the sponge back in the bucket. All hospital patients shared their bacteria. The surgical mortality at Glasgow University was 45 per cent when Joseph Lister took charge in 1860 shortly before Koch and Pasteur were discovering the role of bacteria in inflammation.

General inhalation anesthesia was coming into wide use during 1845–46, but painless surgery did nothing to diminish surgical mortality until a direct attack could be made on the sources of wound contamination. Yet Esdaile, with no knowledge of infection, with no antiseptic methods, found his mortality dropping to a level that was not reached anywhere until after the advent of Lister's antisepsis in 1866.

Why did hypnosis decrease surgical mortality and increase resistance to infection in the days before surgeons washed their hands and instruments? There may be some answers to this question.

Delboeuf, in 1877, studied burns and noted that they healed without blister formation on an arm rendered painless with suggestion. In 1957, Armstrong, Jepson, Keele and Stewart at Cornell found pain-producing substances in blister fluid. These were proteclytic enzymes. Ostfield and his co-workers found similar enzymes released in pericranial transudates of patients during attacks of migraine headache in this same year. In 1959, Chapman, Goodell and Wolfe at Cornell were studying the effect of painful stimuli on release of these inflammatory polypeptide enzymes. They repeated the experiments of Hilton and Fox with "bradykinin" using their methods of collecting subcutaneous fluid and concentrating the enzymes. They found that anything interrupting the continuity of messages from injured site to brain and back would diminish the output of these enzymes. They added a test with the use of hypnosis to block pain. There was moderate diminution of "neurokinin" secretion on the suggested numb side as compared with the normal side. The difference became accentuated when they added an element of alarmed expectancy by telling hypnotized subjects that something really disturbing would happen to the normal arm. This was a major contribution to our understanding of what happens during surgery, particularly with surgery involving personal risk or possibility of finding cancer.

George Crile in the first decade of this century believed that apprehension was the major factor in surgical mortality with toxic goiter. He lowered the mortality by having his patients get used to breathing exercises with an anesthetic machine in their room. After two or three days, he added nitrous oxide to the oxygen until the patients became used to losing consciousness and awakening comfortably. The next day they were anesthetized in the same way in their room, taken to the operating room and their thyroid "stolen." One day a patient died with the horribly familiar thyroid crisis after this treatment. It was learned that a friend had told this patient that the difference between a day of breathing exercise and surgery would be that breakfast would be withheld on the day of surgery. With this and other observations on the role of apprehension, he developed the principles of "anoci-association" in surgery. This included careful handling of tissues, local anesthesia as well as general anesthesia, careful avoidance of scrub-room conversations and clashing of instruments.

METHODS OF ALLEVIATING AND BLOCKING PAIN PERCEPTION

A. Methods which do not seem to alter tissue reactions.
   1. Misdirection of attention.
   2. Recognition of more important threat.
   3. Dissociation in time or place (Erickson).
   4. Fooling the brain's programming with purposeful relaxation.
   5. Altering the meaning of pain (pain means removal from danger).
   6. Manipulating duration and intensity of pain (Erickson).
   7. Direct suggestion of pain relief and comfort.

B. Methods permitting decreased tissue reaction, improved healing.
   1. Mesmeric passes continued to end-point of trance and subconscious analgesia (Esdaile).
   2. Combined analysis of meaning of pain with permissive directions for subconscious pain relief for continued periods of time. Conditioned stimuli must be removed, resistances must be cleared, and the patient must be protected from "this-is-too-good-to-last" phenomenon listed elsewhere as a "slip-back" phenomenon.

Discussion. In Group A, only #6 and #7 might be considered truly related to hypnosis. The others can be achieved with patients who do not seem to be hypnotized and may not show commonly recognized signs of hypnosis. Number 1 (misdirection) had been taught us by children who use their first name in reporting injury: "Mary fell down and skinned her knee," instead of "*I* fell down and skinned *my* knee." It seems to hurt less when the injury happens to self in the third person. The pain tolerance is elevated by recognized danger. The boxer may be badly injured without feeling pain until the fight is over. This is the essence of #2.

Milton Erickson has extended use for the misdirection used by children who have, without direction from elders, often used associations with a pleasant experience to soften a present pain. One little boy told Cheek that he went down to the store in his mind and ate an ice cream cone to ease the pain when he fell on his knee. Erickson may shift the orientation of an uncomfortable patient to another period of life when pain was not part of the experience. By drawing attention to scenery and various happy sensory stimuli, he dilutes the capacity of the mind to pay attention to the incongruous painful messages. He may ask the patient in labor to come out of her body and sit across the room watching her body over on the bed giving birth to her baby. Her thinking mind is therefore free from her feeling body.

The nervous system reacts to danger and pain by acclerating heart and respiratory rates, decreasing circulation to the vegetative organs, and increasing blood supply to skeletal muscles. At the same time, the tonicity of these muscles is increased by the hyperventilation. The reverse of these reactions occurs when the environment is peaceful. Purposeful relaxation of muscles seems to evoke the reactions of peace and freedom from pain even in the presence of danger and injury. The patient must cooperate and therefore should recognize reasons for using suggestions of this sort when they seem ridiculously out of tune with the situation. There are many times, however, when patients seem willing to accept such suggestions as a sort of mental escape from a painful situation.

A man suffering anginal pain can readily understand that slowing his heart rate will allow better filling of his coronary arteries. These vessels get their oxygen and nutrition in the interval between contractions of the heart. It makes sense then for him to hallucinate the peaceful setting and his reaction to the situation of having a lazy vacation, stretched out on a sunny beach. He can be asked to signal with an ideomotor response when he is there, give another signal when he knows his heart is getting better circulation, and another signal when the subconscious element of the pain is totally gone. This is an intelligent way of reprogramming the brain during an emergency. It uses conditioned responses, and the process of attention given the act will also diminish awareness of the pain.

Henry Beecher has pointed out the significance of motivation in the tolerance of pain. A wound in combat may be tolerated without need for pain-relieving drugs if the soldier realizes his right to be removed from danger by virtue of being honorably wounded. Where circumstances prevent complete control of pain, it may be possible to attach some constructive meaning to the pain although we feel a better case can be offered for the complete eradication of pain.

Erickson (1967) has described uses of time-distortion and diminution of pain in increments when circumstances do not permit complete removal of pain. He has struck bargains with patients who need their pain but are willing to suffer in some unimportant part of the body or will compress a long period of mild pain into a few moments of excruciating pain. He has found it possible for patients to substitute night pain during sleep for disabling daytime pain. He has arranged for episodic pain of long duration to seem like pain of a few seconds duration or has exercised patients with forgetting various aspects of pain. These methods are interesting. It seems to us that their general goals are to permit time for the patient to recognize that the pain is really not essential for constructive living and that pain can eventually be eliminated if it can be manipulated.

Direct suggestion of pain relief may work dramatically or it may fail miserably and force the therapist into a position of diminished prestige. We feel it has a place in dentistry and during acute emergencies when patients show spontaneous trance-like behavior. Indirect methods are more successful at all other times.

MESMERIC PASSES

The learning process by which biologically insignificant stimuli are eventually discriminated out of effectiveness is called habituation. Mason has shown that continued stressful avoidance experiments eventually cause diminished output of contrisol derivatives in primates. At first it was thought this phenomenon resulted from exhaustion of the adrenal glands until administration of ACTH demonstrated greater than normal capacity of the adrenals to put out corticoids. Habituation is usually selective as seen in nature.

There is much we need to know about the special kind of habituation caused by repetitive lulling stimuli used by Esdaile in India. He prepared his patients for surgery by gently blowing on their face and repetitively passing his hands down over the face, chest, abdomen and legs. This was alternated by passing the hands over the lateral sides of the head and down to the finger tips. He spoke no words. He seldom touched the skin. He turned the task over to varied assistants while he made hospital rounds. Sometimes total anesthesia was obtained in 30 minutes; sometimes it took more than an hour, even several hours. He returned from time to time and tested reactions to a pinprick. The patient was taken to surgery when there was no reaction to this stimulus.

Research by Becker and Bachman suggests that mesmeric anesthesia may be an electrical phenomenon. Possibly the repetitive movement of hands with their electrical field polarity opposite to that of the head and body produces a state similar to that caused by fluctuating direct current (electro-narcosis). Animals as low on the scale as salamanders and as high as physicians show reversals of electrical polarity during hypnosis, sleep and unconsciousness of chemo-anesthesia, according to these authorities.

They produced trance-like behavior in salamanders by repeated stroking with a nylon brush. They have studied wound healing and bone formation in relation to electrical field potentials and are coming up with interesting results which may account for the results of Esdaile in lowering his surgical mortality with the help of mesmeric passes. The reader may be interested in reading the classic discussions of bioelectric phenomena by H. S. Burr and his associates at Yale University and the interesting contributions of Ravitz. We may eventually discover that the concept of animal magnetism proposed by Mesmer may be closer to the truth than was thought by the French commission of Benjamin Franklin, Lavoisier and others in 1784.

COMBINED ANALYSIS OF PAIN AND PERMISSIVE SUGGESTIONS

General principles involved here will be considered in some detail because the method can be applied to many types of psychosomatic illness. The general format to be followed includes the following:

1. Orientation at a subconscious level to the first moment pain of this sort seemed important.

2. Discover what event made this a personal, significant experience.

3. What reinforced the meaning of this pain (emotional loading, identification, guilt, attitude of doctor, etc.)?

4. Knowing these things so far, does your inner mind feel willing to let me help you get well?

5. Project forward to the time you are completely over this trouble and are no longer afraid of it recurring. When you are there your "yes" finger will lift and tell me the date that pops into your mind.

6. Is there anything else we need to know before we start working toward this goal?

7. Teach the patient how to use auto-hypnosis for brief periods.

8. Rehearse turning on the symptom and turning it off.

9. Instruct the patient of the occasional recurrence of symptoms during a time of discouragement or with unconscious prompting of relatives or physicians. Teach the patient how to use the "slip-back" phenomenon as a learning process instead of a sign of failure.

Discussion. It is hard for a patient to answer question 4 about willingness to get well until the full meaning of trouble has been clarified by steps 1, 2 and 3. The process of orientation to a *first moment* can be used as an induction of hypnosis because it involves some of the requisites already present. Full attention is drawn to the search. When finger signals are assigned, the attention is even more concentrated on whether or not a finger will lift to indicate subconscious knowledge which is not yet available at a conscious level. The introduction goes something like this:

"Your subconscious mind has much information about this pain that would be hard for you to remember accurately. Let's check the history you have already given me by using a deeper level of awareness revealed by the same sort of unconscious muscle movement that we use in everyday talking. Instead of watching for changes in facial expression, movement of your head or changes in voice inflection, I'm going to ask this index finger to lift for a "yes," just as you might nod your head. This middle finger will be your "no," and this thumb will be your method of waving me off for something you don't want to tell.

"Now please don't try to move the fingers purposefully, because you could as well just tell me verbally. I want to know what you think at subconscious levels, and we both need to know a lot of information that is not yet available to you consciously. I feel sure you would have cured your own pain if the factors related only to will power and conscious understanding. I doubt if anybody really enjoys feeling pain or being sick.

"Now just close your eyes to shut out external stimuli and let the subconscious part of your mind orient back to the first moment in your life when pain of this sort *first* became important to you; it might not have been *your* pain. It *could* have been pain that someone else was suffering. When you are there, your "yes" finger will lift. As it lifts, please bring those memories up to a level where you can tell about them."

Suggestions of relaxation can be given before the ideomotor response.

This method seldom fails when it is used directly after taking a history and doing a routine physical examination. It involves an element of surprise and therefore permits mobilization of memories and associations which might be further repressed after too much warning. It saves much time that would be wasted in explanations of hypnosis to a patient whose resistances are going to make ordinary induction fail. These resistances are immediately apparent in delayed responses, distressed facial expressions, restlessness or unwillingness to close the eyes.

After obtaining the initial "first moment," it is always necessary to ask if there is anything *earlier than this*, something which might have *set the stage* for the initial report. Even in hypnosis it is necessary to look for screen memories that make consciously acquired history so unreliable. These can be rapidly cut through by use of ideomotor responses which bypass more conscious reasoning processes.

Items 2, 3 and 4 are self-explanatory. Number 5 is helpful in checking the answer to the question 4 about willingness to let you help the patient get well. The confirmed pessimist will not accept a "cure date." Delay in answering and signs of restlessness or discomfort are valuable indications of resistance.

There is a need to know the answer to #6 regarding other information which might be needed to assure cure. Unconscious resistance may be screened by yielding seemingly significant information requiring one more element before the problem is solved.

Element #8 serves two purposes. It tends to strengthen the ego of a patient who previously has always been a target for treatment rather than a cooperative part of therapy. It also gives valuable evidence about motivation. Guilt-ridden and masochistic patients will show their colors by forgetting to practice their homework or by invention of excuses for this avoidance.

Rehearsal of the symptom (#9) teaches the patient that purposefully invented discomfort can also be eliminated. The result can be achieved by having the patient start from full comfort and develop a fraction of the total pain before turning it off on signal. If pain is already present, it is helpful to have the patient double the amount of pain for a few moments and then reduce it to the initial level before diminishing it to half its initial level. It is always explained that the goal will be achieved at an ideomotor level of awareness before the conscious mind is aware of the response. This tends to eliminate conscious effort effect while the patient is waiting for the ideomotor signal of achievement.

Any successful therapy with a disease or pain state will eventually evoke the dangerous wondering how long the luck will hold out. Discomfort will return hand-in-hand with the feeling of discouragement and assumption that the most recent therapy is no more successful than its predecessors. A recurring symptom can be used very helpfully when you have forewarned the patient. Ask the patient's subconscious mind to orient to the moment just before the symptoms recommenced. The "yes" finger is to lift when he has arrived and he is to "look around and see what is going on at that time; what might have something to do with the beginning of trouble." Inability to discover the cause is either an indication of need for the trouble or an indication that organic pathology may be involved. By discovering the time of onset of symptoms, it is possible to assess the importance of ideation during natural sleep.

PLANNING OF THERAPY SESSIONS

An hour should be allowed for the initial interview and physical examination. At this time it is usually possible to demonstrate postural suggestion, the effort effect of "trying," and the importance of shifting awareness. The second visit should be within 24 hours. Ideomotor responses can be set up and #1-8 can be completed. With persistent pain states of longer duration than one year, this second visit should be for an hour to allow for searching resistances. Major resistances will show up at the third visit a week later. Thirty minutes is usually enough at this time (see chapter on resistances). If the way is clear, you can go on with items #9, rehearsal of symptoms and instruction about the flashback phenomenon. A fourth appointment of 30 minutes is set up to cover possible complications of therapy and to permit the patient to tell us what we have done wrong and what might be done better in the future with other patients. This is not only instructive for the therapist but it is good medicine for the patient who may have spent many years of frustration with other doctors more bent on treating than learning.

Summary. The most significant element in pain is that part which is not consciously recognized. It is necessary to know the meaning of pain to the patient and help motivate the patient to get well for the sake of other people. Prolonged freedom from pain at a subconscious level of awareness seems to accelerate reparative tissue reactions. We must protect the patient from discouragement over recurrence of symptoms after initial relief. The "slip-back" phenomenon may be used as a learning process.

REFERENCES

Armstrong, D., Jepson, J. B., Keele, C. A., and Stewart, J. W.: Pain producing substance in human inflammatory exudates and plasma. J. Physiol. 135: 350, 1957.

Becker, R. O.: The bioelectric factors in amphibian-limb regeneration. J. Bone Joint Surg. 43-A: 643-656, 1961.

Beecher, H. K.: The powerful placebo. JAMA 159: 1602, 1955.

————: Surgery as placebo. JAMA 176: 1102-1107, 1961.

Burr, H. S., and Northrop, F. S. C.: Electro-dynamic theory of life. Quart. Rev. Biol. 10: 322-333, 1935.

————, Harvey, S. C., and Taffel, M.: Biolectric correlates of wound healing. Yale J. Biol. Med. 11: 103-107, 1938.

Cheek, D. B.: Ideomotor questioning for investigation of subconscious "pain" and target organ vulnerability. Amer. J. Clin. Hypn. 5: 30-41, 1962.

Crile, G. and Lower, W. E.: "Anoci-Association". Philadelphia, W. B. Saunders, 1914.

Delboeuf, J.: Concerning the origin of therapeutic results with hypnosis. Bull. Acad. Royale Belgique, 1877. (Reference in H. Bernheim: Suggestive Therapeutics, New York, London Book Co., 1947, p. 411.)

Erickson, M. H.: An introduction to the study and application of hypnosis for pain control. In: Hypnosis and Psychosomatic Medicine, Proceedings of 1965 International Congress, Paris. Berlin, Springer-Verlag, 1967, pp. 83-90.

Esdaile, J.: Hypnosis in Medicine and Surgery, New York, Julian Press, 1950. (Reprinted from the original Mesmerism in India, Chicago, Psychic Research Co., 1902.)

Ostfield, A. M., Chapman, L. F., Goodell, H., and Wolff, H.: Studies in headache. Summary of evidence concerning a noxious agent active locally during migraine headache. Psychosom. Med., 19: 199, 1957.

Ravitz, L. J.: History, measurement and applicability of periodic changes in the electromagnetic field in health and disease. Ann. NY Acad. Sci. 98: 1144-1201, 1962.

Chapter 17

Surgical Uses of Hypnosis

THE GENERAL goals of a surgeon should be exercise of good judgment in deciding on an operation, careful preparation of the patient, meticulous attention to the details of surgical technic and thoughtful care after surgery aimed at rapid recovery of normal function.

This is not a one-man job. We need assistance from relatives, nurses, house officers, laboratory technicians, an anesthetist, and even the unseen helpers in the kitchen. A good-risk surgical patient can be converted to a bad one by careless remarks of relatives and friends on the eve of surgery. The question, "Why didn't you go to Doctor — ?" can have a devastating effect on a patient. The admitting officer insisting on removal of a ring carrying special significance to the patient may initiate very troublesome thoughts at a critical time.

Hypnosis can be of great service in discovering unconscious fears, correcting them, decreasing needs for anesthetic agent, diminishing risks for complications during anesthesia, and assuring rapid recovery of vegetative processes. Hypnosis is, however, not the only means of accomplishing these things.

We must remember that "hypnosis" is still a bad word to many people, including our patients. What may be accepted by our patient may be destroyed by a relative or a well-meaning physician. It is wise to move slowly and discuss the subject of hypnosis sparingly within your hospital until the patients can speak for you with their postoperative behavior. Keep in mind that every anesthesiologist and every good surgeon is and has been using elements of suggestion. All good clinicians and nurses realize that optimistic suggestions get better results than the legally acceptable discussions of possible complications involved in "informed consent." They know that remarks capable of double interpretation will be understood in their pessimistic rather than optimistic light. Some have learned to ask, "Are you comfortable tonight, Mrs. Jones?" rather than "Are you having any pain?"

The quality of hypnosis that makes it a valuable tool in surgery is its use for uncovering information that is not known to the patient at a conscious level of awareness. Ideomotor responses permit us to learn that subconscious pain continues and interferes with healing at times when the patient seems to be comfortable and free of pain. We can block subconscious pain and permit removal of muscle guarding, improve circulation to injured tissue and decrease release of inflammatory enzymes in the surgical field (see chapter on pain).

Many surgeons, including J. B. Murphy, J. M. T. Finney and the senior George Crile, have pointed out the danger of going ahead with surgery after a patient has expressed a fear of dying. It is possible with hypnosis to discover the origin of such consciously expressed fear. The origins are usually ridiculous identifications or assumptions that now is the time to be punished for real or imagined sins. Sometimes they stem from unscientific assumption that the diagnosis will be cancer, and death during anesthesia is preferable to a slow and painful death with cancer.

It is possible for these fears and assumptions to be corrected in the hospital at a time of emergency when the importance of surgery is greater than the risk of an emotional death, but there is seldom such an emergency. The operation should be canceled and the patient discharged from the hospital. Surgery should not be rescheduled until the origin of fear has been discovered and corrected and the patient taught how to control pain perception and sensations of hunger. In a trance state, the patient should be asked to project forward to the *best time for surgery* and have a "yes" finger lift when the optimum time has been selected. It may come as a shock to the surgeon to learn the answer, but he should ask for the patient to "see the surgeon, himself or someone else, who should be doing the operation in order to assure most rapid recovery and return to normal activities."

Patients too often are referred for surgical treatment without being given a chance to decide whether or not they react favorably to the spiritual and emotional climate shown by the surgeon. Surgery, like obstetrics, requires at least an effort on the part of the referring physician either to match personalities or "sell" the specialist so highly that warmth of personality does not matter. Obstetrical patients have plenty of time to decide whether or not they want to go on with the relationship. Surgical patients, however, may have only one chance to meet the surgeon, schedule the operation and make preparations to enter the hospital.

SUBCONSCIOUS FEAR

It is possible that the unexpressed fear of dying may be more dangerous than the kind a patient is able to talk about. No careful study has been made to see how many patients have survived when they thought they would die. We tend to generalize on the basis of the tragic few who died after expressing their convictions. When we compare results of surviving people who had fears of dying before surgery with results when there have been no fears, there is an advantage in favor of those who went into surgery without fear. Since such studies are made with hypnotized subjects in age-regression, we may say that the reported fears must have been subconscious. Differences can be found in the incidence of surgical shock, hemorrhage, postoperative distension, vomiting and wound disruption. It is reasonable that alarm would alter coagulation mechanisms and disturb gastro-intestinal function.

Notice the variants of fear. We can be afraid and freely talk of our fears. We do so usually because we understand that others have had similar fears. We are willing to listen and be reassured in return. We can know our fear consciously but feel unwilling to talk about it because of the conviction that others might think us foolish. We may have a consciously recognized fear and be unwilling to talk about it lest it be justified. We often do not want to "hear the truth." This kind of fear causes people to put off visiting a doctor after discovery of a symptom. It may lead to suicide in older people fearing cancer, heart disease or stroke. In younger people it can lead to suicide or foolish acts prompted by fear of being pregnant or having a venereal disease.

We can experience fear subconsciously in tremendous reality and be totally oblivious to its presence in our conscious thinking. Recent studies have convinced the authors that such consciously unrecognized fears may be responsible for major complications due to hypercoagulability of the blood. In surgery this can cause shock, thrombo-embolic phenomena and fibrinolytic hemorrhage. It can cause abortion, stillbirth and premature labor. It can lead to severe antepartum hemorrhage, placental separation and toxemia of pregnancy.

UNCERTAINTY

Whatever the statistics might show in relation to fear, we can safely assume that surgical patients will do better and recover more rapidly when they have confidence in their surgeon, know what to expect and are free of conscious and unconscious fear. Interviews in age-regression with adults who have undergone surgery in early childhood have strongly emphasized the point that primal fear is initiated and aggravated by uncertainty. New sights, new sounds, new smells followed by loss of ability to talk, move and feel are terrifying only when they come without warning and without assurance that everything will be all right afterward.

The thoughts and dreams of adults during the week before surgery and during induction of anesthesia are literal, direct and as alarming as similar experiences in real life would be to children. Conscious adult reasoning has no place in the thoughts of sleeping and anesthetized people.

Patients who have experienced unpleasant things during surgery are easily able to hallucinate what words and deeds would have made the entire experience *comfortable and safe*. Over and over again we have heard that thoughtful explanation in advance could have solved the problems. Sometimes we have found that real experiences during general anesthesia, as those of dreams, are too unpleasant to talk about in hypnosis. Often it is possible to learn something about the original trauma by asking what would have made the experience more pleasant. We can guess about the real one by hearing of its counterpart. This is like studying a cast in order to learn about the mould.

The phenomenon of habituation is significant in biologic learning processes. Stimuli associated with injury and release from starvation are significant. All other repetitive stimuli from the environment evoke progressively weaker responses. This mechanism explains, in part, the ability of a mother to sleep through traffic noises outside her house but awaken at infinitely less intense sounds of an infant's disturbed breathing. It explains the amusing reaction of the lighthouse keeper awakening and saying "What was that?" when a power failure shut off his fog horn.

William Kroger has pointed out the importance of rehearsing each step of delivery with an obstetrical patient who wants to use hypnosis for analgesia. He has emphasized the importance of this rehearsal method in preparing patients when hypnosis is to be used as the sole anesthesia for surgery. This method is valuable also for patients who will have drugs and chemical anesthetic agents. This is an intelligent use of the habituation phenomenon. It is a feature of Wolpe's desensitization program in psychotherapy. Hypnotherapists have observed it repeatedly in action when they demonstrate abreactions for successive audiences using the same subject. An asthmatic seizure during age-regression to a traumatic experience in childhood becomes progressively less dramatic and the physiological reflections less clear with each repetition.

Go to your hospital admitting office. Listen while the admitting officer confronts a patient with questions about religion, ability to pay and relatives to be notified in case of trouble. Notice whether patients are permitted to tape on their significant rings or are forced to give them up. Go up to a surgical floor between the hours of two and four to hear how patients are greeted by the floor nurses. Learn from the nurses the order of routines such as the visits from a technician, the house-officer, the prep-attendant, the anesthetist. Be able to tell the patient about these matters at the final office visit or have them noted in a brief mimeo-graphed form as a check-list. Add to it notes about whether or not drinking water will be removed from the bedside table and why this will be done. Tell the patient the order of events:

1. Pre-operative hypo.
2. Attendants coming with the carriage.
3. Placement on the operating table and setting up intravenous fluids.
4. The type of induction to be used, whether by inhalation or the more acceptable intravenous route.
5. How there is loss of pain sense first, then of touch and position.
6. Explain about the need for an airway to diminish the requirements for anesthetic agents and assure plenty of oxygen at all times.
7. Positioning for surgery.
8. Preparation of the operative site.
9. Draping.

Explain that the hearing sense continues and that you will keep your patient posted on what is going on. All other sounds and conversation are to be ignored or used as background sound for the recollections that will be selected and talked about during the training period the evening before surgery.

Although these matters may be read only once in your notes or you only talk about them once in your office, the effect will be that of multiple repetitions. All important thoughts are repetitively reviewed. We never nod only once in accepting a thought; we always reject an idea with repeated wagging of the head. Degrees of magnitude in primitive languages are expressed by repeating the descriptive word. Your outlines of events will echo and re-echo in daytime thoughts and the dreams of natural sleep, and with each repetition the stage is being a little better set for minimal response when the real action takes place.

The book *Anoci-Association* written by Crile and Lower contains the essence of thoughtful consideration for the fears, perceptions and needs of surgical patients. It should be read by every surgeon and every anesthesiologist. Crile studied his own reactions to general anesthesia and concluded that the mind continues to function after loss of consciousness. He witnessed at least one example of continued ability to hear under general anesthesia but refrained from mentioning this in a surgical journal. He refers to it in detail in his 1947 autobiography.

It now seems probable that his concept of a mind perceiving painful stimuli under general anesthesia was in general correct although not in the way he believed. More likely is the possibility that continued hearing sense alerts the patient to what is going on during surgery. If the perceptions are alarming there may be central nervous system reactions comparable to those responsible for phantom-limb syndrome and reflex sympathetic dystrophy or causalgia. The central imagery of remembered pain releases inflammatory and pain-producing enzymes at the site of previous trauma as though the brain were reasoning that it must remain increasingly aware of this bad place to prevent any further injury. The result is that any mild threat capable of hurting when the wounds were fresh will continue to evoke painful reactions long after the injuries have healed.

This is the phenomenon sometimes referred to as "tissue memory." Gustav Heyer called it "Hängen-bleiben," noting that symptoms of a disease often continued long after the apparent cure and might again make the same tissues vulnerable to disease. We see evidence of this heightened awareness when we ask subjects to hallucinate various colored lights as representative of feelings from different parts of their body. We frequently find subjects reporting bright lights symbolizing uncomfortable awareness in areas of the body that are presently comfortable but have once been injured. We find that patients who have had Herpes simplex, virus lesions about the mouth in relation to sunburn or emotionally stressful situation may reproduce these lesions after accepting suggestions that they are reliving exposure to the sun or a stressful situation. People who have labile neuro-circulatory systems can produce real blisters when they have accepted suggestions of reliving a painful burn on a hand or arm.

Physiological responses to injury and fear do not shut down during natural sleep when consciousness is obliterated. They do not shut down during traumatic unconsciousness. They certainly continue to act during general chemo-anesthesia.

EVIDENCE REGARDING CONTINUED AWARENESS OF MEANINGFUL SOUNDS

Probably most investigators with hypnosis have attempted to break the conscious amnesia for sleep ideation. Many have considered the possibility that anesthetized human beings might hear conversations. Some psychotherapists have wondered about breaking the amnesia of electro-convulsive-therapy. In 1937 it was possible for Milton Erickson to break through the retrograde amnesia associated with traumatic unconsciousness in a classic study which also demonstrated recovery of physical responses during the reliving of the actual period of unconsciousness.

Several characteristics of unconscious behavior have militated against successful exploration of these amnesic areas:

1. The unconscious mind is economical. It will not work to elevate information to a conscious level of awareness unless the investigator makes clear his knowledge that information is expected and that he knows it is available. Requests for information must be phrased from this standpoint. For example, "Orient back to the moment you lose consciousness. Your 'no' finger will lift each time you are hearing something important. Your 'I don't want to answer' finger will lift when you know you are conscious and out of the anesthetic."

The hypnotized subject will usually indicate "no" when the question is placed in the ordinary acceptable way, "Do you hear anything important while you are asleep with the anesthetic?" It is clear to the subject that a negative would be accepted and this requires no further effort.

2. Most hypnotized subjects find it very hard to talk. When they talk at all they are limited to information which is near the borderline between unconscious and conscious thought. Information perceived during unconsciousness or fabricated during the dreams of natural sleep is far below this border. Dreams that are consciously remembered on awakening are usually garbled with symbolism and are screens for the thought sequences capable of influencing physiological behavior.

It is a mistake to ask the hypnotized subject to report information which is not yet available at a speaking level of awareness. A thoughtful observer will see, on reviewing traumatic dream material or the events of general anesthesia, that changes in facial expression and respiration occur many seconds and even many minutes before it is possible for the subject to talk.

3. Elevation of deeply suppressed or repressed information toward conscious awareness for verbal reporting occurs as a result of multiple repetitions. Erickson was the first to report this phenomenon in his study of a return to an unconscious state (1937). The student of hypnosis will see evidence of this repetitiveness of review if he asks a subject "to review an important dream last night and tell me about it." When a designated finger is to lift for the beginning and another for the ending, you will see that the fingers lift alternately many times before a change in facial expression or an effort to speak indicates readiness to talk about the dream. This occurs spontaneously without need for instruction about repeating the review.

In studying the amnesia of sleep, general anesthesia and traumatic unconsciousness, it is necessary to allow time for review. This occurs very quickly when the review is carried out at a subconscious level with ideomotor signals for beginning and end of the experience. Assign some other ideomotor signal to let you know when the information is ready for verbal reporting. It may take several reviews, occupying a total of four or five minutes, before a report is ready. It may take much longer if the experience has been particularly unpleasant. Sometimes it may be necessary to ask for an hallucinated counterpart that would have made the experience more pleasant.

CONTINUED HEARING: HISTORICAL NOTES

In his autobiography, Crile tells of an incident occurring about 1907. A patient of his was unconscious and ready for abdominal surgery. The anesthetic agent was nitrous oxide. A resident physician presented the clinical history to the gallery of physicians. At rounds a few days later she was asked by Crile how much she could remember. She then proceeded to recite her clinical history as given by the resident when everyone had thought her unable to hear.

In a personal communication, Milton Erickson told Cheek that Waters, Professor of Anesthesiology at the University of Wisconsin, had commented about 1923 on the possibility that anesthetized patients could hear remarks.

Dave Elman, a stage hypnotist who became a teacher of physicians and dentists after World War II, told Cheek about his first experience discovering that anesthetized patients could hear and react badly. It was about 1947. He was asked by a surgeon to hypnotize a woman and cause her to stop vomiting. Vomiting had been a prominent symptom before surgery, but her gallbladder full of stones had been removed and she should have been eating well by the time Elman was called. Elman had no preconceived notions about anesthesia experiences. He intended only to place her in a deep trance and suggest that she feel hungry on awakening. In deep hypnosis she became agitated as she was asked if she knew why she continued to vomit after surgery. She quoted her surgeon as saying, "She'll never be the same after this." This had seemed a worse alternative than the vomiting which had existed before surgery. Elman called in the surgeon who explained to the patient that he had intended to mean she would no longer vomit now that the diseased gallbladder had been removed. When this misunderstanding had been corrected, she stopped vomiting and made an uneventful recovery.

In 1953 Cheek attended a symposium on medical and dental applications of hypnosis. The instructors were Erickson, LeCron and Aaron

Moss. Both Erickson and LeCron expressed themselves with assurance that anesthetized people could hear much more than surgeons believed possible. Both had found examples of it. LeCron told of a female patient who had refused to go back to her surgeon. She had liked him very much before surgery. In hypnosis she quoted him as saying while she was anesthetized, "Well, that will take care of this old bag!" Of course the anecdote seemed amusing, but Cheek was convinced, from nine years of exploration with hypnosis, that anesthetized people could not hear. These conclusions were drawn on the mistaken premise that hypnotized people will answer questions in the affirmative when they know a negative would stop the need for further effort.

In October 1957, at a Hypnosis Symposium in Houston with LeCron, a physician continued to indicate with ideomotor signals that he was hearing two unpleasant things during his appendectomy. An ideomotor response indicated beginning and end of the operation. Between these signals he persisted in signaling with a finger that he heard two disturbing remarks. His pulse and respiratory rates increased just before each signal. His facial expression showed distress each time, but he could not tell the group what was going on. He was asked to go over the experience again and stop when he got to the bad part. Then Cheek asked, "What do you hear?" Verbally he would say, "Nothing," with an appropriate shake of his head. When asked to have a finger answer the question "Do you hear anything frightening or disturbing?", he would appear puzzled as he found his "yes" finger lifting. After 13 repetitions of the entire experience, he was able to verbalize the two unpleasant comments: (1) "It's gangrenous!" This was spoken in an ominous way. He had no knowledge of that word, but it sounded bad. (2) "Okay, let's get out of here and go home." This was disturbing because he knew his abdomen was still open. As a youngster he did not know the figure of speech often used by surgeons. He believed they were planning to go away and leave him there on the table with his abdomen open.

The meaning of this accidental experience can be summarized as follows:

1. Deeply repressed information of a traumatic sort will be indicated first by physiological indications of distress, then by an ideomotor response, and finally by verbal reporting.

2. Verity of the experience can be assessed on this sequence. Verbal reporting without prior unconscious indications must be suspect until proven otherwise.

3. If physiological signs of distress can occur during hypnotic age-regression to a misunderstanding of intended meaning, the same could be true during the actual experience. Some complications of surgery could

be caused by remarks which the surgical team might think inconsequential.

4. If misunderstandings could be disturbing, how much more disturbing could be factual comments by a pathologist reporting cancer from examination of a frozen section? Could a diagnosis of inoperable cancer rob a patient of the chance to prove the surgeon wrong? Could verbal expressions in the operating room account for the rapid spread of previously slow-growing cancer?

Time and experience seem to be supporting some of these possibilities and conclusions.

LeRoy Wolfe, an anesthesiologist, was present at the First Annual Convention of the American Society of Clinical Hypnosis when Cheek presented the first formal discussion of this subject in 1958. Wolfe decided to test the possibility by suggesting reassurance and ordering freedom from pain at some time during the operation when he believed the patient was in a surgical plane of anesthesia. His evaluation of the surgical plane was clinical and as accurate as the estimate of those who have insisted that "adequate anesthesia" certainly obliterates the possibility of continued hearing sense. Better than 50 per cent of the patients required no pain-relieving drugs after surgery. A point he brought out during his presentation in 1959 was that some patients did not have pain in the operative area where he had ordered them to be free of pain. One man following surgery on his pancreas had pain in a leg instead. In a subsequent study, Wolfe gave the less specific order that the patients could "remain comfortable in every way."

Donald Hutchings and Robert Pearson, who were also present at the first two annual conventions of the society, followed with interesting studies. Hutchings repeated the work of Wolfe with slightly less dramatic but still convincing results. Pearson exposed patients to tape recordings in a double-blind study. Unfortunately he did not recognize that tape recorded messages are unconvincing to anesthetized patients. Some of his tapes contained music, some were blank, and some had suggestions for comfort, good appetite and rapid healing. There was a slight but statistically acceptable difference in results favoring patients who heard the suggestions. They went home sooner than those who heard music or the hissing of a blank tape. Wolfe and Millet, Hutchings and Pearson did not attempt to question patients in hypnosis to see if they reported hearing suggestions. Kolouch has expressed his conviction that anesthetized patients can hear.

Bernard Levinson is an anesthesiologist who changed his specialty to psychiatry. Working in South Africa, he recognized the importance of making test suggestions meaningful to the patient and backed his estimate of surgical plane of anesthesia with evidence from electroenceph-alography. He had read Cheek's paper of 1959 and had set up a test with a patient who was to undergo plastic surgery on her face after an automobile accident. It was his initial plan to test her hearing by play-ing music and then to question her later to see if she had heard it. This test would have failed to demonstrate anything if a fortuitous accident had not occurred. The surgeon felt a lump on the lip of the patient and exclaimed, "My gracious, this is not a cyst. It could be cancer."

The pathologist reported the lump as benign and the findings were passed on to the patient, but in spite of her conscious understanding she became progressively more anxious and depressed until Levinson was able to place her in hypnosis three months later and discover the origin of her alarm. She quoted the remark of the surgeon, changing only the word "cancer" to "malignant."

With this verification, Levinson set up a test experiment with ten patients who were told only that EEG tracings were to be made during their operation. At a signal from him when he believed the EEG tracing indicated surgical plane with nitrous-oxide, oxygen and ether, the anesthetist told the surgeon to stop because the patient looked as though he needed oxygen. After a pause for rebreathing with the bag, the anesthetist told the surgeon to go ahead because the patient looked all right again. On age-regression, using the LeCron method of ideomotor questioning, three weeks after surgery it was possible for four of the patients to report verbatim the remarks in the operating room. Four of them showed evidence of alarm on reliving the experience.

One other report of a study by Abramson and Heron at the University of Minnesota has reached the literature. These investigators paid no attention to the often repeated statements that sounds have to be either threatening or reassuring to be remembered. They did not test their sub-jects after surgery to learn if they could remember the test stimuli in hypnosis. Their conclusion, based solely on the negative evidence of electroencephalography, was that patients in deep surgical planes of general anesthesia cannot hear.

It should be remembered that unconsciousness is an alarming state which probably mobilizes all possible ways of keeping contact with the environment. It is not beyond the realm of possibility that anesthetized human beings are depending on a more generalized vibratory sense awareness independent of the eighth cranial nerve. We have not yet excluded the possible explanation that what seems to be heard was per-ceived by thought transference. The fact remains, however, that sur-geons, nurses and anesthesiologists will help their patients by thinking and talking optimistically in surgery and around recovery rooms.

PRINCIPLES OF PREPARING PATIENTS FOR SURGERY

In the light of our understanding as offered by experienced patients, we can state the following:

1. Keep all statements phrased in optimistic terms, stating as well as implying your faith in the patient's ability to do very well.

2. Avoid statements which could be interpreted pessimistically, such as directions associated with words like "if," as in "You can go home in five days *if* all goes as expected."

3. Tell the patient what you plan to do, even at the risk of a malpractice suit, *without equivocation*. If unexpected reasons for doing otherwise occur at the operating table and you discuss the reasons at that time, there will be little cause to fear litigation. Few things are more disturbing to a patient on the eve of surgery than feeling the surgeon does not know what will be done the next day.

4. Outline the sequence of events after admission to the hospital, including the steps before an incision is made.

5. Teach the patient how to relax, how to make one part of the body numb, and how to transfer that numbness to other parts of the body such as the intended site for operation.

6. Place the patient in deeper hypnosis and ask for hallucination of rapid recovery of consciousness after surgery, early desire to move about in order to improve circulation in the incision area, and immediate feelings of hunger to insure early ability to take food, prevent nausea and eliminate gas. Suggestions can also be made as to normal body functions and elimination postoperatively, thus preventing urine retention.

7. Terminate the rehearsal by hallucination with request for the patient to visualize on a blackboard the date or day when he is very well recovered and ready to go home from the hospital. This is the most important part of the preparation and should be left until this point because many unrecognized fears will have disappeared. Unwillingness to hallucinate a discharge date is a danger signal that must not be passed over lightly. Cheek asks for an ideomotor response when the date is clear at a subconscious level. The number or date is to pop into the patient's conscious mind as the finger lifts. This method, which developed from work with habitual abortion patients, uncovers fear without suggesting it.

8. Ask the patient to orient to the origin of a reason for not selecting a date for discharge or for indicating "I don't want to answer" if either of these has happened. Be sure to check the nighttime ideation during the night before admission to the hospital when you suspect a fearful or pessimistic attitude.

9. Ask the patient to select some very pleasant experience of a vacation trip. Ask for an ideomotor signal when the best experience has been selected and ask for a verbal report when this comes into conscious awareness. Tell the patient to remember this in detail, starting with the preoperative hypodermic injection. This is to be the ticket for the excursion. Tell the patient there will be noises in the operating room but you want them to be associated with sounds on the vacation. Explain that you will keep him posted on all important things but will always address him by his first name. Everything else is to be ignored. You want your patient to make the detailed review stretch from the time of the hypodermic until return to the regular room. Explain that the purpose of this exercise in memory is to keep the appetite and all the normal vegetative processes ready for resumption of duty on awakening from the anesthetic instead of carrying the worries and alarms of surgery as a pattern of behavior on awakening. This makes sense to patients and keeps you from sounding mentally deranged.

10. Either keep the patient informed of each new action yourself after induction of anesthesia or be sure it is done by your anesthesiologist. We are not yet past the time of skepticism on continued hearing ability, and you must be prepared for laughter and derisive remarks from associates. Important events to be announced: intubation, positioning, cleanup, catheterization, transfers to carriage and thence to bed.

Although many surgeons have found it helpful to suggest that patients will be able to void after surgery, it has been Cheek's experience during 25 years of work with gynecological patients that this is unnecessary. Unlike defecation which often has become a conditioned problem with men and women during toilet training, urination is a natural process. Mentioning that urination after surgery will be easy suggests that you think the opposite might be the case. An exception to this rule would be when a patient has already had difficulty with previous operations or delivery.

Patients who have indwelling catheters and/or vaginal packing at the time of recovery from anesthesia will have an unpleasant subconscious feeling that they are unable to empty the bladder. Cheek leaves a retention catheter only when he has opened the bladder or interfered with bladder circulation. Vaginal packing is used only when radium has been inserted for treatment of cancer. This is an important point because gynecologists who routinely use vaginal packing and indwelling catheters seem to have much difficulty with urinary retention after vaginal plastic and vaginal hysterectomy operations.

FOLLOWING SURGERY

Before leaving the hospital, visit the recovery room. Thank your patient for good behavior. Explain what you have done. Outline what you want him to do as soon as he is awake. Ask the recovery room nurse to speak quietly and to address your patient by his first name or nickname.

Regardless of conscious evaluation of pain or absence of pain, ask the patient for an ideomotor answer to the question "Is there any pain, stiffness or discomfort in the operation area?" Some patients will answer verbally in the affirmative when their subconscious answer is "no." In any case, you have implied that you do not feel that there should be any pain. Follow this request for a finger signal when the patient is sure at a subconscious level that there will be freedom from all discomfort for the next 24 hours. Ask that the patient also reinforce this suggestion from time to time with auto-suggestion.

Check with the charge nurse on your 3 to 11 shift to see if it is necessary to write an order for no pain-relieving drugs to be given unless requested by the patient. In some hospitals short of staff, the evening nurse may give narcotics *as ordered* to diminish her work load. On a patient using hypnosis, unrequested sedation will have a stronger effect than expected. This is a very important area that is often ignored by surgeons.

If a patient complains much of pain or seems overly distended on the morning after surgery, be sure to check for possibly disturbing thoughts or dreams during the night.

HYPNOTIC ANESTHESIA

For cleaning up dirty wounds, for suture closure of wounds, and in many other forms of minor surgery, hypnotic anesthesia can be induced and used in several ways.

1. *Dissociation.* The patient may be led to talk about some experience which was not associated with pain: some hobby, a sport, a recent trip. Fortunately, the shock associated with an injury tends to raise the threshold for pain, and it is only a matter of keeping the patient from centering attention on what you are doing. Towels may be used to screen off the working area. Your body may be kept in a position so that the wound cannot be seen. The reader will probably have used this method many times without associating it with hypnosis.

Solutions of various colors may be helpful for raising pain tolerance and distracting attention from the idea of being hurt. This works best with children and requires recognition that you are using suggestion, that you are not dishonest in calling colored aqueous zephirin a magic new local anesthetic, and that you are really teaching a youngster to use his imagination in a constructive way. One doctor keeps three bottles with different colored solutions. He uses the "weakest one" first to see if that will be enough to make the wound numb. He may rarely have to use the "powerful one" which he handles with forceps in order not to anesthetize his own fingers while applying it.

2. *Formal induction of a medium trance state* followed by direct suggestion of anesthesia in an unimportant part of the body. It can be suggested that anesthesia will follow when you have stroked the area three times with your hand. The patient is to indicate with an ideomotor response when he has accomplished the anesthesia at a subconscious level and is to tell you when there is conscious awareness of the numbness. There is usually a lag of 15–30 seconds between ideomotor response and verbal reporting. Explain that pressure will be felt but that there will be no discomfort. Have the patient test the numbness himself and then transfer the numbness to the wound area. An ideomotor response is to indicate completion of that assignment. Have the patient tell you when to go ahead with treatment. The degree of anesthesia can be "doubled" or "trebled" as necessary. It is wise also to use dissociative methods along with this use of formal hypnosis.

3. *Sudden disorientation method* first demonstrated to us by Lester Kashiwa of Maui, Hawaii. This should only be used if there have been no injuries that might be made worse by a sudden change in posture.

The patient is seated on an examining table and told to look up at the ceiling. You support his weight with your forearm and with finger pressure at the base of the neck. He is told to close his eyes as you let him down toward a reclining position on the table, through the first 30 degrees of the arc. When his shoulders and head are about a foot above the table, the arm support is suddenly removed and he is allowed to drop onto a pillow or folded blanket. Disorienting suggestions are then made rapidly and commandingly in a rather loud tone, instructing him to relax completely. You then seize one arm and jerk it into a stiff position above his body. Continue to hold the arm in this position until you note that it has become cataleptic.

Suggestions are then added forcefully that the entire body will become totally unable to feel any pain and that a designated finger will lift unconsciously when he knows this has taken place. Tell him this total anesthesia is to continue until you have finished the treatment.

Experience alone will tell whether you are able to use this method. It is a technique capable of producing a profoundly deep trance state within a matter of seconds. We have never seen it cause resentment. Obviously it should not be used with someone who may have sustained injury to his neck, back or head.

4. *Pseudo-injection method.* Before using this technique it should be learned if the patient has ever experienced a local anesthetic injection as with novocaine. If not, it may not be successful.

The patient is told that you are about to inject some purely imaginary anesthetic drug such as novocaine or xylocaine into his hand or arm, using an imaginary needle. The skin should be rubbed at the area and a pencil point or other object not too sharp is pressed against the skin for a few seconds. It is suggested that a large dose of the drug is being injected, that this drug works very rapidly, and that numbness in the area will develop quickly. It is well to outline the area that is to be anesthetized, using a finger. An ideomotor finger response is to indicate as soon as anesthesia has developed.

5. *The electric light-switch method.* This technique is successful with adults and is particularly effective with children, even as young as four years old.

It is explained that pain nerves work on a tiny electric impulse and that this impulse must register in the brain or pain is not felt when it is stimulated. The hypnotized patient is told, with his eyes closed, to imagine a long row of electric light switches as though in his head. Above each switch is a little colored light, each one a different color or shade of colors, mentioning several colors and shades. All the switches are turned on and the lights lit.

The patient is then told that some certain switch, perhaps the one with the light blue light above it, goes to his right hand. He is to turn that switch off and see the light blue light go out and nod when he has done this. It is stated that this cuts off all nerve current to the hand and that it will then become numb and insensitive, though pressure will be felt if the skin is pinched as a stimulus. A finger signal is to indicate when the anesthesia has developed.

It should be remembered that a termination to the anesthesia is to be suggested with the use of any of these methods unless it is desired to maintain it for some time.

PYRAMIDING SUGGESTIONS (REINFORCEMENT)

To any of the above methods may be added suggestions that each time you move the patient's right arm the numbness will be increased. Each time you touch the injured area with liquid or an instrument or pinch the skin it will feel as though contact is being made through a greater thickness of dressing. This type of suggestion seems to work because it centers attention on what he is expected to experience rather than what pain might be felt if he is touched in the injured area. It is another form of dissociation of awareness.

While such techniques do not necessarily produce complete anesthesia in the area, the pain threshold may be raised considerably so that discomfort is minimum.

Discussion.   These methods are helpful for office diagnostic procedures such as uterine curettage, cauterization of the cervix and cystoscopy. Some have even used it successfully for the removal of thrombosed hemorrhoids and the incision and drainage of perirectal abscess. Prime value is with the injured patient who might be hypersensitive to local anesthetic agents and may not be a good risk for general anesthesia.

Remember that the human mind is capable of standing stimuli which are usually considered painful if you explain what you are going to do, that there may be some discomfort but that this will be minimal when he follows your directions exactly as you give them. This direction gives hope for comfort as opposed to the normal apprehension for possible sources of discomfort. It also puts the emphasis in his thinking on what directions to follow in diminishing pain rather than being subjected to the feeling of being passively at the mercy of painful forces.

When working on an extremity you have one additional trump card of dissociation. You can ask your patient to imagine that you are working on the opposite extremity and you want him to make that extremity increasingly cool as you progress. Ask him to hold an imagined piece of ice in his hand and spread the cold over the entire arm until it is completely numb.

HYPNOSIS WHEN CHEMO-ANESTHESIA CANNOT BE USED

When there are contraindications for the use of general anesthesia, it is possible to resort to hypnosis for the purpose, although the patient must be able to enter a deep trance. Here motivation will probably be strong.

During World War II, anesthetic agents were unavailable in a number of prisoner of war camps. An excellent report on the use of hypnosis in this situation on experience in the Tanglin compound in Singapore was given by the Australian physicians, Woodruff and Sampinon.

Many reports have been made of the use of hypnosis in major surgery. Lester Millikin of St. Louis has performed breast amputation, cholecystectomy and gastrectomy with no other help than hypnosis for pain relief in poor risk patients. His immediate surgical results have been dramatic in that ambulation was immediate. His patients were able to eat and drink on return to their room. His technique, tested by more than 40 years of experience, is as follows.

He shows his patient how uncomfortable the teeth of a small Allis tissue forceps can be. He explains that he does not expect his patient to do any more or less than he can do himself. Thereupon he demonstrates by putting himself into hypnosis and making an arm numb. He then applies the clamp to his arm with no show of discomfort, even when he moves it around.

Next he places the patient in hypnosis with relaxing suggestions until he is able to evoke a catalepsy. This step is followed by the suggestion that this arm will become too stiff to bend, absolutely rigid. This is a confidence-building test before moving on to the control of pain. The arm is then made more flexible as he moves each joint. With each movement he adds the suggestion that the arm is getting increasingly anesthetic.

He starts with elbow and wrist, adding movements of the joints of each finger. This is followed by the announcement that the arm is now numb enough that it could not possibly feel any pain. The patient will feel some pressure as the Allis clamp is applied to the dorsum of the forearm, but with each application the feeling will be less and less until there is no feeling at all.

Millikin verbalizes with complete conviction that these events will take place. His faith is infectious in the patient. Having established the fact that the teeth of the Allis clamp on the arm are painless, he spreads the anesthesia to the site of surgery or to the entire body. He talks to the patient during the operation and concludes with suggestions that healing will be rapid, that he wants him to enjoy his food.

A number of obstetricians including Kroger and Ralph August have performed Caesarean section using hypnosis as sole anesthetic. Only once in 25 years has Cheek found a patient so afraid of general anesthesia and all chemical anesthesia agents that he felt hypnosis was absolutely necessary. This was for a breast biopsy. An arm was first made anesthetic, then suggestion transferred it to the breast with further suggestion that healing would be without any soreness or inflammatory reaction in order that the breast would heal without scar tissue. A tape was prepared with his voice reading an anecdote from a book of dog stories. The recorder permitted Cheek to cut in with verbal suggestions if these should be necessary. Ear phones cut out sounds from the operating room. It was interesting to note the complete absence of bleeding in a normally vascular organ.

The patient showed contact with the immediate environment by having her pulse rate climb from 84 to 120 at the moment of cutting into the tumor to see if it looked suspicious. Pulse rate dropped again to normal when it was announced what the frozen section verified, that it was benign. She happily announced during the closure that there had been absolutely no pain.

Conclusion. Space does not permit covering all the many applications of hypnosis and anesthesia in surgery in this chapter. It has been important to discuss thoroughly the continued hearing sense, because this is, so far, only available in special journals and because much of the information stated here can be given you by your own patients if you use the questioning methods discussed here.

The problems of illeus, hemorrhage, urinary retention, postoperative pyelitis and renal shut-down will be diminished by including consideration for the subjective world of your patient along with your knowledge of techniques in surgery and manipulation of biochemical behavior.

Orthopedists will suffer less with problems of nonunion of fractures when care is taken to remove guilt feelings related to the injury and care taken to assure freedom from pain and muscle spasm after realignment of the bone. Similarly, orthopedists will have less difficulty with unmodified disc syndrome after successful surgery when they have explored the meaning of pain before surgery and made sure it is removed along with the offending herniated nucleus pulposus at surgery.

Unconscious people tend in their reactions to flashback to previous times when they have been exposed to some threat similar to the one causing unconsciousness. We had wondered why so many people show a fear response on entering hypnosis during group inductions at symposia on hypnosis. It was soon clear, as we explored the subjective responses of our subjects, that something about the hypnosis reminded them of a time when they were very frightened losing consciousness with an anesthetic or about to be injured in an accident.

Then we began obtaining histories suggesting that a very bad experience with an anesthetic in childhood would make the reactions unfavorable with subsequent anesthetics, no matter how well given. When we inquired further into this type of reaction we learned that it could be obliterated if the hypnotist or the next anesthetist would make constantly clear in communications that this was a new and separate experience, that new behavior was expected. We learned that this communication should continue with anesthetic administration well into the surgical phase. Ask your anesthesiologist to continue talking and instructing long after it seems impossible for his patient to hear.

Be careful as you talk in the operating room. Your patient is listening and may not understand words as you might intend them to be understood.

REFERENCES

Abramson, A., Greenfield, I., and Heron, W. T.: Response to or perception of auditory stimuli under deep surgical anesthesia. Amer. J. Obstet. Gynec. 96: 584-585, 1966.

Cheek, D. B.: Unconscious perception of meaningful sounds during surgical anesthesia as revealed under hypnosis. Amer. J. Clin. Hypn. 1: 101-113, 1959.

_____: The meaning of continued hearing under general chemo-anesthesia. Amer. J. Clin. Hypn. 8: 275-280, 1966.

Kolouch, F. T.: Role of suggestion in surgical convalescense. Arch. Surg. 85: 304-315, 1962.

Levinson, B.: States of awareness under general anesthesia, primary communication. Brit. J. Anaesth. 37: 544-546, 1965.

Pearson, R. E.: Response to suggestions given under general anesthesia. Amer. J. Clin. Hypn. 4: 106-114, 1961.

Simon, A., Herbert, C. C., and Straus, R.: The Physiology of Emotions. Springfield, Charles C Thomas, 1961.

Werbel, E. W.: One Surgeon's Experience with Hypnosis. New York, Pageant Press, 1967.

Wolfe, L. S., and Millet, J. B.: Control of post-operative pain by suggestion under general anesthesia. Amer. J. Clin. Hypn. 3: 109-112, 1960.

Chapter 18

Insomnia

ONE OF THE commonest and most annoying of all complaints from which people suffer is the inability to sleep well. The average physician will shrug his shoulders helplessly and prescribe a barbiturate for this complaint. The sale of sleeping pills is measured by the billions each year, indicating the great prevalence of this condition. While a person may be drugged into sleeping, he is not cured, nor is the cause of his difficulty removed. In most cases this is a condition in which hypnosis can be of great benefit. Of course drugs are not the answer. The cause must be treated to cure the symptom. Knowing why insomnia has developed is a great step toward ending the condition.

THE TWO FORMS OF INSOMNIA

Most of the patients with insomnia have difficulty in going to sleep after they have gone to bed. This is the more common form. After tossing, perhaps for hours, eventually the victim drops off. With the second type, there is seldom difficulty going to sleep, but after a time there is awakening and then it is impossible to go back to sleep. A few unfortunates will have both types. Insomnia is a serious matter and certainly is a source of great discomfort, although no one ever died of insomnia. Loss of sleep brings fatigue as an accompaniment. Most sufferers sleep more hours than they realize.

With the majority of insomnia cases, the causes are superficial, usually a matter of bad sleeping habits which may be easily overcome with hypnosis. No statistics are available, but probably 75–80 per cent of all cases would fall into this category. On the other hand, insomnia may be a very deep-seated neurotic symptom with complicated causes. Most cases can be helped with the methods given here, but sometimes much longer and deeper psychotherapy may be required, with referral to a psychiatrist or psychologist. Sometimes barbiturate addiction may also require treatment.

THE USUAL CAUSES OF INSOMNIA

If bad sleeping habits are present, they must be broken and new habits formed. Hypnotherapy can break up habit patterns and establish good sleeping habits. Habits are related to conditioned reflexes and sometimes such a reflex is a cause of insomnia.

Some of our seven keys to neurotic and psychosomatic problems are sure to be involved if there is more to the condition than habit. Identification may be a part of the picture. A parent or someone else close to the patient in childhood may have suffered from insomnia. The therapist should also consider the possibility of masochism being a cause, for insomnia is certainly a punishing symptom.

There may be a conflict over sex. One of LeCron's patients, a frigid woman, always went to bed later than her husband in order to avoid his attentions. She would lie awake for some time fearing he might awaken and make love to her. Her going to sleep late enabled her to sleep later than he did, thus avoiding his attentions in the morning. Thus there was motivation in her case. Care should be taken in assessing possible unconscious motivations leading to insomnia. A person with a neurotic need for love and affection may use insomnia as a means of getting sympathy and attention, where this patient used it in reverse to avoid attention.

FEAR-CAUSED INSOMNIA

Without being consciously aware of their fear, some people are afraid to go to sleep. Insomnia is a danger signal with pregnant women who have had frightening dreams about their babies. Their frightening dreams are repetitive, and the symptom should alert the obstetrician.

Subconscious fears are seldom reasonable, but they must be uncovered to be resolved and the problem corrected. An exception would be a woman living alone in a location where attack or burglary was possible. Her fear of an intruder in the night has a rational basis. Her sleep would probably be normal if she were not alone.

The fear of death, usually an unconscious fear, is a common cause of insomnia. We tend to associate sleep with death. It is often called "the eternal sleep." On the death of a relative, children are often told the person went to sleep and did not awaken. There is even the appearance of sleep if a child is forced to look at a dead person. Prior frightening experiences with delirium, general anesthesia or near-drowning have been causes for this type of insomnia.

In searching for the causes, we have encountered still another reason for associating sleep with death. Strangely, this is the common little prayer often taught children:

> Now I lay me down to sleep;
> I pray the Lord my soul to keep.
> If I should die before I wake,
> I pray the Lord my soul to take.

This prayer originated in days when fulminating infections often killed children in their sleep. From the child's viewpoint, this is a horrible prayer. It says he may die during the night while asleep. Therefore sleep means danger and also doubt if the Lord will take his soul. Why ask such a question of God if there is no danger? While a child may not have much difficulty going to sleep with a strong physical need for sleep, later something may happen accenting the possibility of death during sleep. The prayer could be said to be the originating cause, the later event the precipitating one bringing on insomnia.

A fear of a different type can be present with a person who has frequent nightmares. Here the insomnia is an effort to stay awake to avoid having a terrifying dream.

A neurotic fear would be when one is afraid to go to sleep because something terrible might happen, nothing definite, just something horrible. Such an emotion is irrational.

BAD SLEEPING HABITS

Undoubtedly the most common of all causes for insomnia is bad sleeping habits plus the expectation of having difficulty in going to sleep or waking during the night. Anticipating trouble acts as a suggestion, and trouble is almost sure to follow. The Law of Reversed Effect may be operating in this situation. With doubt in his mind, the harder a person tries to go to sleep, the wider awake he becomes. When he is worn out and stops trying, he falls asleep.

A person with insomnia often complains that his mind is so active that he cannot get to sleep. Probably no one's mind is any more active than anyone else's mind. It is more what is in the mind than the amount of mental activity that interferes with sleep.

One who tends to worry a great deal or who has problems to be solved and decisions to be made may have difficulty going to sleep. He takes these things to bed with him, considers them or worries about them. Bed is not the place for solving problems. This tendency can become a very bad habit, and if continued, insomnia may become chronic. Reading in bed may also lead to such mental activity that sleep patterns are disturbed.

TREATING THE INSOMNIA PATIENT

As with all the conditions we are discussing, the questioning technique usually will uncover the causes for insomnia. Ideomotor replies to the following questions should eliminate some possible causes and point out those which are present in a particular case.

Is there some emotional or psychological reason for your sleeping difficulty?

Is your insomnia serving some definite purpose?

Does worrying and thinking of problems prevent you from going to sleep?

Does your expectation of not going to sleep at once serve to keep you awake? (Or cause you to awaken during the night?)

Does nervous tension and inability to relax keep you awake?

Is there some inner conflict preventing you from sleeping well?

Are you identifying with someone who had insomnia?

Are you punishing yourself by not sleeping well?

Is sex in any way involved?

Is there some fixed idea (imprint) acting to keep you from going to sleep? (Or waking during the night?)

Is there some past experience, or more than one, which affects your ability to sleep well?

Are you fearful that something bad will happen during your sleep?

Are you afraid you may have nightmares during your sleep?

Do you unconsciously associate sleep with death?

Are you afraid you might die during your sleep? If the answer to this question is affirmative, further inquiry should be as to why: the little prayer, a past experience where a dead person was seen, being told something which connects sleep with death, etc.

Is some other kind of fear involved in your sleeping difficulty?

Is there any other reason why you have difficulty going to sleep (or waking during the night)?

When the causes for insomnia have been learned, the therapist is better able to treat the condition. The patient's recognition and insight into the causes is a big step forward in overcoming the difficulty. While the patient is in hypnosis, suggestion and reassurance can help him digest the information he has brought out. Further treatment will depend on what causes are involved.

For the person who has merely developed bad sleeping habits, they can usually be corrected voluntarily. He must learn to think only of pleasant things on going to bed. The expectation factor can be overcome by some explanations and advice from the therapist. After all, insomnia is not too serious a condition, no matter how unpleasant and uncomfortable it is. What if he doesn't go to sleep for a time? If he can take an attitude of "What of it? So what if I don't go to sleep right away?", a don't-care viewpoint, the expectation problem is ended. Often it is easier said than done, but some practice can bring a change in attitude. Hypnotic suggestion can also help to accomplish this.

Travis, the leading authority on habits, has said that one of the best ways of breaking any habit is to exaggerate it greatly. This can be very successful with insomnia. The patient could be told something like this, which he is to say to himself on going to bed, "I'm having sleeping difficulty. I would get to sleep eventually, but tonight I'm going to try to keep from going to sleep. I'm going to stay awake all night, if I can. I don't care if I never get to sleep tonight. I'll be tossing for a while anyhow, so I'll just toss some more, and I'm determined I'll not go to sleep tonight." The harder he tries to stay awake, the more ridiculous this will seem, and before long he will become so sleepy that he can't stay awake.

If fears are located as causes, they must be dealt with and seen as irrational. Again, hypnotic suggestion can help eliminate them. Fears have probably originated in past experiences which must be located and understood.

If conflicts, sex, identification, masochism, or other causes are found, they should be worked out with the patient.

Once the causes have been located, one of the best aids for the patient in getting to sleep is to teach him self-hypnosis. When he has learned to hypnotize himself he should use it in this way. While in hypnosis he should give himself the suggestion that *within a few minutes* he will drop off into a good normal sleep and will sleep well all night. If the difficulty is the other type of insomnia, waking and not being able to go back to sleep, he uses self-hypnosis in exactly the same manner. The phrase "within a few minutes" is indefinite. It may be two or three minutes or 15 or 20.

Following such a self-suggestion, it is important for the patient to keep his thoughts away from sleep and from problems and worries. He should think only of something pleasant, something he has done or would like to do that would be pleasant. Thinking about going to sleep or about anything unpleasant will negate the sleeping suggestion and prevent him from dropping off to sleep. When the patient is to use this method, the therapist can make a similar suggestion to the hypnotized patient, saying that when he has hypnotized himself he will go to sleep quickly and will have an excellent night's sleep.

Another problem for the physician is the insomnia patient who has become accustomed to taking sleeping pills. He may have become very dependent on them. Barbiturates may not result in a physical addiction, but they certainly can cause a psychological one. Furthermore, the tolerance for them may lead to steadily increasing doses and increasing chronic toxicity.

During the first part of treatment, no attempt should be made to eliminate pill-taking. Sometimes it is well to substitute another type of pill. Ordinarily they can be dispensed with when the patient learns that he can fall asleep after hypnotizing himself. Sometimes a posthypnotic suggestion can be helpful here. During hypnosis by the therapist, a suggestion can be given that the patient will forget to take his usual pills that night. He will be so sleepy as soon as he is ready for bed that he will forget all about taking his pills. This may or may not be effective.

At the time drugs are discontinued, prescribing a tranquilizer as a substitute is advisable, to be taken only for a few days.

The methods given here will enable the physician to end insomnia in most patients who come to him with this condition. However, it should be remembered that there will also be some failures, as in treating any other condition. The neurotic needs or causes may not be easily overcome or perhaps can never be eliminated. Nevertheless, these methods will be successful with most cases of insomnia. When there is failure, there should be referral to a psychotherapist who may be better prepared to deal with the case, having more time to devote to it than the ordinary physician.

NARCOLEPSY

The reverse of insomnia is variations of narcolepsy which may be a mildly bothersome symptom occurring during lectures, with unstimulating gatherings of friends, or while driving an automobile. It may be so severe that it takes over most of the daytime concerns of the patient and the family and may take the patient through a series of frightening tests for brain, liver and kidney disease. It is always necessary to rule out organic disease in such cases, but the possibility of sleep becoming too important because of imprint type experiences should always be considered. With such a condition, there is always the possibility that the patient is using sleep as a means of escape from problems or his environment.

A CASE OF NARCOLESPY

This was the rapid solution of a narcolepsy problem with a physician who could not stay awake whenever he sat down to study for a certification examination. He was attending a symposium held in Columbus, Ohio. It took approximately 20 minutes to discover the cause, correct it and set up acceptable habit patterns of alerting interest and enthusiasm for his studies.

Subject: I'm really worried. I get enough sleep at night, but I have to prepare for these exams, and every time I sit down to study I get so sleepy that I just can't keep my eyes open.

Instructor: Let me ask this right index finger to lift unconsciously for a "yes" answer and this middle finger to lift for a "no" answer. The thumb here can go up if you don't want to answer my question. Now, knowing that we slip into hypnosis every time we review some past experience, please orient your thoughts back through the years to the first time in your life when sleep became too important, some time when sleeping or not sleeping was very important to you. When you are there, your "yes" finger will lift, and, as it lifts, please bring that experience up to a level where you can talk about it.

Subject: (After a lag of 70 seconds, the finger slowly lifts. This is followed by an amused change of expression and this, in turn, brings out a description of an incident) My brother and I have just finished scrawling with crayons all over the wall in the dining room and mother is pretty mad. She says for us to go right to bed without any supper. She doesn't punish us. She says that Dad will punish us when he gets home.

Instructor: How old are you at that time?

Subject: Four, four and a half. We're twins.

Instructor: Go on.

Subject: Well, my brother and I talked it over and we decided it would be a good idea if we were asleep when Dad came home. (He chuckles.) Dad didn't punish us.

Instructor: Is that what makes sleep so important?

Subject: (Finger indicates "yes." The finger indicated "no" to a question about any other possible factors.) I guess I must be afraid about that exam. That's crazy, isn't it?

The subject was then asked to feel all the sensations associated with being very wide awake and interested in all the things he will be relearning and fixing in his mind. He was asked to develop the feeling that the examination is just a way for him to show how much he has learned and how very much qualified he is to treat human beings who need his help. The "yes" finger was to lift when he had experienced these feelings at a subconscious level, and he was to say when consciously aware of that feeling of confident alertness which he will have every time he sits down to study, no matter where he plans to study.

It took about two minutes before his finger lifted with the characteristic trembling motion. Another minute elapsed before he took a breath, opened his eyes and indicated by gesture as well as voice that he was wide awake.

He was then asked to rehearse all the feelings of his next study period and to have an arm levitation indicate the moment he *knew* he would never have to worry about being sleepy or going to sleep at times when he wanted to be wide awake and alert. He was allowed to take three minutes for this while the therapist reviewed the steps of the session with the other members of the class. The steps here were simple:

1. Set up ideomotor responses.

2. Induce hypnosis by requesting a review of an important experience relating to sleep.

3. Orient to first experience making sleep too important.

4. Allow subject to explore reason for selection.

5. Allow subject to resolve the problem by exposing it to reasoning processes.

6. Obtain commitment of optimistic outcome by pseudo-orientation in time to a successful experience studying.

This subject was merely reacting to an imprinted past experience without any conscious realization of doing so. He reported later that he had no further difficulty.

REFERENCE

Erickson, M. H.: Historical note on the hand levitation and other ideomotor techniques. Amer. J. Clin. Hypn. 3: 196-199, 1961.

Chapter 19

Hypnotherapy of Obesity

HYPNOTHERAPY undoubtedly is the most effective treatment of the problem of overweight. As every physician is well aware, the usual medical treatment of perscribing some diet plus appetite-killing drugs is far from successful. If the patient continues the program and loses weight, a few months later it has returned. The problem is mainly psychological, and results can be permanent when the emotional causes are understood and corrected. However, no treatment is always successful with this stubborn condition. There will be failures with hypnotherapy, but there will also be many successes.

The real problem in obesity is not overweight but overeating. The reasons vary in individuals, but some causes are common to all cases. There may be a hereditary tendency, but there usually is identification as well with one or both parents. Willpower will never control compulsive overeating, and a frequent complaint from the obese person is that she has no willpower. While the condition is prevalent with both sexes, we will use only the feminine in discussing it, since women are more apt than men to seek treatment.

The original cause for overeating is likely to have had its genesis in infancy. A baby who is uncomfortable is probably hungry. Feeding brings comfort and is then associated with feeling good. It becomes a conditioned response, the infant associating food with feeling better. As an adult, this carries over, and the obese person heads for the refrigerator whenever emotionally upset or disturbed.

In the Freudian sense, every child goes through an oral stage of development. Many who suffer from obesity never seem to grow out of this stage. The oral need continues. Food satisfies; the more food, the greater the satisfaction.

In applying our seven keys to emotional problems to this condition, identification has been mentioned. Motivation may be another. What purpose does being overweight serve? Sometimes a woman will put on weight in order to make herself sexually unattractive to her husband or perhaps as a way of punishing him. If she does not enjoy sex and is frigid, this may serve as an escape for her.

Involving somewhat the opposite motive is the woman who does not receive enough sexual gratification and then substitutes stomach appetite for sexual appetite. This is often the case with an unmarried woman. Such a woman may keep herself unattractive in order to avoid sex, as gratification might cause her to feel guilty.

A compulsive desire for sweets may arise from parental rejection as a child or when there is a neurotic need for love, which could arise when a child has not been shown affection. Sweets then symbolize love.

Parents who go away from home often bring back some food treat for a child when they return. A conditioned reflex can then be set up in this way, associating the idea of food or candy with the return of a loved one.

Feelings of unworthiness and inferiority are often present in the obese individual. There is rejection of the self, the self-image denying an attractive appearance, for it is not deserved. Guilt feelings with self-punishment over them may bring on obesity.

A very common cause for overeating is conditioned associations which have been set up in the subconscious mind. Children usually go through stages of development where eating is a problem to the parents. Then potent thought associations are established from statements made by a parent, usually frequently repeated: "You mustn't waste food," "You must eat to be *big* and strong," "You must eat everything on your plate," "You can't have your dessert until you've eaten everything." These and similar statements become fixed ideas and are carried out even into adulthood. They act as do posthypnotic suggestions and are often found to be present with obese patients, as can readily be determined with ideomotor response to questions when this possibility has been explained to the patient.

Past experiences are often involved in connection with this key and others. Perhaps there is conflict over sex, and certainly there is conflict over the need to eat compulsively, meeting the desire to have a good figure and be good-looking. Organ language is an unlikely factor in obesity.

Investigation with ideomotor answering will bring out the emotional causes which are present and will eliminate those not involved in a particular case. Insight into the causes is the first step in treatment to bring weight reduction.

DIET

Every few months some new dietary fad appears. People, mostly women, try the latest one, sometimes with good results but often with only slight loss of poundage. Eat this or avoid that is a part of every diet. Too many calories, or calories don't count, starvation, eat only grapes for a time. The latest is the brown rice diet. The results from fad diets are usually good during about two weeks at most. Obviously we do not know enough about nutrition and metabolism or we could better cope with overweight.

When diet can be rigidly controlled, it has been found that one person will lose weight rapidly on an 800-calory diet. Another may actually gain a little with exactly the same food supplied. This proves that individuals absorb energy from food at different rates. It also shows that calories are not the only thing involved in overweight. While it would be difficult to prove scientifically, it is possible that hypnotic suggestion can affect the rate or amount of absorption of food. A suggestion can be aimed at accomplishing this. With a person weighing 200 pounds, it can be suggested that she will absorb only enough from the food eaten to maintain 170 pounds. When this weight is approached, the suggestion is reduced to 140 pounds, or such a weight as would be about normal for the person. This may be one helpful means of controlling weight.

To the obese person, "diet" is a nasty word. Dieting has been attempted again and again. She probably knows all about the various recommended diets and can tell the calory count of most foods. There is always resentment on the part of the obese case at having to diet, at being forbidden to eat desired foods. It is much better for the therapist to begin his approach to the problem by telling the patient that she does not have to diet. She is to forget about diet and calories. This invariably brings a happy smile. Explain that all that is necessary is to make some changes in the person's eating pattern and habits. Certain foods should be avoided: those which are fattening. It makes little difference what dietary ideas you may recommend, but avoid expressing it as dieting.

While most dieticians believe that calories are very important, this seems to be questionable. Some successful diets pay no attention to cutting the number of calories consumed. We think it best to tell the patient to pay no attention to counting calories, which is a great nuisance. If better eating habits are established, there will be less calories consumed. It seems that the kinds of food eaten are much more important than calories.

A part of the treatment for overweight should be to avoid the resentment and consequent rebellion that is so often involved in dieting and counting calories. Many who start on such a program soon revolt and abandon it. To prevent this tendency, telling the person not to diet or count calories is very helpful. It can also be pointed out that no one is forcing the patient to lose weight. She could put on more pounds if she wishes, but of course this is not desirable. She will lose weight only because that is the sensible thing and what she wishes to accomplish. Being ordered or forced to reduce is a natural source of resentment.

The physician should learn if the husband of an obese woman complains about his wife's condition. Since this can be another source of resentment. It is often well to advise the husband to stop this practice and instead be sympathetic and give praise and encouragement in his spouse's efforts to shed her excess pounds.

Almost every obese person has been warned by her physician that excess weight shortens life and may bring on disease. This is recognized but has no effect whatsoever on the patient. Her view is that it might happen to someone else but not to her. Masochistic tendencies seem responsible for this attitude. Instead it is better to develop as much motivation as possible along other lines.

When any factors of self-punishment and unworthiness have been worked out, the desire for good personal appearance can be a helpful motive for weight loss. Normally everyone likes to look his best and not feel conspicuous. The comfort and relief from fatigue that accompanies normal weight can be stressed as another motivation.

If mother is obese, her children will probably copy her and be fatties. Mothers do not want their children to be overweight. For her to become slender sets a good example for her children, which should be pointed out to her.

Still other possible motivations in a particular case can be stressed. The person who is greatly overweight is unhappy, frustrated and despairing. Regaining normal weight will relieve these emotional states and bring contentment as well as better health. Mentioning all these motives while the patient is hyptonized will make them much more effective. It is good practice to have a patient write out in detail every reason she has for wanting to be at a normal weight.

Some dentists who have been consulted believe the following theory to have merit. It is that one unconsciously needs to exercise the jaws a certain amount as this helps keep the gums and teeth healthy. If food is bolted with little chewing, there is a need to eat more food in order to have the proper amount of jaw exercise. If an obese person is questioned, it will almost invariably be found that food is bolted. We have yet to find an obese person who doesn't admit to bolting her food with a minimum of chewing.

To overcome this tendency, the patient should be given hypnotic suggestion that she will be aware of this whenever she eats and will develop a new habit of eating leisurely and chewing her food well. She will not only benefit because she will then eat less, but she will also begin to have full taste enjoyment of the food eaten. Bolted, the good flavor of food is not noticed. She should become a gourmet instead of a glutton. The gourmet tastes and savors his food, enjoying each mouthful. It is the quality and tastefulness of food that brings enjoyment, not the quantity.

Of course there is another physical benefit from chewing food longer in that more saliva is secreted, which is beneficial in the digestive process.

Almost every overweight person tends to eat everything on her plate. This may be due to one of the conditionings mentioned. Suggestions should be given that henceforth she will serve herself, or will see that she is served, small portions of all foods. If more is desired, there can be a second helping, but this seldom will be wanted.

Food is a symbol of hospitality. Guests are always plied with large portions and urged to have seconds. A hostess will take no offense if she is told the person is reducing and if some food is then left on the plate. A similar situation occurs in restaurants where large portions are usually served. Again, something can be left on the plate.

Food is also used as a reward. Parents will bribe their children with goodies. This may set up an unconscious association of food with being good. The thought is that behaving well and being "nice" should be rewarded with food, and the obese person rewards herself with excess eating.

A very large part of anyone's excess weight is liquid. Frequently too much liquid is consumed: water, coffee, tea, soft drinks, etc. The physician can give advice on this, suggesting cutting down to a normal, needed amount of liquids. Often this is an important part of weight control. Some dieticians believe giving a diuretic at the start of treatment is helpful. While the result is only temporary, it certainly has a good psychological effect for the patient to lose several pounds during the first week of treatment. Other dieticians frown on this practice.

Snacking is a bad eating habit and is prevalent with most obese people. If there is a strong compulsion present, it is useless to tell the patient not to snack, unless the compulsion is removed. It can be suggested that eating between meals can be reduced somewhat and that non-fattening foods low in calories can always be kept on hand for snacking.

It is well to tell the patient that sweets and other fattening foods are to be avoided but not to set up a prohibition against sweets. "You can avoid these foods most of the time, but do not feel that you must never eat a piece of candy or a slice of pie or cake. You will only do this rarely, however." This avoids resentment at coercion, with resulting rebellion.

To reduce snacking, the patient can be advised of a technique which may cause some amusement but serves well. This is to place a piece of red cloth or paper (a danger signal) on the refrigerator door, fastened with Scotch tape. It serves as a reminder and warning when the door is opened other than at mealtimes.

In starting treatment, the patient's weight at the time of her first visit should be noted. She should be told only to weigh herself once a week, at the same time of day. Watching the weight daily is discouraging, particularly if there is a gain one day. A woman should also be reminded that a slight gain of weight at the time of her periods is to be expected.

While control of appetite by means of drugs is a frequently used method of treatment and may be helpful when results are not satisfactory with the methods given here, our belief is that drugs should be avoided. They are a temporary crutch and side results are sometimes present, the patient becoming nervous and jittery. It is common experience that these drugs quickly lose their effect on the appetite, and patients will eat even when they are not hungry when eating is compulsive.

In health food stores and supermarkets, many excellent dietetic foods can be found. Patients can be urged to investigate the dietetic shelves. Any craving for sweets can be satisfied with such foods which are nonfattening.

Is exercise beneficial in reducing? Few obese people exercise enough, either through laziness or because they quickly become fatigued. A moderate amount of exercise is excellent, though patients often exercise as an excuse to eat more. Exercise does tend to tone the muscles and burn up energy; it should be recommended. It seems to increase the patient's motivations toward losing weight.

Massage, if available, is a good substitute if time or other conditions prevent exercise. Exercising machines are widely advertised but are expensive and not worth bothering with. Isometric exercises not requiring equipment are readily learned and easily performed. Some of them are very helpful in weight control, particularly for excess weight on the abdomen and hips, where excess usually accumulates.

The techniques for weight control given here will often be unsuccessful unless the causes for overeating or excess weight are dealt with at the beginning of the program of treatment.

QUESTIONING THE PATIENT AS TO CAUSES, WITH IDEOMOTOR RESPONSES

To ascertain the factors which may be causing either overweight or overeating, questioning could include the following:

Is there some emotional or subconscious cause for you to be overweight (or to overeat)?

Is your inner mind willing for you to know the reasons for your overeating (or overweight)?

Are you identifying with someone, perhaps a parent, who was or is overweight?

Do you overeat when you feel rejected?

Do you overeat from frustration?

Do you overeat to feel more secure?

Is one of the causes because when you were a baby you felt better when you were fed?

Does food act as a bribe or reward for you?

Do you think of food when you are emotionally upset?

Do you like your appearance now?

Do you tend to dislike yourself as to your body image?

Do you dislike yourself in other ways?

Are you punishing yourself by being overweight?

Are you unconsciously trying to harm yourself by being overweight?

Do you substitute food (stomach appetite) for sexual appetite?

Is there some conflict in your inner mind over sex that leads to overeating or overweight?

Are you carrying out some fixed idea implanted in your mind as a child about eating, an idea about not wasting food, that food is good for you, that you must clean your plate, or other similar ideas?

Are you using your overweight condition for some purpose, possibly as an alibi of some kind?

Are you trying to make yourself unattractive to avoid sex or members of the opposite sex?

Are you using this condition as a revolt, to be contrary toward yourself or someone else?

Are there any other motives or reasons for overeating?

Are there any other motives or reasons for being overweight?

Other questions can be devised, depending on the individual case. When some of the above have been answered, it may be necessary to learn more. For instance, with self-punishment as a factor, the source of guilt feelings should be uncovered. If conditionings are located, the triggering ideas should be discovered and removed.

GROUP THERAPY IN WEIGHT REDUCTION

As overweight is such a common condition, many physicians will see enough patients with this affliction for group therapy to be possible. It is far cheaper for the patient and many could afford the lower fees where private treatment would be too costly. It will be found of great advantage and results are even better with group treatment. Experience has shown that the best number in a group is from six to eight. A smaller group does not work out as well and a larger one is too unwieldy.

During a first private session with each patient, a case history is taken and a physical examination is made with such laboratory tests as may be indicated. The use of hypnosis is suggested as the best procedure. The usual misconceptions are dealt with. As soon as possible a group is formed and the first session is held.

The group should meet once a week for five or six weeks. Then there should be one meeting two weeks later, and after that, two or three meetings a month apart if required. Meetings are best held in the evening, lasting an hour and a half or two hours.

In the first group session, there should be a discussion of the usual causes for obesity. One patient can be selected for questioning with the ideomotor technique while the others observe. The person selected should be the one believed by the therapist to be the best hypnotic subject. After questions have shown the causes active in her particular case, the others can be instructed to do "homework" in the same way with a pendulum, asking the questions given in this chapter, thus locating the causes in their own cases. Notes should be made of those found to apply, to be given to the therapist.

The selected patient is hypnotized before the group. The group situation usually facilitates induction. Some of the others may spontaneously become hypnotized also during this demonstration. While the demonstration subject is still in hypnosis, a group induction talk can be given to the others. Probably all will enter hypnosis. If any prove resistant, they can be dealt with later in the next group session or perhaps privately.

A group posthypnotic suggestion is made to allow rapid induction in later sessions. This should be a key word or phrase followed by the escalator technique for deepening. The group should then be awakened and at once rehypnotized using this key. While the group is in hypnosis, much that has been mentioned in this chapter can be discussed and suggestions given: chewing food longer, taking small portions, leaving food on the plate, what foods to avoid and what to eat. Mental imagery can also be mentioned for homework.

At each meeting, each patient should bring her present weight written on a piece of paper. These figures can be added and the total group weight announced. This prevents anyone who has gained slightly or failed to lose from feeling guilty or discouraged about it. It will bring a desire to do better during the next week, so as not to let the group down.

Later sessions follow this general pattern, each person's problems being discussed openly, with consideration for the particular causes of overweight. This will help each work out her problem. Free ventilation should be encouraged during the first part of each session before hypnosis is induced.

After the group has become acquainted and accustomed to being hypnotized, it will be of advantage to have one of the group act as the hypnotist, taking turns, in other meetings.

Either with the group or with individual patients, insight into the causes of overweight and overeating is important in order to obtain permanent results. Development of new eating habits and the encouragement felt as weight is lost makes it easier for patients to maintain proper weight once the excess is gone. While there will be failures and some will relapse, overall it will be found that most overweight patients will benefit greatly and will not regain lost weight.

It might be pertinent to call attention to some patient's resentment towards doctors seeming to need to prove that their eating is justified by failures of doctors to "cure" them. In discussing resentments and motivations of obese patients, Kroger has said, "These people collect doctors like Indians used to collect scalps."

It should be realized that the goal is not just weight reduction but changes in habits and an understanding of the problem and its causes. Then loss of weight follows and a normal weight can be retained.

REFERENCES

Kroger, W.: Clinical and Experimental Hypnosis. Philadelphia, Lippencott, 1963, pp. 172-177.

Mann, H.: Hypnotherapy in Obesity. *In*: Techniques of Hypnotherapy (L. M. LeCron, Ed.). New York, Julian Press, 1962.

_____: Group hypnosis in the treatment of obesity. Amer. J. Clin. Hypn. 1: 114-117, 1959.

Chapter 20

Emergency Uses and Spontaneous Trance States

WE EMPHASIZE repeatedly that frightened and unconscious people are hypersuggestible and may be treated as though already in a hypnotic state. If conscious, their thinking processes are literal, direct and somewhat paranoid. They move slowly when able to move. They tend to hold new positions even though these might be uncomfortable. Facial expression is "ironed out." If the eyes are open, they seem not to focus on objects; if closed, they may move about slowly and apparently without convergence. If the eyes are open, the lids will flutter several times with each blink. Speech tends to be slow and without inflection. These are all signs of hypnosis.

Utilization of spontaneous trance behavior can diminish dangers of hemorrhage, shock and overwhelming infection at critical times of emergency and may pave the way for continuing successful therapy. There is no need for ordinary induction methods. Merely assume that the patient is going to behave as though in hypnosis and you are going to take advantage of this fact.

Keep suggestions simple and optimistic. Avoid negative statements and statements containing "if," "perhaps" and "maybe." These always imply unfavorable possibilities and may act as damaging suggestions. You can never harm a frightened patient by offering a positive, hopeful target and detailing hopeful steps along the way. The neutral scientist and the pessimist can justify neutrality and pessimism according to the way they express their thoughts.

Frightened patients are peculiarly sensitive to touch. Do not touch such a patient if you are worried or pessimistic. Take a few moments to size up the situation. Your voice will sound more confident when you are directing someone to do something you know about. This carries to the patient and makes it easier to sound honestly hopeful when you talk to him. If you are sure of yourself from the start, put your hand on the patient before speaking. Give yourself time to outline a plan while you are catching your breath.

Unconscious or seemingly unconscious people should be informed of each thing you do. They should be notified at least 15 seconds before you start to move them. Sudden, unheralded movements may throw the unconscious, injured person into cardiac arrhythmia or may produce massive intravascular coagulation. It is a grave oversight to start treating a person for cardiac arrest or profound shock without telling him he is doing well, congratulating him on relaxing so well, and informing him about steps to be taken in returning him to a normal state. The few seconds it takes to do this are far from wasted. It can be done after telling him why you are positioning him for mouth-to-mouth breathing. It can be done while you are making your preparations. Reassurances can be most helpful at this time.

It is well to remember that pain is diminished when thoughts are shifted from the source of pain. Attention should be drawn to some other part of the body by questioning or direct suggestions. It can next be shifted to some external object or to some prior experience associated with peace and calm (Chapter 15). During a state of fear and alarm, the patient is wasting energy in unnecessary muscle action, increasing the need for oxygen and increasing the load on the heart. These handicaps are reversed when a person is vividly able to recall memories of times when his body was relaxed and comfortable. Initial diffidence can be brushed aside by directions first to tighten the forehead and neck muscles and then relax them. This is accompanied by direction that the brain is less able to feel pain and fear when you purposefully relax these sets of muscles that are always tight in the presence of pain and fear.

A CASE OF OBSTETRICAL SHOCK ASSOCIATED WITH SCHIZOPHRENIC REACTION

A 30-year-old Para I, Gravida II was visited on the day following delivery of a profoundly anoxic but surviving baby. This patient had requested care by Cheek but failed to appear for two of her last prenatal visits. She had not wanted this pregnancy, had insisted that her husband be sterilized, and became increasingly hostile toward him during the pregnancy.

On the day of delivery, she developed a fulminating pneumonia which in retrospect was probably due to amniotic fluid embolism from a precipitate delivery. She delivered on the carriage in the hallway of the hospital. The baby was flaccid and apneic. The attending doctor made the remark in her presence that the baby would probably not live. At this point, the patient went into profound shock. Her respiration was shallow, blood pressure unobtainable and color cyanotic. A tracheostomy was done and continuous oxygen started. A catheter was inserted. Portable X rays showed infiltration of the right lung with presumed pneumonic process since she had been coughing for several days.

Twenty-four hours after delivery, her husband called Cheek to ask if he would come to the hospital to see his wife. He wondered if Cheek might be able to help, because the attending obstetrician and internist had both told him she could not survive. Permission to consult was obtained from the hospital and from the doctors, who both expressed themselves as holding out little hope for her recovery.

The nurse was adjusting a tracheostomy tube as Cheek entered the room. The patient was motionless except for her gasping, irregular respiration at the rate of 50 per minute. Pulse was thready at 116. It was reassuring to see that she was still putting out clear urine from the catheter in spite of a variable systolic pressure of 70 to 80.

The baby was a boy and was doing well after his imperforate anus was opened. It seemed possible that the patient might have some guilt feelings about not wanting the baby and then hearing at delivery that it might not survive. This assumption had been strengthened by learning from the husband that she had commented on not caring to live just before she lapsed into coma.

She was told the following: "Hello, Grace. I'm Dr. Cheek. I'm sorry to have missed your delivery, but you chose the wrong hospital. Your son is doing very well now. You wouldn't want him to grow up feeling he had made you very sick, would you?" There was no change in expression and no responsive movement.

"You are relaxing very well right now. Take advantage of this rest and go a little deeper to sleep for the next two hours. This is the kind of rest that can be valuable to you after you are home with your baby. I'll show you how to turn it on and off next week. Take a couple of deep breaths, now, Grace." She took two quick deep breaths but showed no other signs of recognition.

"In two hours you'll feel like awakening, and during that time I would like to have you begin to feel really hungry, because you have not had anything to eat for 24 hours and you need nourishment to speed up your recovery from this pneumonia you have had. That tube in your throat gives you the maximum amount of oxygen, and it will be removed in a few hours because you are already recovering from the pneumonia."

Three hours later the same suggestions were given of enjoying the rest and relaxation, feeling hungry and hurrying her recovery for the sake of her husband, her children and her parents. Her color was good and her respiration more regular, but blood pressure was still too low to measure. It was felt that her chances were poor unless she could be motivated to live for the sake of her family.

Three hours later she still showed no response, and it was not possible to obtain ideomotor responses from her fingers, either because she was too listless or because she was mustering hostility.

Twenty-four hours later she was awake, talking to her family, and was sucking soup through a straw. She had a hostile attitude toward Cheek, who was told by the husband that she had resented, through misunderstanding, something that Dr. Cheek had previously told her.

Her family doctor and the consultant both agreed on the need for urgent psychiatric care for her. She was suicidal and needed motivation to live. She recovered and went home with her baby in a few days. She divorced her husband a year later.

It is perhaps a significant point that she was willing to accept hope and could be motivated toward physical recovery by a person toward whom she had taken a great dislike. The working principle here involved was accepting her behavior and encouraging her to shift her rebellion into channels that would permit recovery for the sake of her baby. It was not possible to trace the course of cause and effect, although her husband and her two sisters believed Cheek's intervention had changed the course of unfavorable events.

AN EMERGENCY CASE

While giving a course in Jamaica, we attended a performance at a North Shore hotel. A drunken visitor attacked a native entertainer and struck her on the temple with a beer glass during the show. A laceration three inches long extending down to the bone was bloodless until the stunned girl saw blood on her arm and dress. This was not her blood but that of her assailant whose hand had been lacerated by the broken glass. Sight of the blood made her start moaning in fear. Her expression changed to frightened animation.

By this time the hushed surprise of the audience at the unexpected, an example of mass hypnosis, changed to a noisy clamoring. Cheek reached her side just as she shifted from a spontaneous trance state into frightened alertness. To misdirect her attention from the blood and gain her attention for what might be given in the way of suggestion, he put his thumb on her forehead just above the nose and said loudly: "Listen to me. You are all right. Stop that bleeding!"

The native woman's eyes looked at the source of these commands and then seemed to go out of focus as her facial expression changed back to the one she wore immediately after the injury. There had been a gush of blood from her lacerated scalp as she began to cry. It diminished to a slight ooze within two minutes of going back into a hypnotic-like state. Cheek ran his finger the length of the laceration looking for glass fragments and evidence of depressed fracture. This did not cause further bleeding. There was none during the hour before the arrival of a local physician who cleaned and sutured the laceration in one of the most vascular areas of the scalp.

Advantage was taken of the confusion and the frightened state of the injured woman. The original shock had produced a hypnoid state which recurred when her attention was taken from the sight of blood and was held by placing a thumb on her forehead and the intense sound of a voice telling her what to do.

The reason for the sudden cessation of arteriolar and venous bleeding could be speculated upon as being due to massive outpouring of epinephrine followed by relaxation of the neck and scalp muscles. Increased coagulation speed caused by epinephrine is normally followed by rebound fibrinolytic activity which may open the way for secondary bleeding. This is the basis for fluidity of blood with sudden death from trauma, electrocution and asphyxiation. Cadaver blood requiring no anticoagulants is collected from people killed suddenly. It can be used for massive replacement of blood with people who might be damaged by the antigenic qualities of blood from multiple donors.

A frightened person shifted into hypnosis will often stop hemorrhage if treated with expectancy that this will happen. This is true for obstetrical hemorrhage, and it seems to work for traumatic hemorrhage. We do not know whether this is brought about through changes in force fields, changes in muscle tone, or inhibition of the transfer of precurosers to active fibrinolysins in the injured area.

Concluding remarks. Emergency uses of hypnosis are numerous and the valuable possibilities obvious with such urgent situations as highway accidents, burns, cardiac arrest, surgical shock, status asthmaticus and any crisis where a patient seems to have lost motivation toward recovery. We have not explored all the ways in which a body can cope with cancer, with acute dermatitides like poison oak and the initial disabling pain of back strain, ankle, wrist and neck injuries. It can be a great help in the long range recovery from injury if initial pain is obliterated by subconscious acceptance of analgesia.

Accident victims tend to augment the tissue reactions of trauma by meaningless and sometimes dangerous self-punitive thoughts beginning with "If only I had ———." It is helpful to point out this failing at the very beginning as being a most selfish and destructive force before moving on to active therapy. It may be missed during the early emergency situation but can be picked up on secondary visits by questioning about willingness to stop pain or asking for time commitment on final recovery. Ideomotor responses are helpful here because self-punitive patients will not accept relief. They will give none or an "I don't want to answer" signal when requested to orient forward to a time of complete recovery.

In treating accident and other traumatic cases, later therapy should include regressing the patient while under hypnosis to the experience, causing the patient to relive it. This should be repeated several times until all fear and other emotions which were present have been discharged. This will serve to prevent possible later psychological reactions to the trauma.

REFERENCES

T. J. Hudson: The law of psychic phenomena. *In*: Suspended Animation and Premature Burial. Chicago, McClurg & Co., 1893.

Macfarlene, R. G. and Robb-Smith, A. H. T.: Functions of the blood, New York, Academic Press, 1961.

Quackenbos, J. D.: Hypnotic Therapeutics. New York, Harper Bros., 1908.

Simon, A., Herbert, C. C., and Straus, Ruth: The Physiology of Emotions, Third Annual Symposium, Kaiser Foundation Hospitals, San Francisco. Springfield, Charles C Thomas, 1961.

IN PREVIOUS CHAPTERS we have dealt with psychosomatic disease where the causes are often superficial and may, with luck, be removed quickly in the course of two or three hypnotherapeutic sessions. Associations of unrecognized guilt feelings leading to passive acceptance of disease or militant, subconscious resistance to goal-directed therapy may greatly lengthen the time of treatment for psychosomatic illness even in the hands of experienced hypnotherapists. Purely psychiatric disorders with little or no physical distress may yield sometimes to brief hypnotherapy but may require 40 or 50 treatments to bring the patient to a comfortable balance with his environment. Under any circumstances, it is reasonable to expect that a method of communication allowing rapid recognition of subconscious repressions, masochistic tendencies and unfavorable identifications will yield better results more quickly than ordinary conversational methods of psychiatric therapy.

Among purely psychiatric disorders would be included severe depressions, prolonged anxiety states, pure hysteria, phobic, obsessive-compulsive behavior, character disorders, anxiety-producing homosexuality, alcoholism and frankly psychotic behavior. In contrast with the mental disorders associated with pain or malfunctioning of organs, it is not possible to obtain a temporary plateau of advantage by using hypnosis to alleviate pain or demonstrate a hope-giving temporary improvement of organ function by suggestion. It is necessary to search for the origins of trouble, discover and correct reinforcing environmental factors, and construct a more favorable adaptation to present and future living conditions.

It seems clear from the observations of Sontag and his associates at the Fels Institute in Yellow Springs, Ohio, that prenatal influences may have an important bearing on nervous system and neuroendocrine function in postnatal life. It seems reasonable that single-impact type of learning demonstrable in birds and lower animals (usually referred to as *imprinting*) can also occur in man and can influence human adaptations at levels of awareness too primitive to be discovered with ordinary talking methods of analysis.

It is more than a probability that serious disorders in mental processes may be initiated and continued as conditioned responses during the unconsciousness of natural sleep and that only the least noxious of screening dreams and nightmares will be recalled on awakening. Cheek has found that only 10 per cent of dreams responsible for onset of uterine bleeding during pregnancy are remembered by the patients on awakening, and that discovery of repressed dreams can permit cessation of bleeding and continuation of pregnancy during a psychotherapeutic interview over the telephone. If this is possible, it is also possible that the fears, guilt feelings and misunderstandings related to purely psychiatric disease may interfere with any sort of therapy which is restricted only to consideration of daytime thoughts or the meagre evidence of remembered dreams. The physiology and the psychiatric meanings of sleep are just beginning to take their place of importance in research since the pioneer work of Kleitman at the University of Chicago. Talking psychoanalysis without the aid of hypnosis cannot touch the amnesic areas of natural sleep and early life. We are at least getting glimpses of these areas with the help of ideomotor questioning methods and hypnosis.

It should be emphasized again that hypnosis is not a method of treatment but is a clinical tool. It affords a more rapid and a broader approach to mental problems because it permits a cutting through to the origins of problems with less time wasted on satellite or screen memories. It is unfortunate that the dictums of Freud, based on too little knowledge and too little experience, are still influencing heads of psychiatric departments in our teaching institutions. It is unfortunate that too much enthusiasm for hypnosis has been shown by many physicians, dentists, psychologists and lay people speaking and writing without understanding or respect for the methods of scientific observation. It is unfortunate that the scientific and the unscientific have too often ignored the role of hope involved in the *placebo-effect,* permitting the often forgotten patient to cure himself. Hypnotherapy can be and should be a builder of ego strength for the patient as long as the therapist is willing to respect the great capacity of the human mind to adapt well and to fight for survival.

In psychiatric treatment, the hypnotizability of patients differs from that of a general public. Earlier works on hypnosis have stated that psychotics are very poor subjects or cannot be hypnotized. More recently it has been learned that this is not true. Many psychotics respond well and become excellent subjects. The relationship with the therapist probably is an important factor in the hypnotizability of such patients.

Patients with other disturbances vary considerably in hypnotizability. Compulsive-obsessive patients are often poor subjects. Hysteria was formerly a very common illness but now is seen much less frequently in a pure form, free of conversion into organ disfunction. Such a patient is likely to be a somnambulistic subject. Most phobias are easily remedied and such patients are average in hypnotizability. The same is true in most character disturbances. As to psychotics, of course paranoia patients seldom can be hypnotized. Manic-depressives are very difficult subjects in the manic stage or if deeply depressed, but sometimes they are readily accessible with hypnosis at other times. These statements are all merely general, and all depends on the individual. There are many exceptions, and even some paranoia patients have been good subjects.

Psychiatric hypnotherapy will differ only slightly from the methods given in previous chapters. The psychiatrist will have available techniques, such as dream interpretation, which few non-psychotherapists would be able to employ. Merely having a patient in hypnosis will make the results of any method more successful. With a hypnotized patient, free association is found to be much easier. Undoubtedly the greatest benefit is not so much in the better successes obtainable with hypnosis but in the greatly reduced time required for therapy. Thus it makes psychiatry available to many patients who cannot afford long treatment.

Those psychiatrists who have learned our uncovering technique by means of ideomotor responses to questions have found this of tremendous value. So much can be learned with it in such a brief time that treatment is greatly abbreviated. The psychiatrist here has an advantage over others in that he is better prepared for its use in knowing better what questions to ask. There is both knack and knowledge necessary in selecting and phrasing the questions. In our case histories, we have tried to show the way questioning should be conducted.

Hypnosis also affords greater ease in handling transference. It is seldom an important factor when therapy is brief. Hypnosis is helpful in overcoming resistances, and repressed material can be brought to consciousness easier when the patient is in hypnosis.

One technique possible here is to bring out repressed matters while the patient is hypnotized, but with posthypnotic amnesia suggested so that the patient does not consciously remember it after awakening. Told beforehand that he will not remember what he brings out, it is far easier to reach the repressed material. The knowledge the therapist then gains enables him to handle the case better. Later, when it can be tolerated, the material can be brought up to a conscious level.

Psychotherapists unfamiliar with hypnosis may overlook the great importance, frequency and effect of imprints and verbal associations as they have been described in previous chapters. Often they are factors in emotional disturbances, and many a difficult case will be found to have one of the blocking-type imprints preventing progress. A patient may have been told, "Nothing will do any good," "You'll never get over it," or "You must learn to live with this condition." Working as a posthypnotic suggestion, these imprints act as a command and can block progress until located and counteracted. When progress seems to be blocked, it is well to suspect such a "command phrase" and to investigate the possibility with the questioning technique. If located and brought to awareness, it can be removed.

One of the most amusing instances of such an imprint was one present in a young woman undergoing therapy. Regressed to age ten when her mother was whipping her for some transgression, the mother had said, "Don't you ever say 'no' again! Don't ever say that word again!" The young woman then exclaimed, "So that's why I've always been a pushover! I never can say 'no.'"

The phenomenon of age regression is one of the most useful of all hypnotic phenomena. It makes possible much greater catharsis where this is important. The patient who is age-regressed seems to be able to vent bottled up emotions far better than when he merely remembers some experience.

Another great advantage in the use of age-regression is that very early memories are accessible. Sometimes these are of great importance. We have mentioned the possibility of there being an actual memory of birth which may be producing some effect on behavior. Undoubtedly many readers will be skeptical of this, but we have become convinced of the actuality of such memories. We have both had patients regress spontaneously to their birth experience with no recognizable suggestion having been made in that direction. This has happened most frequently in asthma cases and in chronic headache cases. With asthma, the difficulty of drawing the first breath seems to be a factor, and in headaches forceps delivery or prolonged second stage labor appears to have been the cause. Of course other causes are also present in these illnesses, but the first conditioning factor may occur at birth. When it is remembered that both Freud and Rank called birth traumatic and believed it could cause aftereffects, it is apparent that there must be some unconscious memory of it, or no such spontaneous result could occur.

In this regard, it might be found of interest to use the questioning technique with some patients and ask if there is an actual memory of birth deep in the subconscious mind. The question needs careful wording. Apparently there are deep levels of the subconscious and the wording might be "In the deeper levels of the inner mind, is there an actual memory of your being born, of the birth experience?" Almost every time this is asked, the answer will be positive.

When this birth memory matter was mentioned in one of our courses, one psychiatrist who was attending ridiculed the idea in a very vehement way. He was asked if he would be willing to give his own subconscious answer as to whether he had any such memory. He agreed to this. His ideomotor responses with the pendulum were established and the question was asked. The pendulum signaled "yes" in reply, swinging very emphatically. He tossed the pendulum to the questioner and snorted, "The damn thing lies! It isn't so."

A technique during age regression where catharsis is sought has been advocated by Kline. This is to suggest that the patient will find his emotion increasing to a point where he can barely tolerate it, but strong suggestion is made that it will stop short of being intolerable. Of course this must be handled with great care and undoubtedly should not be attempted by anyone other than a competent psychotherapist.

Undoubtedly one of the fields where hypnotherapy will be of the greatest use is in psychiatry. We have been impressed with the fact during the last three or four years that many more psychiatrists have shown interest in hypnosis and have attended courses.

Chapter 22

Hypnosis with Children

*By Raymond L. LaScola, M.D.**

OF ALL AGE GROUPS, children are undoubtedly the best hypnotic subjects. With them induction can be rapid and most will enter a deep trance.

Because of their capacity for visual imagery, it is possible to use fantasy situations and illustrations in a therapeutic way that the adult patient many times is unable to grasp. The child will slip into hypnosis so very rapidly and with such ease that the inexperienced operator may not feel that the patient has achieved the hypnotic state.

One marked difference in the child and adult subject that should be pointed out is the behavior of the child while in any stage of trance. A child may squirm, twist, scratch, pick his nose, etc., and remain quite deeply hypnotized, while these same actions in an adult subject are considered signs of resistance.

It is often asked at which age children are the best subjects. Most experienced therapists feel that the 8–10 age group respond best. However, in my experience, children seem to respond equally well at any age, and the response is primarily dependent upon the rapport the operator is able to establish with the child.

A few minutes spent visiting, talking about the child's interests, family situation, etc., will very quickly establish a feeling of camaraderie that is invaluable for a later therapeutic situation.

The first session with a child is without doubt the most important in so far as therapeutic results are concerned. By approaching the child on his level, using his language, and avoiding any attitude that might be interpreted as demeaning or talking down to his level, one is able to make successful results seem logical and attainable.

As an initial induction, it is best to use a shortened modification of the "lullaby technique." Since children go into hypnosis so very rapidly, one

* Instructor with Hypnosis Symposiums.

finds it unnecessary to relax the child subject in the same slow progressive manner used with the adult. Instead, simply suggesting "Now, as you close your eyes, you can let your whole body just go limp, just the way a wet towel does when you drop it on the floor." Or, "When I snap my fingers, your whole body will become as limp as cooked spaghetti."

A simple deepening technique is to suggest walking down a stair as the operator counts down from ten, "taking a step and going deeper with each count." However, since the child slips so rapidly into deep hypnosis, it is not usually necessary to use additional deepening technique at all. It is very effective with a child to talk of his becoming drowsy and sleepy and even to use the word "sleep" in the induction but to specify that it is a "kind of sleep" and that the child will hear everything you may say.

Often no formal induction is needed. Depending on his age, the little patient may be asked if he enjoys watching television and asked his favorite program. It can be mentioned that you have a "magic" TV set, and he can be asked if he would like to see it and see a repeat of one of his favorite programs. To do this, the child must hallucinate, and he can only hallucinate something previously seen. In order to hallucinate, he will spontaneously slip into hypnosis.

When he has indicated the program he would like to see, he is asked to close his eyes. He can then be told he is to imagine the magic set with his eyes closed. A true hallucination is not then involved with this method. Alternatively, he can be told that he is to open his eyes when instructed to do so and that he will then see against the wall in front of him a set just like the one at home. Wording could then be something like "Now I'm putting my magic set there in front of you against the wall. When you open your eyes, you will see it there, and then we'll turn it on. Now open your eyes and there is the set. You see it clearly. There it is right in front of you. Now I'll turn it on, and there come the wavy lines and the sound. First there's a commercial. You can see it and hear it now. And now the program is starting. There it begins. Just watch it now."

It is surprising how easily most children can hallucinate in this way. To do so they will enter a deep trance. It is also very easy to distort time during the hallucination of the TV program, speeding it up to a remarkable degree. The child can be told that you are going to count to ten and that this represents all the time needed to see a half-hour program. The count is then made during an elapsed time of only about ten seconds, and yet the entire program can be seen during this brief period. Questioned about it afterwards, the little subject will elaborate on just what he saw and heard.

This method is particularly effective to use with either the frightened child or one who is obstreperous and hard to handle. Almost any child is interested in magic and enjoys television and would much rather watch a program than have some unpleasant treatment from the physician, whatever he is there for. While he is watching the hallucinatory program, he can be given an injection and seldom will give any sign of noticing it. Dentists who use hypnosis find this an excellent way of dealing with the child patient while his teeth are worked on. All his attention is on the TV program.

ASTHMA IN CHILDREN

The child asthmatic responds most dramatically to the hypnotic approach, and the cure is so gratifying that it seems incredible for any other method of treatment ever to be considered. When first dealing with asthmatic children, the author spent a great deal of time bringing out all or as many of the underlying etiologic factors as possible. Later, however, very little time was devoted to uncovering these factors, and the children did just as well. In the adult, just the opposite seems to be the case.

To illustrate the technique in detail, first the child is induced by any methods appropriate to his age. Assuming the hypothetical patient is in the 9–11 age group, the following approach might be used.

"Not many people understand what asthma is. Most people think that you wheeze and can't breathe because you can't get the air into the lungs, but you and I know differently. We know it's just the opposite. When you're having an attack, you can't get the air out of the lungs to let fresh air in." The child asthmatic will usually show agreement by a smile or a nod of the head.

There should then be a simple explanation of the mechanics of the anatomy of the respiratory system. Particular attention is called to the small muscles that encircle the smaller bronchi, and the patient is given as vivid an image as possible of how the tightened musculature acts very much like a purse string in trapping the air in the alveoli.

The anatomic description bears little resemblance to the way *Gray's Anatomy* puts it, but this oversimplification does permit the patient to see his problem as one of a mechanical nature. The dialogue continues. "So you see, all a person has to do to be able to breathe comfortably is just let all of these muscles relax." The term "let all of these muscles relax" is used to stress the lack of effort needed, in contrast to saying "make these muscles relax" or "you can relax these muscles."

At this point, other illustrations are given to show as vividly as possible the effect of contracting or relaxing musculature. Children enjoy blunt and crude humor, especially if it is aimed at the adult. Their vivid imagery and sense of the ridiculous make it possible to put these illustrations on a fun or joke basis.

As soon as the concept of relaxing the musculature is clearly understood, an example is given as follows. "If you were holding a hot potato in your hand and it was burning you, too hot to hold, what would you do to get rid of it? Would you tighten all of your hand muscles? Of course not. That would be stupid. You'd just relax the muscles and let the potato roll out." The patient will usually nod and smile at the use of "stupid," the implication being that only stupid people tighten muscles when they are supposed to relax them.

Another illustration used is: "Suppose you lit a match and were holding it as it burned. Pretty soon the fire would get closer and closer to your fingers. Would you tighten all of your hand muscles to hold the match tighter?" Wait for a shake of the head. Then, "Of course not! Only a *fool* would do a *dumb* thing like that. All you'd need to do is to relax the muscles and you could drop the match before it burned your finger."

At this point you have established a friendly camaraderie with the patient. You've implied that *you two* know what to do if there is a problem that can be solved by simple muscle relaxation. You've been implying by your choice of words that "other people" who are not able to solve such a simple problem are either stupid, dumb, or are fools.

We then very casually return to the problem of asthma. If the child is having an attack or is having any wheezing at all, the following suggestions are given. "Now we both know that asthma is a condition in which a person *without realizing it* tightens all of the little muscles around the air sacs of the lung and holds the old air in so that there is no room for fresh air. This simply means that they are holding these muscles so tight that they can't breathe out. Right?" Wait for a nod of agreement. "Now notice that you're wheezing. Don't you feel silly?"

A child will usually smile at this point. Continue in this simple casual vein. "Of course this isn't your fault. No one ever explained asthma to you before. So now that you know, let me see you relax those tiny muscles that are holding the air in and get all of this wheezing stopped."

Invariably the child will lean slightly forward, lower his chin, and in a few seconds the respirations become much slower and the asthmatic noises begin to subside. One must keep in mind that the child's ability to do this is in direct proportion to his conviction that *he can do it*. It is, therefore, vital that this conviction be reinforced as much and in as many ways as possible. One excellent way of doing this is to take out a stethoscope and listen to the chast *after* there has been a noticeable improvement and find an area where there are still some rales. Then say, "There are a few whistles here. Let's clear them up next." Notice particularly that the approach is one of positive conviction. At no time does one say, "Let's see if you can clear these up." If a term is used that gives the patient any doubt it would bring failure as would such an opening as "We don't know what we can do for your asthma, but it certainly won't hurt to *try*."

When the chest is entirely clear, some complimentary comment is indicated, such as "Now it's as clear as a bell. That's fine!"

In order to get the child freed of the dependence on drugs and to give him a feeling of "Now that I know, I can handle this," the following is interjected, being sure to depreciate those who are archaic and "not in the know." "Now I'm sure in the past when you've had an attack of asthma and couldn't breathe, somebody gave you a *shot* of adrenalin or amenophillin or some other *shot*. They gave the shot just to do what you now know how to do all by yourself. Isn't that silly? If you had known then what the problem was, you wouldn't have needed any of those shots, would you?" Wait for a nod of agreement.

"Suppose you woke up in the middle of the night with an attack of asthma. Naturally you'd realize that you must have had a bad dream that brought it on. So what would you do? Act like a gooney bird and stay awake all night and wheeze? Of course not. You'd simply relax those little muscles and go right back to sleep, wouldn't you?"

We have now established in the child's mind that asthma is a matter of choice. "Since you now know how to stop an attack of asthma, you naturally have already figured out how to start one, so let's see you start a real bad attack. I want you to tighten all of those little muscles so much that you'll sound like a leaky steam engine. Make your face turn blue."

Requesting the most severe attack possible reinforces the fact to the child that he can clear any attack, no matter how severe, and that the therapist knows he can do this. In a surprisingly short time, the child will have produced a severe, bonafide attack of asthma. He should be complimented. The therapist conveys by his attitude the more severe the better. "It's more fun to clear these up than it is those little piddly ones."

When the attack is full-blown, the therapist says, "Now I'm going to time you with my watch and let's see how fast you can get it completely cleared." If there is time or if there seems to be any reservation in the child's manner, the procedure is repeated one or two times.

Just as soon as the therapist feels that the child knows that he is in control of the situation, the therapist says, "Now do you think you ever need to have another attack of asthma again?" Wait for a shake of the head. "If you ever wake up in the middle of the night after a bad dream and you should be wheezing, do you think you will remember what to do?" Wait for a nod. "Well, I guess that's all there is to it. Do you feel that you're cured of asthma?" Wait for a nod. "Do you think you'll ever have another attack? Don't you wish somebody had explained this to you sooner? Isn't asthma kind of a dumb thing to have, now that you know all about it?" Wait for a nod. "So that's all there is to it."

When the above is finished, the author usually takes the child on a fantasied skin-diving trip or on some other excursion where respiration is controlled or restricted. Much play and fantasy about finding treasure is used to prolong the trip. This all tends to reinforce further the child's new feeling that he is no longer a slave to the caprice of contracting musculature.

In developing this imagined skin-diving expedition, the therapist brings out details, describing the trip to the ocean and donning all of the skin-diving gear which includes a nose stopper, mouth-breathing bit connected to tanks worn on the back, etc. Putting on all this respiratory-inhibiting equipment is treated quite casually with no mention of the limitations it imposes.

The fantasied descent into the water is described with all of the pleasurable associations possible. While in the depths of this fantasy, sea fish are sighted, a sunken pirate ship or a sea cave is explored for treasure, being sure to "find" a chest containing coins (for boys) or jewels (for girls).

When the fantasy trip is finished and the hypnosis terminated, the author asks, "How did you like that trip?" The child is usually very enthusiastic. "But you forgot your coins (or jewels)." The child usually smiles because of his awareness of the fantasy. "Well, I thought you might forget, so I brought them up for you." This always produces a hearty laugh as the author brings out a few coins or a dime-store necklace from his pocket.

In cases involving real or supposed allergy to various foods (wheat, eggs, chocolate, etc.), the child is asked at the end of the session, after he has learned how to control his symptoms, "Do you think you can eat (mentioning the specific allergen) and be completely free of symptoms?" He invariably says yes. "Then how would you like to come with me to the restaurant across the street and have a chocolate malt with an egg in it and a piece of cake?" This is greeted with enthusiasm. The accompanying parent usually becomes pale. However she has been told privately before the session that she is not to comment or interfere with anything the therapist suggests. The excursion to the restaurant is made and what was previously considered pure poison is eaten with relish and without any ill effect whatsoever.

It is wise to point out to the child that he may never have another attack of asthma, but there is always the possibility that he will. He is then reassurred by being told, "The big difference now is that it won't matter, because now you know how to turn it off."

Another point to be emphasized is the fact that attacks can occur during the night, precipitated by a dream. "Suppose you awoke in the middle of the night and were having an attack, what would you do?" The child may look puzzled. "Why, you'd turn it off just like you would if one started in the daytime, wouldn't you?"

It is wise to have a consultation with the parents to explain their role in supporting the child in his new-found freedom in being able to control the asthmatic attacks. Any display of skepticism, doubt or apprehension on the parents' part may completely negate the positive results obtained. Parents should be reminded that the child will only be able to succeed in freeing himself of asthma if he is convinced in his own mind that he is able to do so.

One child patient was used as a demonstration before those attending one of the Hypnosis Symposiums to learn hypnotic techniques. Several weeks later, his mother wrote a glowingly grateful letter telling how pleased she was that her nine-year-old son had been completely free of his asthma for the first time in six years. Several months later, this same mother was contacted regarding her child's progress and stated that the attacks had returned. Further questioning revealed that the child had been seen in a Navy medical clinic for a routine visit. The officer who had previously attended him was no longer there. In his place was an all-knowing resident. After carefully reviewing the boy's chart, he proceeded to explain to him how he could be certain that the attacks would return, and further that they could never be controlled by any measure other than chemical vasodilators. The mother who had accompanied the child left the clinic armed with inhalators, etc., after accepting the resident's suggestion that she make an appointment to resume desensitization shots just as soon as he had his next attack. Before they reached home, the boy had begun wheezing. That night he had a severe attack just as had been suggested.

It may seem that such a superficial treatment would seldom be successful, particularly in severe cases, but it is actually very successful.

THUMB SUCKING

Persistent thumb sucking in a child past two or three years of age is often an annoying problem for many parents. It is often so poorly handled that it becomes a compulsive mechanism for the child. The forceful measures used to curb the habit are often responsible for the development of other behavioral disorders. The following approach has been found to be effective in most cases.

After inducing hypnosis by any of the techniques suggested, an understanding and sympathetic attitude is taken. "I understand that your parents feel you should stop sucking your thumb. Now I don't see anything wrong with thumb-sucking, do you?" There is usually some hesitation, then agreement. "There's nothing wrong with it as long as you play fair." The child will seem puzzled by the last statement. You continue to explain. "By that, I mean since you have ten fingers. Each one of them should be entitled to the same amount of attention. That sounds fair, doesn't it?" Wait for agreement.

"Now I can tell you haven't thought of it this way, because I can see that you've given all of the attention to one thumb. Is that so?" The child with usually nod in agreement. "Well, now that you realize that you haven't been playing fair with the other fingers, would you be willing to be a good sport and play fair with all of them?"

When presented in this manner, agreement is the only choice. You can then state what "playing fair" entails. "Now that you understand that being fair to all of the fingers you can still suck your thumb, but whenever you do, you'll suck each of the other fingers just as long as you did the thumb, one after the other. In this way you'll be giving each of them the same amount of attention."

When this is stated very matter-of-factly, stressing the word "fair" as often as possible, it seems quite reasonable. Rehearsing the procedure in hypnosis will further reinforce the suggestion. "Now let's go over this one time. I'm going to count to ten, and when I start counting, you can begin with the thumb. With each number, change to the next finger." After going over all ten fingers, the last suggestion can be, "Now that's fine. All of your fingers have had the same amount of attention. You can suck them any time you like, but remember always to do it this way."

The child leaves with a feeling of triumph. He hasn't been told that he can't suck his thumb anymore. An appointment is made for two weeks later to hear how things are going. In most instances, the second appointment is canceled. After being a "good sport" and "playing fair" for a few days at home, the whole procedure of thumb and finger sucking becomes dull and boring, and the habit is usually given up. If at any time it is resumed, the parent is told to give a gentle reminder of what the child promised the doctor about playing fair with the rest of the fingers.

PAIN CONTROL

It is much easier to teach children the control of pain than to teach it to adults. The technique of glove anesthesia commonly used with adults can be used here. However, another method taught in our courses is simpler, and children seem to enjoy the visual imagery involved.

After hypnosis has been induced, the child is asked to visualize a long row of light switches as though they were in his head. Above each switch he is to see a colored light bulb, all turned on and each one a different color or shade of color, several being mentioned by the operator. He is then told how this system of lights is analogous to the nervous system, the description being tailored to the child's age and level of understanding.

He is then told how, by turning off any one of these switches, he can make a particular part of his body numb. It is specified that a certain switch, with its light, controls a hand (the predominant one). Turning it off and seeing the light go out means that the nerve current is turned off and the hand will then become numb and lifeless. With a young child, it might be mentioned that it will seem as though the hand has gone to sleep. In this practice, an area, such as the hand, should always be an area distal to the one where anesthesia is desired later. The area is then tested, being sure to mention first that the child will feel touch and pressure but that there will be no discomfort. The word "pain" should be carefully avoided. After an innocuous area such as the hand has been anesthetized in this way, the child should always turn the switch back on and see the light come on, thus restoring sensitivity. The child can test himself by pinching his own hand. Then anesthesia can be developed where it is really needed.

With pediatric patients, the author routinely teaches them this technique before any need for anesthesia arises, so that when the occasion does come up, it can be more easily applied. Simple lacerations can be repaired, and it can be very effective for immunizations. Often it is even possible to use it in setting a broken bone with little or no discomfort.

Another method of suggestion for anesthesia that works well with young children is as follows. The child is told, "I want you to close your eyes, and when I rub this cotton on your arm, it is going to feel like I'm using an ice cube. The colder you can let it feel, the better. If you can let the spot where I'm going to give you the shot get really frozen, you won't even know when you get the shot."

After a few seconds, the cooling of the evaporating alcohol from the swab becomes noticeable and the child is asked, "Is the ice cube making it real cold so that it is beginning to be numb? Good!" After a short pause, "Is it numb enough now for the shot? It will be as though I were only pushing on the place. Okay, now watch how easy it is."

BED-WETTING

Enuresis is undoubtedly one of the most difficult pediatric problems to treat medically. Various child therapists consulted agree that the usual approach is of questionable value unless a long-term analytical therapy is used, wherein the bedwetting is looked upon as part of a symptom complex. This is a time consuming, very expensive undertaking.

The hypnotherapeutic approach, by going directly to the problem, is much less costly, less time consuming, and offers a great deal more as to the percentage of cures obtained.

Again the understanding, permissive approach is used. In hypnosis the child is told, "From now on we are going to ignore the 'wet' bed. We are only interested in the 'dry' bed. So are you willing to go along with me and start thinking how good it's going to feel to wake up every day in a nice, clean, 'dry bed?" The patient will nod agreement.

"Now of course we all know why people wet their beds. It's because they urinate while they are asleep. Well, as far as you are concerned, this will never happen again. Let's find out if the inner part of your mind is willing to make it impossible for you ever to urinate again unless you are wide awake."

The ideomotor questioning method with finger signals is used here to elicit a response. If there is a negative reply with the fingers to the question, it then becomes necessary to go farther into the problem in order to find out the reason for the negative response. Since the condition is dynamically based on various hostility factors, these can usually be brought out and considered at this time. However, it is much more usual for the response to be affirmative. Incidentally, the child is fascinated at having his fingers move in reply to questions.

The suggestion of always waking to urinate is repeated and stressed several times. Counting dry beds and ignoring wet, uncomfortable, messy beds is also repeated. In order to prevent discouragement, the child should be told, "Now of course you must remember that anyone can have an accident. By that I mean that if you do wet your bed ever again, just think of it as an accident, because now you no longer are a bed-wetter."

This can be reinforced by finger questioning. "Let's see what your inner mind has to say." The question is then asked, "Can we now feel that you are no longer a bed-wetter and that if it ever happens again it will only be an accident?" The "yes" finger will invariably lift. Go on to say that the child should not feel discouraged if there are accidents. He will find that there will be fewer and fewer of them until they won't happen at all.

It is also helpful after the hypnotic session to tell the child that he can practice during the daytime to learn how his bladder is going to feel just before his inner mind wakes him up to urinate at night. Suggest that when he feels like going to the bathroom during the day, he take a drink of water, then wait as long as he can before going, just to get used to the feeling of having a real full bladder. After he has waited as long as he can, he can say to himself, "Now this is how it's going to feel at night, and this feeling is going to wake me right up so I can run to the bathroom."

The child can also be told that as he urinates with a full bladder he is to shut off the stream two or three times so that he can learn just how to control urination.

The patient should be seen weekly. Each time the number of dry beds is noted, the wet ones not mentioned, and the above suggestions are repeated.

Three of the most common pediatric problems have been discussed. Others can also be handled in much the same way, keeping in mind the principles involved.

It should be emphasized again that children are usually such good subjects that formal induction of hypnosis may not even be necessary. The child usually will go into hypnosis spontaneously while closing his eyes to view an imagined television set, and the same is true if he is merely told to close his eyes and to imagine the switches and colored lights for anesthesia.

One precaution might be mentioned in dealing with older children. Most are intrigued by the idea of being hypnotized, and a brash boy may want to try hypnotizing his young friends. With an 11- or 12-year-old, it is well to warn against such attemps. A posthypnotic suggestion may be given to prevent any such attempts.

AARON Moss, one of the leaders in this area of dentistry, coined the word "hypnodontics" as a term for the use of hypnosis in dentistry.

Freud has pointed out that there are two major human drives: the pursuit of pleasure and the escape from pain. The motivation to escape from pain by the patient brings better acceptance of hypnosis, which is of great advantage to the dentist. While the usual misconceptions may lead some patients to be unwilling to be hypnotized, few refuse it when hypnosis has been explained and its value to the dental patient described.

With the desire to have dental work performed with the least discomfort, the dentist finds his patients more hypnotizable than will the physician or psychologist. Even the beginning "hypnodontist" will have few failures. With more practice, his patients will usually enter a deeper trance.

While hypnosis in dentistry is effective if the patient is only lightly hypnotized, greater depth has advantages in that there is less discomfort with more depth. There is more relaxation, more phenomena can be produced (such as hallucinations), and anesthesia is easier to develop. Therefore the dentist tries to induce as great a depth as the patient can reach within the time available for induction.

It is commonly believed that the main use of hypnosis in dentistry is for purposes of anesthesia. This is a relatively minor use. Anesthesia is important at times, but it is too easy to use drugs rather than take the time to produce hypnotic anesthesia unless there is some reason which contraindicates the use of drugs. There are other more important uses.

The dentist practicing with hypnosis is selective of the patients with whom it will be applied. For patients who will need frequent attention and will require extensive work rather than occasional prophylaxis, it may be advantageous to teach them hypnosis. The patient found to require extensive work is a good candidate. It may offer the only way to control a phobic patient.

Most people fear dentistry but overcome their fears and have their work performed. It has been said that more than half the people in this country never visit a dentist. This may be partly for economic reasons, but the main reason for this is simply fear. Many such people are buying cars and household equipment without realizing that dentists are also able to arrange easy payments for dental work. While lack of money may be one reason for avoiding dental work, undoubtedly fear is the prime factor. It is here that hypnosis is of utmost value to both patient and dentist.

Almost every dentist has encountered patients who are terribly fearful of dentistry. They cannot bring themselves to visit the dentist. Appointments are made and broken. If they do appear, the dentist may have great problems dealing with these fear reactions. For such a patient, hypnosis can be a welcome solution of the problem. When the dentist knows an appointment has been made by such a person or when he discovers the situation, he should explain that no dental work will be performed during the first visit. He can assure the patient that he has means at his disposal to do away with most of the discomfort and pain which the patient fears. However, he should not promise complete elimination of pain.

PREPARING THE PATIENT FOR HYPNOSIS

In this first session, hypnosis is recommended for the patient, with explanations of the misconceptions and description of how it will be used. An induction can be carried out but with full assurance that no work will be done during the visit.

With a bad phobic case, it is best for the dentist to learn the reasons for such great fear. This can be accomplished through the ideomotor questioning technique. It will usually be found that some childhood experience is behind it, probably a traumatic visit to a dentist. It is somewhat surprising to find how many people in middle age or older have been subjected to apparently brutal dental treatment as a child. They may have been forcibly held down in the chair while work was performed. With older people, it may have been at a time before novacaine was introduced, although it is sometimes difficult to separate the memory of fear from that of fact.

Sometimes fear has been instilled by remarks of parents or of other children. The dentist is fully entitled to carry on simple psychotherapy to remove such fears. With regression to the traumatic experience, plus reassurance, such phobias can usually be permanently resolved.

Before induction it is best to have the patient empty his bladder if necessary and to see that his clothing is loose so that he can be comfortable. Induction can be performed in the dental chair by means of the technique selected. With the first visit of the phobic patient, it is better to use some other chair for induction the first time. The counting-backward method while rotating the subject can be used with the patient sitting up in the dental chair rather than standing.

Deepening methods are utilized in order to induce as great a depth as possible within the time allotted. Some dentists think it best to do no dental work with any patient during the first session with hypnosis, unless it is an emergency case. If hypnotic anesthesia is to be used, a glove anesthesia should be induced. A posthypnotic suggestion of a signal for subsequent inductions is given.

Many dentists think hypnosis may be time consuming and with a busy practice believe they cannot afford time for hypnosis. It is true that the first session does require perhaps a half-hour, but in the long run, time can be saved. If much work is involved or if the patient will return regularly, time is not a factor. More work can be carried out in the same length of time with a hypnotized patient than if he were not hypnotized. Fatigue can be largely inhibited, and periods of rest are unnecessary. Where much work is required, there may be an actual saving of total time. As will be considered under fees for hypnodontia, the dentist is paid for any extra time he must spend.

Some dentists who use hypnosis fear to become known as hypnotists or that their colleagues will disapprove of hypnosis. They then use it in disguised form, with indirection methods of induction. There are some advantages in this, but the disadvantages outweigh them. There is the possibility of the patient realizing he has been hypnotized without his permission. Conversely, the person who knowingly has been hypnotized usually is enthusiastic and pleased to have found his work accomplished with so little discomfort.

DENTAL USES

With the relaxation developed while under hypnosis, there is a spontaneous raising of the pain threshold. It is a primary goal in dentistry to achieve relaxation for the patient. A frightened patient cannot relax. He therefore feels pain to a greater degree. A hypnotized patient will relax in spite of his fears.

Probably due to the greater degree of relaxation and the consequent raising of the pain threshold, the same amount of anesthesia can be obtained with only about half as much drug used as would ordinarily be necessary. Some patients will be quite unaware of the insertion of the hypodermic needle. While hypnotic anesthesia is not often indicated as the sole anesthetic, there are some situations where anesthetic agents are contraindicated and hypnosis will then be sufficient because of the patient's need for relief. The success of hypnosis depends much on motivations of therapist and patient.

The effect of any drug wears off within a short time and pain may follow. Here is one application of hypnotic anesthesia which is of great advantage. It can be extended for several days if necessary. When the patient has been injected with a drug, it often is easy to continue the effect with hypnotic anesthesia. This can be accomplished merely by suggesting that the area will remain anesthetized for a certain number of hours, overnight, or even for several days. There can be frequent applications of hypnotic anesthesia in this way, inducing it on top of drug anesthesia.

Distraction of attention under hypnosis can allow the patient to be much more comfortable while work is performed. Even without hypnosis, some dentists use music to distract patients. While hypnotized, a patient can be instructed to listen to hallucinated music of his own selection, or he can hallucinate a TV program or a movie. With his attention concentrated in this way, he still will respond to directions from the dentist, such as to empty his mouth, etc. Such a hallucination may require a medium depth of trance, but many patients find it possible to hallucinate in this way. It is particularly effective with children.

With a patient in hypnosis, it will be found that bite registration is better accomplished and impressions can be taken more accurately. Dentures can be better fitted. This is largely due to the greater relaxation of the jaw muscles.

Every dentist encounters patients who claim their dentures do not fit and cannot be worn comfortably. Some people will have several dentures, none of them satisfactory, although the dentist will probably find some which do fit. In this situation, the patient probably is unconsciously rejecting the idea of wearing dentures. Hence none are comfortable. If this is true, it can be brought out with the questioning method. Often hypnotic suggestion given in a positive way can bring comfort. To establish motivation, it can be mentioned that the patient looks so much better with dentures, that he can chew better, and that he can even forget about his dentures when he has become accustomed to them. It can be said that some slight adjustment to a denture has been made and the patient is assured that he now can wear it comfortably, this being strongly emphasized. While in hypnosis, the denture should be inserted, with comments on how well it looks and how comfortable it now will be.

Some other situations where hypnosis can be helpful are frequently encountered. Gagging is one. There is a normal gagging reflex, but it is possible to control it voluntarily. Some people find this impossible, and it then presents quite a problem for the dentist. If the patient continues to gag, it may be impossible to continue work. Gagging can be controlled sometimes with suggestion under hypnosis. A person is unable to gag while holding his breath. The patient can be told to press one nostril shut with a finger and to hold his breath, then expel it, breathe in and hold again. It should be stated that he will then find he need not gag.

While most gagging can be controlled in this way, the tendency may be so strong that other methods must be used. Brief psychotherapy can remove the condition permanently. It will invariably be found that this tendency is psychologically caused. Ideomotor questioning can locate the cause. It usually requires no more than 15 or 20 minutes for such treatment which then enables the dentist to proceed with his work.

Behind the gagging symptom will be found some past experience, or perhaps two or three related ones. They usually go back to childhood. At some time the patient gagged, was nauseated, or choked. While he may not consciously remember the event, it is lodged in his subconscious and any approach to the mouth is unconsciously associated with the prior experience and hence is a threat. Gagging is an attempt to be rid of the threat.

With questioning, it is first asked if there is some past experience, or more than one, causing the gagging. Then it is asked if there is more than one and the number ascertained. The earliest one in point of time is then located, the age of the patient when it happened. Questions can determine the type of incident. Was it a nauseating one? Was it choking? Was it while undergoing an operation? Was it during an illness?

One of the most common experiences will be found to be a tonsillectomy. Choking on something is also a common one. Other questions locate where the event occurred. When the dentist knows what was involved, the patient is regressed to the incident. It should be specified that he may find himself gagging but he will not be nauseated, otherwise it may be necessary to clean up a mess.

The patient should be taken through the event two or three times and then asked a question if he can now be free of the need to gag. If the answer is negative, other similar or related experiences are sought and the patient regressed to them.

When an affirmative answer is received, the patient, still in hypnosis, should be given a tongue depressor and allowed to explore his mouth with it. Strong suggestion should be made that he now no longer needs to gag, although he may feel some tendency to do so. Now it can be controlled. After the patient has proved to himself that he no longer gags, the dentist can proceed with his work.

Steingart, in a personal communication, has noted that the gag reflex is absent with people who learned to reject food by tongue-thrusting. The two habits are mutually exclusive.

Tongue thrusting and thumbsucking in children can often be controlled or eliminated with hypnotic suggestion. The latter is much more easily accomplished. Thumb sucking is normal in a young child but it usually ends by the age of four. If it persists, it is usually an evidence of emotional disturbance. Psychiatrists believe that thumb sucking should not be stopped as it is a needed symptom. The dentist looks at the matter from another viewpoint, for thumb sucking may cause mouth malformation. The psychiatrist is correct, but, with most children, stopping the thumb sucking will not be emotionally damaging, particularly if the child can be led to want to stop the practice. If a child is greatly disturbed, the situation is different and there should be no attempt to stop the habit. It is a matter of degree as to disturbance.

The dentist should try to learn something about the child before attempting to stop thumb sucking. If he can determine that the child is reasonably happy and not seriously disturbed, the symptom can be terminated with no harm done. With a seriously disturbed one, it should not be attempted. Consulting the parents may be indicated in order to determine the degree of disturbance, though sometimes parents will deny disturbance when it is obviously present. If the little patient is also a bed-wetter, it can be suspected that his mental disturbance is too great.

Tongue thrusting has been the subject of extensive investigation at the University of North Carolina Dental School. A long series of experiments has been conducted there, and it has been found that hypnosis can be very effective in controlling this tendency and in teaching these children proper tongue movements. We do not know if the results of this research have yet been published.

Another dental problem often of psychological genesis is bruxism. While malocclusion may be present, the grinding of teeth often is purely a psychological symptom. Usually it can be ended by locating the causes through the questioning method, though some hypnodontists report control as difficult.

There seem to be one of two possible factors behind this symptom. Sometimes both are present. It may be organ language, one of our seven factors causing psychosomatic conditions. One phrase involved is "grit your teeth and bear it." When this is functioning, there is probably some environmental situation with which the patient is contending which he cannot resolve, at least at the moment.

Feelings of hostility, anger and resentment may bring a need to grind the teeth. It is a common expression to say, "He ground his teeth in rage." In most bruxism cases, the patient has strong feelings of hostility which are repressed. Then he grinds his teeth to express them. If these emotions can be discharged or vented in an acceptable way, there is no further need for teeth grinding.

An understanding of the causes is often enough to end this symptom. Sometimes better ways of venting such emotions can be suggested and suggestions can be made to the effect that grinding the teeth is detrimental and should be ended. Sometimes it is possible to substitute another symptom which is harmless. This is to suggest that the patient will clench his fists during the night as much as is necessary instead of grinding his teeth. Verbalizing his hostility can be a good way of venting it.

PHYSIOLOGICAL CONTROLS

With a patient in hypnosis, it will be found that certain bodily processes can be controlled through suggestion. Salivation is one. It can be suggested that it is well during dental work to have less flow of saliva. The suggestion should be that the flow will diminish until there is only enough secretion to keep the mouth normally moist. It should not be said that the mouth will be dry, as that is uncomfortable. With a good subject, it is often unnecessary to use a saliva ejector.

Often it is surprising how easily bleeding can be controlled. This has been mentioned previously. With a tooth extraction, the suggestion should be that a few drops of blood will enter the cavity as the tooth is lifted out, and that the blood vessels will then shut off completely. Whenever there is bleeding from dental work, suggestion can usually stop it. Dental treatment of a hemophilia patient is fraught with danger, and the dentist dealing with such a condition can find this ability to control bleeding of great advantage with such a case.

Since the rate of healing of any injury varies considerably with different individuals, it is difficult to prove scientifically, but dentists and others who use hypnosis are aware that the rate of healing can be greatly accelerated. Suggestions for this should always be given when hypnosis is used.

Hypnodontists have noted that there is little or no edema following an extraction when the patient has been in hypnosis. This is true whether or not hypnotic anesthesia has been used, but this effect is more frequent when such anesthesia has been induced. It seems to be a spontaneous matter, with no suggestions given to cause it.

Miscellaneous comments. A deepening technique available to the dentist is to have the dental chair elevated for induction of hypnosis. As suggestions for deepening are given, the chair is slowly lowered, so that the patient actually feels himself sinking.

A beneficial posthypnotic suggestion is to tell the patient before he is awakened that he will only remember the session as a pleasant experience. This tends to produce amnesia for anything unpleasant or painful which occurred during the dental work. Another posthypnotic suggestion can be that the patient will return for a checkup at the end of six months. Suggesting this is for the patient's benefit and is therefore ethical. He is much more likely to return at that time.

When dental surgery is performed with general anesthesia, all of the uses of hypnosis as given in the chapter on surgery and anesthesia can be utilized. Postoperative shock and nausea can be prevented and rapid healing instigated. Hypnotic anesthesia can prevent postoperative pain.

During the hypnotic session, the patient should be given frequent reassurance, with inquiry as to his comfort. It is not necessary to talk continually. Greater depth can be suggested when emptying the mouth, deeper anesthesia if the slightest pain is felt as the tooth is rocked or when a drill is pressed against a tooth. The patient's behavior should be noted. Movement may indicate discomfort or lessening of trance depth.

Having a prospective patient observe another who is in hypnosis is an aid for induction. This can be particularly impressive to a child patient.

Use only permissive suggestions for control of bruxism, tongue thrusting, thumb sucking, or when suggesting the elimination of any symptom. Before awakening the patient, suggestions given during the session should all be removed except for those intended to be effective posthypnotically.

The use of hypnosis with child patients will be found to be of very great advantage. Children are usually such good subjects that they are readily hypnotized and easily controlled for dental work. The apprehensive, fearful child or the spoiled brat can easily be dealt with. It allays apprehension if such a child is asked if he would like to watch a television program while he sits in the dental chair. Of course he would. Told he need pay no attention to what the dentist is doing in his mouth and that he need feel no discomfort because he is watching a program, he will be so intent on what he is hallucinating that he pays no attention. However, he will respond when told to open wider, to empty his mouth, or whatever is required of him. If older children have ever heard about hypnosis, they are usually greatly intrigued at the prospect of being hypnotized.

Should the parent's permission be sought for the use of hypnosis? Here opinion is divided. If written permission is asked, the parent will take this to mean that hypnosis is dangerous and may refuse. Some dentists tell a parent that handling children is often very difficult and ask if it is "all right to use some psychological methods in handling the child?" Hypnosis is a psychological method, and if the parent agrees to this, he has given permission for its use.

Many dentists do not mention hypnosis to the parent or child. The word is not used in induction and the child does not know he has been hypnotized. He may tell his parent that he watched a TV program while in the dental chair. The parent will think, "What an imagination!"

Often no formal induction is needed with children. Told how pain can be shut off by the use of imaginary switches and colored lights, the child slips spontaneously into a trance while producing the anesthesia. The same is true when told he can close his eyes and watch a TV program. He goes into hypnosis spontaneously in order to produce the hallucination. Most children between the ages of 5 and 12 can easily hallucinate in this way.

Many dentists make an addition to their fees when hypnosis is utilized. When estimating the total cost of the work to be performed, the addition is included without stating that it is for hypnosis. On the other hand, others specify that some additional amount is charged for hypnotic treatment. This amount varies considerably. It is based on the additional amount of time estimated as required. Probably a half-hour is all that should be estimated. Many dentists feel that no extra time is spent when much work is to be performed, and that there is even a saving of time. Few patients are unwilling to pay something extra for the benefits of being hypnotized for their dental work.

The hypnodontist invariably finds his patients pleased when the work has been accomplished with so little discomfort. Such patients are the source of referrals.

How much use of hypnosis will be made by the average hypnodontist? The amount would increase as more regular patients are conditioned for hypnosis. Probably the average use will be only three or four times a week, perhaps even less. Use would increase as other patients are referred for hypnosis. Some few dentists have become specialists in hypnodontics and seldom work without hypnotizing their patients. Some dentists familiar with hypnosis use it only in exceptional cases but apply its principles much of the time. Much depends on the individual dentist's interest and experience.

The dentist is fully covered by his malpractice insurance as to the use of hypnosis. However, this applies only when it is used for dental purposes. The dentist should always keep within his competence. Patients will sometimes ask for help to stop smoking or perhaps for relief of some condition such as a headache. This is not dentistry, and the operator should never step outside his own field. To do so will subject him to criticism from other branches of the medical profession.

When learning induction, it is quite permissible to practice with friends or the family. However, it certainly is inadvisable to use hypnosis for entertainment in a social situation. When it is known that a person uses hypnosis in his practice, he is likely to be asked to hypnotize someone and to demonstrate in social groups.

REFERENCES

Burgess, T. O.: Hypnosis in dentistry. *In*: Experimental Hypnosis (L. M. LeCron, Ed.). New York, Macmillan, 1952.

Moss, A. A.: Hypnodontics. Brooklyn, Dental Items of Interest Publishing Co., 1952.

Shaw, S. I.: Hypnosis in Dentistry. New York, Saunders, 1958.

Chapter 24

Recognition and Handling of Resistances

PROBLEMS of getting people into hypnosis are similar to the problems of getting people well. It seems that prior conditioning, subconscious misunderstandings, guilt, self-punishment and unfavorable identifications are matters that must always be considered.

Study the failures carefully, for you can learn much about the art of living when you give your patients a chance to examine their seemingly perverse behavior and give them a willing ear for criticism.

You will find that patients who used to irritate and frustrate you into referring them elsewhere are usually rather nice, shy people who were picking up the wrong cues from you. When you felt frustrated because you seemed not to be helping them, they understood your anger at yourself as anger directed toward them. They became more confused and less able to function successfully. It is human for us to become angry with apparent sources of injury or obstruction. The child who has stubbed his toe may kick the rock that did it. We often act similarly with patients.

The interplay of pyramiding misunderstandings and resistances is largely responsible for protracted failures of therapy in psychiatry and in other areas of the healing arts. It seems to explain, in part, the recurring problems of gastrointestinal disorders, urinary tract infections, chronic dermatitides and disc syndrome.

It is possible to study the successes and failures of patients with their previous doctors just as it is possible to learn some of the keys to successful and unsuccessful marriages. The impressions a patient and therapist have of each other at the first interview are largely responsible for the course that follows. Each is subconsciously alert to nuances of action and reaction based on habit and, perhaps, even genetic learnings. This hyperawareness does not seem to be there on subsequent occasions. Persuasion and politeness are strong forces in continuing a hopeless doctor-patient relationship, just as they may lead two young people into a miserable marriage.

The authors have tried to estimate some of these factors of initial bias by asking new patients the very significant question, "Does the subconscious part of your mind feel willing to let me help you with this problem?" The ideomotor response to this question may tell you that the future looks fruitful or it may alert you to trouble. Some of our students ask themselves this question after an initial interview to assess their subjective reactions to the patient.

There are several types of resistance to hypnosis and to hypnotherapy. We will attempt to classify them in outline before discussing them.

SOME FACTORS IN RESISTANCE

I. *Intrinsic factors* primary in the patient.
   1. "Flashback" to unpleasant spontaneous hypnoid state.
   2. Previous frightening association (watching demonstration).
   3. Unresolved need for symptom or problem.

II. *Extrinsic factors* arising from the environment.
   1. Unfavorable reaction to the therapist.
   2. Rebellion against request for therapy by someone else.
   3. Association with critical or intrinsically resistant people.

Discussion. Children in a friendly environment and all people in an intensely threatening environment may be considered as though hypnotized. The thinking processes of children under five years of age and of all people when highly alarmed or unconscious are literal, direct and humorless. T. J. Hudson, in his *Laws of Psychic Phenomena*, has compared conscious and unconscious thinking processes. He uses the term "subjective" for the ideation of frightened and unconscious states and pointed out its similarity to the ideation of hypnosis. Bernheim drew attention to the non-reasoning, hypersuggestibility of acutely ill patients and said that we only have to know it occurs before we are able to recognize and use it for the benefit of the patient. Hudson pointed out that seemingly unconscious people may fail to recover, may die or enter a very deep hypnotic-like state of pseudo-death in accordance with suggestions of hopelessness picked up from relatives and medical attendants. Quackenbos has written about a young woman who recovered from a moribund state which was due to bronchial pneumonia. Although apparently unconscious, she responded to his encouragement and commands to get well.

This phenomenon of apparent non-critical willingness to accept suggestions must be considered here in the chapter on resistance for two reasons. People who have interpreted tactile, visual and auditory stimuli in a discouraged or hopeless way while very ill, asleep or unconscious, may show great resistance to any kind of therapy which medical attendants think should be helpful. As stated in the chapter on surgery, the pessimistic perceptions of anesthetized patients are not corrected by simple conscious level reassurance after recovery from anesthesia. The unconscious understandings must be exposed to conscious reason. It is not easy to do this with the amnesia of chemo-anesthesia, natural sleep, traumatic unconsciousness, or the events of very early life before conscious memory begins. This is where the repetition of subconscious review and the use of LeCron's methods of ideomotor questioning are most helpful.

The second reason for referring to spontaneous hypnoid states of hypersuggestibility is to show their value even in situations when a would-be therapist might feel the most handicapped. Apparently non-reacting people will accept sincerely given helpful suggestions from a person they might strongly dislike on recovery of consciousness and good health. It is possible at such times to override hopelessness and self-destructive attitudes.

Some people have intrinsic reasons for rejecting hypnosis and any constructive therapy. Some patients willingly accept hypnosis and can experience all sorts of phenomena of hypnosis until they recognize the direction is toward a therapeutic goal. They may not be ready to give up a disease or adverse habit.

Some patients will accept hypnosis and appear optimistic at their first experience but will cancel or appear at the wrong time for a second visit. Some do well the first time but regress and are unable to enter hypnosis at the second visit.

Some apparently willing and motivated patients enter hypnosis easily but start to laugh and come out of hypnosis. Others appear uncomfortable, open their eyes or complain about the room temperature or their position. They may think they should go to the bathroom or put another coin in the parking meter.

Some stay in hypnosis with troubled expression, perspiration, pulsating neck vessels and rapid respiration that say they do not want to go on with this experience. Sometimes they will muddle past this troubled stage and continue comfortably but will resent having to do so. They may save this resentment to build resistances at the next visit. It is wise for the therapist to watch for such initial discomfort and check its cause. This is the phenomenon of "flashback." It may be helpful as well as distressing. It always seems to indicate a previous experience which has a bearing on the patient's problem.

"Flashback"

In 1957 we began each of our symposiums on medical and dental hypnosis with an induction of the entire group in attendance. We used suggestions about muscle relaxation associated with ideas of peaceful places. We used no ideas that might suggest accidents, general anesthetics or serious illness. In every group, however, there would be individuals who would start to relax and then would appear disturbed and perhaps open their eyes. In each group of highly motivated professional men and women wanting to learn about hypnosis, there were approximately 10 per cent who showed this distress reaction. Search into factors responsible for this revealed in each instance that the hypnotic state was reminding the subject of some experience associated with great fear, great physical stress, or loss of consciousness. Some individuals found they had also become similarly distressed when they had tried inducing hypnosis in their patients before taking our course. They had worried over doing harm to their patients because their patients would also become disturbed, sensing it in the operator.

This was the period of great interest in hypnosis in the United States. The chairman of the Committee on Hypnosis for the American Medical Association had not yet begun his fear campaign regarding the dangers of hypnosis (1958-1962). We wondered why so many seemingly thoughtful and enthusiastic professional men and women were either not using hypnosis or were taking course after course on hypnosis but doing nothing with it themselves. One physician took 13 courses but did not "feel ready yet" to use it in his practice. In studying our students, we learned that flashback fear after repeated exposure during symposiums gradually disappeared. It faded out in an atmosphere of confidence among experienced instructors but recurred when individuals either tried to put themselves into hypnosis or tried to hypnotize a patient.

We had been mistaken in assuming that apparent comfort with the experience of hypnosis during symposiums was the answer. It is necessary for the therapist to understand the origin of his apprehensive reaction and know that it need not continue to bother him now or in the future.

Case: The Physician who gave up hypnosis because of flashback

A physician in his sixties had to leave the conference room several times during the first day of a symposium in Salt Lake City. During an intermission, he came forward to tell us that he had been forced to leave each time we had given a demonstration of an induction method because he had felt short-of-breath and could not control the pounding of his heart and the strong feeling of apprehension. He added that this feeling had been responsible for his giving up the study of hypnosis 30 years earlier. He had read everything he could find about the subject and was convinced hypnosis could be of great service to him in his practice of medicine until he tried it on his first patient. The terrifying reaction in himself during this experience had led him to believe that hypnosis was not for him.

Finger signal replies to questions revealed that he had had an experience something like the one he had described before the experience with his patient. Other questions brought out that it was a tonsillectomy performed in a doctor's office. His parents had not told him he would have the operation and he had forcibly been "put to sleep with ether." After discovery of this memory, his fingers signaled that he might now use hypnosis without being reminded of this unpleasant childhood trauma. Thereafter he was able to use hypnosis on his colleagues at the course and was comfortable in letting them practice on him as the subject.

Cheek has written a paper on resistance caused by equating a hypnotic state with distressing experiences during which the subject has entered a hypnotic-like state.

Space has been given to this flashback mechanism for intrinsic resistance to hypnosis because it affects results with patients directly by making them afraid to go into hypnosis. It also may influence them indirectly because some close friend, relative, or physician may be reacting to the same mechanism and be unaware of this cause for prejudice against use of hypnotherapy. A patient who has already learned to feel comfortable may be turned against hypnosis by a trusted advisor.

Previous Frightening Association

Patients often rationalize reasons for rejecting hypnosis when they do not know the cause is the flashback type mentioned here. One of the more common explanations is that the patient has once been frightened at the control exerted by a stage hypnotist or enthusiastic amateur. Usually they rely on one of the clichés commonly listed under misconceptions in texts on hypnosis. The correctness of their statement can be checked by an ideomotor response to the question, "Has there been any earlier experience that could have made you vulnerable to the objection you have just given?" The answer is usually yes. You can then ask the patient to orient back at a subconscious level to the beginning of that experience, have the "yes" finger lift and then bring the memory up to conscious awareness where it can be put into words.

Unresolved Need for Symptom or Problem

Distress seemingly calling for hypnotherapy may be self-punitive, but it may also be used to punish someone else. In the latter case, we frequently find the target is the person who called to make the appointment. You should always be alert to potential resistances when a patient comes in to keep an appointment made by a relative or a person referred to as "a very good friend."

Among reasons for self-punishment should be mentioned some of the following:

Injuries or disease arising from accidents of any kind.

Disease starting after an accident that caused death or serious injury, when the patient feels in some way responsible.

Death, serious illness (or divorce) of parent or parents before the patient is ten years of age.

Serious illness or death of a parent or sibling for which the patient held feelings of resentment or hatred.

Need for patient to sign commitment papers for a relative needing custodial care.

Imprinted remark of judgment by a parent, such as "You're a disgrace to the family; you will never amount to anything," etc.

An illness, injury or allergy which once saved the patient from expected punishment or drew comforting attention from a seemingly hostile parent or loved one.

A short step separates the last item from use in a self-punitive way and use for manipulation of loved ones. Later it may take on subconscious meaning in punishing others who were not even known during the first conditioning process. An innocent husband may suffer for the real or imagined deeds of the patient's father. A man who began his problem drinking in marriage to a rigid and inhibited first wife may unconsciously punish a loving and compatible second wife with the same habit.

An unresolved need for a symptom or problem is usually extrinsic rather than intrinsic in origin, but it is classified here as intrinsic because it manifests itself sometimes at the first visit and requires understanding of causes before it can be corrected. The external cause is not as important as what happens to it in the subconscious thought processes of your patient.

Here are the factors that originate more clearly with the environment.

Unfavorable Reaction to the Therapist

Some people just do not click with each other and we should not forget our possible role in this problem which has two sides. It may start with the first or second visit because of dislike. Much later it may show itself when you and the patient are approaching the therapeutic goal but the patient is not ready to break the relationship. All progress may stop because you have sounded too optimistic. You can save much waste effort and embarrassment by asking for an ideomotor answer to the question, "Does the subconscious part of your mind feel willing to let me help you with this problem?" It should be asked at the first interview involving hypnosis and can be repeated whenever you run into apparent trouble. A negative answer should lead to the question, "Would you be willing to let someone else help you?"

When in doubt about a personality clash after one or more unsuccessful interviews, you can say something like this: "I feel sure you could have made much more rapid progress than has been accomplished. I must have been doing something or saying something which interferes with what you want to accomplish. Is it possible that there is something I could have said or done to let you progress more rapidly?"

It is better to ask about what could have been done rather than to ask about what you did wrong. You need not fear too much that you will not be told your mistakes. Patients in hypnosis are much like parents in this respect. It is, however, important to know what constructive path to take.

Occasionally resistances of this sort can be overcome with subjects capable of reaching a fairly deep level of hypnosis by using a pseudo-orientation into the future (age-progression). The therapist states that he is glad to see the patient again now that he has returned after so many years, and a date some years in the future is stated. Since it has been a long time, the therapist does not remember the details of what was done to overcome the patient's difficulties, and it is certainly nice to note how well he did recover. Would the patient please tell him just what it was that was done? Thereupon the patient may explain what "was done" and of course the therapist then uses these means in his therapy.

Some complaints of patients about therapy errors

You are too busy answering the telephone, writing notes, being restless. You sound distracted, angry or uninterested.

You do not apologize to the patient when you are interrupted.

You are critical of previous therapy. (You tacitly insult the patient's judgment when you criticize what has been done previously. He has had an investment in those actions.)

Something went wrong during a period of unconsciousness. Usually this has occurred with the patient under general chemo-anesthesia. Examples are:

> An assistant was told to come around and do the operation when you were expected to be the surgeon.
>
> Remarks were interpreted by the patient as being critical. These include "What a mess!", "She sure is fat.", "This is a bad one.", and "She's bleeding too much."
>
> Pessimistic remarks during surgery were not corrected by conscious explanation after recovery. "This ulcer is bigger than we thought.", "Better get a frozen section on this one.", "This isn't working." (needle-holder, hemostat, suction).

Rebellion against Request for Therapy by Someone Else

The one who makes the appointement may be the butt of punitive illness or behavior and may need more punishment. A patient feels discredited and rejected by the person who has suggested therapy. A patient may be resistant to therapy when a friend or relative has called for an appointment before consulting the patient.

Two questions are helpful in discovery of factors in this category. "Have you been using this trouble in any way to do harm to yourself or someone else?" "Is the subconscious part of your mind willing to let me help you with this trouble?" You will need to clarify the intent of this last question if the ideomotor answer is affirmative. Obviously punishment could be helped by having the distress grow worse rather than better.

"Poisoned referral"

This means a type of referral by a colleague who has, consciously or unconsciously, diminished chances of your helping the patient. There are two major types of this faulty conduct.

Conscious poison. The referring doctor does not believe in hypnosis. He has knowingly done his best to convince the patient, or a relative of the patient, that hypnosis would be of no value or might even be dangerous. Having failed to dissuade, he now calls you or writes as though he were recommending hypnotherapy on his own initiative.

The referring doctor believes in the value of hypnosis but either has been afraid to talk about it with the patient or has mentioned it and has persisted in his enthusiasm in spite of the horrified or apathetic reaction of his patient. From the way the referral is made, you think that you have carte blanche to start right in with a discussion of hypnosis. This error can arise when the appointment has been arranged between the doctor and your secretary or between the two secretaries. It can come from the referring doctor feeling embarrassed at telling you how to conduct the interview when he should have advised a slow approach to the subject of hypnosis.

Unconscious poison. The colleague has had his feelings hurt when the patient requests hypnotherapy. This may bring a raised eyebrow on the part of the doctor, a tone of voice or choice of words showing disapproval. The loyal patient feels guilty for hurting the doctor's feelings and is unable to continue in his care or make a new relationship succeed.

A variant of this problem is the recommendation for hypnotherapy initiated by the physician who has become discouraged at failure with other means of treatment. The patient feels rejected and will always find it difficult to believe hypnosis will be of use if his doctor only considered it after trying everything else first.

Discussion. There is nothing about "poisoned referral" for hypnotherapy that could not be said about other referrals in the healing arts. Be aware of its possibility until hypnosis has been better accepted by medical schools and in psychiatry.

Association with Critical or Intrinsically Resistant People

Be aware of this possibility when a patient suddenly resumes symptoms or becomes unable to use hypnosis after initial success. Consider differential diagnostic points when this occurs:

The problem is organic and cannot yield to psychotherapy.
You have done something to harm the relationship.
The patient is not ready to give up the problem.
Someone with a negative attitude has influenced the patient.

You can pick up clues by asking questions. "Do you feel subconsciously that there is some physical distress?" (A "yes" answer at an ideomotor level does not necessarily mean that the condition is organic, but then you should rule out that possibility before going on with psychotherapy.)

Another way of handling it would be "Orient your thoughts to the last moment at which you were doing very well. When you are there, your "yes" finger will lift. Then come up to the moment something went wrong. Bring it up to a conscious level where you can tell me what has interfered with your progress."

METHODS OF OVERCOMING RESISTANCE

These will vary with the personality and inventiveness of the therapist. The general principle within each method is essentially that of the placebo effect in medicine.

Learn as much as you can about diagnostic studies made by others before the patient came to you. Remember that patients who do not want to face the reality of organic disease may consciously ignore symptoms and forget advice and warnings of physicians. This mechanism of repression is the greatest factor in handicapping the treatment of cancer.

Get the name and address of every physician who has seen your patient for this or a related complaint. Have the patient sign a release for all information which pertains and send it to the doctor with a covering note. Follow up if the doctor does not reply. Keep carbons stamped with the date of mailing.

It is well to have printed or mimeographed forms containing such questions as:

Have you been treated for this or any related condition by a physician or psychologist? List names, dates and addresses.

Have you had any X rays or other diagnostic studies made within the past year? Give name of examination, date and your understanding of the outcome.

Have you ever had any reaction to drugs, antibiotics, narcotics or anesthetic agents? List which if any.

Has shock treatment ever been advised or given? At the bottom of this form, leave space for the signatures of the patient and a witness, and a place for the date. California physicians, dentists and psychologists are increasingly vulnerable to legal action in case their actions result in failure to cure. The above recommendations may not be needed in more friendly environments.

HANDLING THE EFFECTS OF GUILT AND SELF-PUNISHMENT

Guilt feelings serve no good purpose for anyone. Bring this out in your questioning. Ask for ideomotor responses to such questions as "Does this situation make your husband happier or more prosperous?" The subconscious mind looks only at end results rather than possible side effects, and masochism also hurts everyone close to the person punishing himself.

Adroit questions and statements may point out the selfishness of guilt. Success is yours if you can motivate such patients to get well for the sake of someone else. It is well to point out that we are all human and err at times. We learn from our mistakes and sins. Is further self-punishment really warranted? Through the questioning technique it can be learned if this can now be relinquished. If the answer is negative, further work is necessary to locate the main sources of guilt. One main source is in the area of sex, though there can be many other sources.

There is always some motive behind resistance or some definite reason for it. Ideomotor answers to questions are of great value in uncovering these causes which may not be consciously known to the patient. He is then dissociated from the process and can look upon the answers as though given by someone else. If resistances are strong and deeply buried, it is not always possible to have success. Even the most experienced therapist, whether or not hypnosis is used, is sure to have failures at times. This is regrettable but should not be too disturbing to the therapist.

Before giving up with a difficult patient, try a group situation with other patients who are doing well. Success is infectious. Sometimes you can barter for fractions of improvement on a protracted time plan.

REFERENCES

Cheek, D. B.: Removal of subconscious resistance to hypnosis using ideomotor questioning techniques. Amer. J. Clin. Hypn. 3: 103-107, 1960.
————: Importance of recognizing that surgical patients behave as though hypnotized. Amer. J. Clin. Hypn. 4: 227-236, 1962.

Chapter 25

Office Procedure, Fees, and the Planning of Visits

OFFICE PLANNING in the application of hypnosis poses no problem for the psychotherapist. His practice will be handled in the usual way. He will find the time spent in treatment much shorter and, undoubtedly, he will see much better results from his therapy. With hypnotherapy there may be some change in the frequency of the patient's visits. So much more is accomplished in an hourly session that the patient should have a few days in which to digest any insight he has gained, for suggestions to become effective, and for problems to be worked through. Depending somewhat on the individual and on the particular situation, probably no more than two sessions a week should be planned. Frequently only one is good practice. An exception might be where there is a time factor, the patient coming from out of town or planning to be away.

The physician in general practice or who specializes must plan differently. His routine will change only in that he should allot certain hours for hypnotic treatment. The average physician who uses hypnosis sets aside certain hours for this purpose. Sometimes patients will be seen for the "50-minute hour." Often only a half-hour is needed. Some devote one or two afternoons to such practice or do evening work. Office personnel should not interrupt hypnotic sessions unless it is essential for some reason.

For use with hypnosis, a couch or comfortable arm chair is needed. Best for this purpose is a contour chair with a back which can be adjusted so the patient can sit up or recline as is preferred. Such chairs have a footrest which extends when the back of the chair is pushed down. Our observation is that some patients have a definite preference as to whether they sit up or lie back, and best results will come if selection of position is permitted.

Fees will vary with the individual physician. He must charge appropriately for his time and must consider his overhead in setting his fees. Probably his overhead will exceed that of psychiatrists who have much smaller office space and less rent and may or may not have a secretary. Other types of physicians may have several employees.

Psychiatric fees usually amount to around $25 to $35 for a visit of an hour, although some psychiatrists and analysts may charge up to $75. Other physicians using hypnosis may find that they must charge at least $35, depending on their expenses. With a developed practice in hypnosis, it may be possible to hold group sessions, keeping fees much lower. This is particularly practical in obstetrics, for weight reduction, and for some other conditions where there are enough patients to warrant group work. Group hypnosis will be found most effective. Obstetricians usually have a flat fee for care regardless of methods used. This should allow for time required in therapy with hypnosis.

In this matter of fees, the physician must realize that he will accomplish much more in a session than is possible with more orthodox methods. The total that a patient pays will be relatively low in comparison to the costs of orthodox treatment, even if the fee is higher per hour. Many obstetricians and surgeons feel the time used for hypnosis is more than justified by time saved during the hospital period.

Hypnodontists vary considerably in regulating their fees. Many dentists feel that the use of hypnosis entails more time than they can afford, but those who use it usually find that it saves time. Some dentists add to their fees if hypnosis is used; others do not. If there is an additional fee, it is probably best to quote a total amount without specifying an additional charge for hypnotic treatment.

Before beginning to use hypnosis, most practitioners feel that they should first become fairly proficient with inductions. Beginners usually lack confidence, but a few practice sessions will provide this. A deep trance is usually unnecessary. Inductions are really easy, though they may loom as difficult to the beginner.

Probably the best way of gaining some experience with inductions is to use children as subjects, your own or those of friends. As we have mentioned, children are usually excellent subjects and enter a deep trance very quickly. Those old enough to have heard about hypnosis are often eager to experience hypnosis.

While "parlor hypnosis" for the amusement of friends and acquaintances is to be avoided, using friends for practice is both feasible and suitable. Wives and other relatives may also serve and often will be found to be good subjects, although family relationships sometimes make it difficult to hypnotize a spouse or someone close to you.

For practice, it is best to select some induction method which is not too brief and which will give good results. We can recommend either having the subject concentrate on a pendulum while the talk is about relaxation or, even better, the use of the technique where the subject stands while counting backward from 100, the operator moving him in a circle during the count. For initial practice of induction, a talk such as is given in this book can even be read to the subject. We do not recommend this because it is neither very effective nor an exercise in formulating suggestions.

Beginners usually try to say entirely too much and talk too rapidly. The voice should be kept low, in a monotone, with slow cadence. Early in the induction talk, there should be much repetition of suggestions as to heaviness of the eyelids until they close and of the words "heavier and heavier, heavier and heavier" a number of times. During the use of deepening techniques, the phrase "deeper and deeper" can also be repeated frequently.

It is not necessary to keep up a continual chatter during an induction. If the beginner wonders what he should say or do next, it is quite all right to say nothing at all for a moment or two while he decides on his next procedure.

Plenty of time should be taken for the induction, continuing with deepening techniques. It is well to spend about ten minutes or more for this. Avoid challenging tests at first. It is better to use an arm levitation or ask for subconscious finger signals of acceptance of suggestions. Glove anesthesia is easy to obtain if you suggest the feeling of numbness occurring when one lies on an arm for a long time. Give the subject time to accept these thoughts and ask him to test his own analgesia when he knows it has developed. Sometimes the beginning operator is fortunate enough to find a practice subject who readily goes into a deep state, as is particularly apt to occur with children.

With a little more proficiency and experience, some of the phenomena most easily produced can be utilized, such as the partial form of regression to some recent unimportant experience such as a meal.

When beginning the use of hypnosis in the office, the physician should assume that his suggestions will work. This is a fact. Subjects will behave poorly when the therapist expects or is afraid of failure. They will do well when he expresses confidence in their ability to perform well. Confidence is important and comes only with practice.

It should be kept in mind that it is always best to have someone else present in the office when dealing with women patients. It is not necessary to have anyone in the room, but an office assistant or nurse should be in the office suite. Malpractice insurance covers the use of hypnosis unless the contrary is stated in your policy, and we know of no insurance company that fails to cover the physician or dentist.

Something might be added here as to religious prejudices about hypnosis. The only religious sects which seem to be opposed to the use of hypnosis are Jehovah's Witnesses, Christian Scientists, and Seventh Day Adventists. With the last named, some physicians who are members of this church are trying to secure a change in attitude since they have used hypnosis themselves and realize that this attitude is based on misconceptions. The Catholic church is not opposed to hypnosis, although an individual priest may be against it and so advise a member of the church. Many Catholic physicians use hypnosis.

As stated, physicians other than psychiatrists should confine themselves to treating psychosomatic illnesses rather than to deal with psychoses or the neuroses which are hard to handle. It is best to refer to a psychotherapist any patient who seems to be extremely disturbed, deeply depressed, or who may be suspected of being psychotic or near a psychotic break.

When hypnotherapy is indicated, the first session with the patient may be merely the taking of a case history, laboratory tests, diagnosis, and making some explanation to the patient about hypnosis, ridding him of the usual misconceptions and possible fears about hypnosis. It should be remembered that your patient comes to you believing you competent and gives you prestige. Some doctors fear to become known as hypnotists and use hypnosis disguised as relaxation, not as out-and-out hypnosis. We think it much better to suggest hypnotic treatment. It will be found that very few patients will refuse hypnosis when it is recommended and when explanation is made as to its benefits and about hypnosis itself. If time permits on the first visit, there can be an induction, but often this is reserved for the second visit.

Psychoanalysts usually see patients on a daily basis. With psychosomatic and most other conditions, only one or two visits a week is best, as has been mentioned. Ordinarily one visit a week is best. With progress, this can often be cut to a visit every two weeks or even to one a month toward the end of therapy.

CLASSIFICATION OF PATIENTS

There are many ways of introducing patients to the use of hypnosis, and each of us has to formulate technics best suited to our own backgrounds and to the needs of our patients.

In general, there are three major categories of patients: (1) those who expect hypnosis and are interested in its use, (2) those who have no understanding of the subject and may resent its introduction and (3) those who are unconscious or so badly frightened that they will accept hypnosis without struggle even though they might reject it if they were in good health.

Class 1: Ready and Interested Group

The method which we have found most readily demonstrated and incorporated into a teaching process is a combined use of postural suggestion followed by a "challenge" involving the word "try," a resolution of the challenge, and finally a setting up of ideomotor symbol responses for answers to questions. The introduction is verbalized as follows:

"I would like you to know how easily muscles can become tense or relaxed in association with changes of thought. Muscles that are held tight for too long will become painful. Muscles always tighten up unconsciously around painful areas, and part of the art of getting injuries to heal rapidly depends on getting the regional muscles to relax. The circulation to an injured area or an operation site is improved when the muscles are allowed to contract and relax intermittently rather than staying tight all the time.

"It is also a fact that the association between real pain and muscle tension is so constant that the brain seems unable to recognize painful stimuli when a person purposefully achieves total body relaxation. It may sound deceitful to talk about relaxing when you are in pain, but I think you will soon discover for yourself how valuable this apparent deceit can be. Our minds work for us in very much the same way as the nervous system of a chameleon which changes its coloring to match the environment in which it rests. This is why we ask someone to remember a picnic or a trip through beautiful country when she may be initially very uncomfortable with active labor. Neither the picnic nor the trip was associated with pain. She will soon find the labor pains becoming unimportant contractions as the mental imagery associated with the comfortable experience becomes more vivid and real in hypnosis.

"Now hold up your arms on a level with your chest, close your eyes and imagine how this right arm would feel if you had your purse or a couple of books hanging from your wrist."

Steps after this will depend on the reactions of the patient and the clinical problem. Remember that willing and seemingly cooperative patients may demonsrate strong resistances on entering hypnosis or at the moment you begin attacking the major problem (see the chapter on resistance).

Class 2: Presentation to Those with No Understanding of Hypnosis

The best example of this class of patient is the resentful masochist who has not recognized that the headaches, bursitis, "whiplash" injury, disc syndrome or colitis have strong emotional components. Here the technic developed by LeCron using a Chevreul pendulum may break the ice better than a long-winded lecture on the blessings of hypnosis. It would go something like this:

Therapist: Have you ever considered the possibility that these very real and painful bouts of bursitis might be related in some way to emotional stresses in your everyday life?

Patient: Doc, are you trying to tell me I imagine these things? Look here at this X ray. See all that calcium around the joint? Sure, I got things that bother me, like everyone, but I take them right as they come. They don't have anything to do with my shoulder.

Therapist: Sometimes we can get information about pain of this sort with the help of a little gadget here that might interest you. What we need to know is the relationship between things that happen and the onset of trouble with your shoulder. There is a deep part of your mind that keeps track of all important events. This pendulum is like a ouija board. It can help discover things you might have forgotten.

The pendulum movements are explained and the patient becomes interested in the unconsciously controlled movements. He is asked to let the pendulum answer the question "Do worries, anger, or fear have something to do with your shoulder trouble?" A "yes" answer will usually open the way for therapy that might otherwise be totally rejected. You have not told the patient that there is an emotional background for the condition. He has told you.

Much of the unwillingness to accept psychological factors in illness stems from early-life conditioning that all obstacles yield to willpower and that failure must be ascribed to laziness or stupidity. Obstinate refusal to accept even the evidence of a pendulum would suggest some unresolved need for the disease.

Class 3: Those Unconscious or Too Ill to Seem Reasonable.

These should be treated as though already in hypnosis, as discussed in the chapter on emergency uses of hypnosis. Make sure you speak slowly, firmly, and in terms that do not offer any loophole for pessimistic interpretations. It helps very much to address the patient by first name. A gentle but firm touch on the arm or head answers as well if you do not know the patient. Be sure of your own position before you touch an unconscious person. Perception of attitude is very keen in the frightened or unconscious person. Excellent voice tone, timing and inflection may be inactivated by your indecisive or trembling touch.

In general, you should introduce yourself and then explain the situation as you see it, followed by an explanation of steps to be taken in correcting the problem. Give suggestions for relaxation, comfort and increasing appetite, and end with the suggested projection to a time of full recovery with all systems working in a healthy, happy way.

Few physicians who become interested in hypnosis wish to become out-and-out psychotherapists. In this course we have given enough of the general principles of how to use hypnosis so that it is not necessary to have extensive knowledge of and experience with psychotherapy, provided the safeguards given are utilized. Of course the more any physician knows of psychotherapy, the more psychologically oriented he becomes and the better doctor he will be. Every physician uses some psychotherapy in his practice. The "bedside manner," general attitude and behavior toward the patient are indirect psychotherapy. In adopting hypnotherapy, you are merely adding something to your armamentarium and will undoubtedly help far more of your patients.

HYPNOSIS IN DENTAL PRACTICE

For the dentist, much that has been said in this chapter will apply to him as well as to the physician. However, there are some other considerations.

Many dentists who take courses in hypnotic technics feel that too much time is involved to warrant the use of hypnosis except very occasionally. Those with experience find that this is not so and that in most situations there is actually a time saving in that more work can be accomplished in a given time when the patient is under hypnosis.

In considering the time element, some dentists add to their fees if hypnosis is used. Others feel that the time saving and the benefits of hypnosis make this unnecessary. Certainly if more time is spent, it should be charged for.

A few dentists who have learned the use of hypnosis become so interested that they have become hypnodontic specialists. Others refer to them, usually sending them their most difficult patients. Word-of-mouth advertising from patients to their friends also brings other patients for hypnotic treatment.

The average hypnodontist will use the principles of hypnosis and suggestion with most patients but will not actually induce hypnosis more than perhaps two or three times a week. If a patient needs only a small amount of dental work, obviously it is not worthwhile to resort to hypnosis except with such patients as may be phobic about dentistry. In such an event, an additional charge should be made, as more time is needed.

Patients who require much work, or those who will be returning frequently, are good prospects for hypnosis. It is undoubtedly indicated with most children, as they are such good subjects and usually are very fearful. Still other indications for its use are with gaggers, hemopheliacs, and when drug anesthesia is contraindicated. Still other indications are cited in the chapter on hypnodontics.

We have tried to make this book as thorough as possible within the limitations of space. We feel that the reader is prepared to use the knowledge but probably will find further reading material valuable. There are many excellent texts and other books on hypnosis, too many to list fully. The following list is suggested for further reading:

AMBROSE: *Hypnotherapy with Children*
AUGUST: *Hypnosis in Obstetrics*
DORCUS: *Hypnosis and its Therapeutic Applications*
ESDAILE: *Hypnosis in Medicine and Surgery*
GORDON: *Handbook of Clinical and Experimental Hypnosis*
KROGER: *Clinical and Experimental Hypnosis*
LECRON AND BORDEAUX: *Hypnotism Today*
LECRON (EDITOR): *Experimental Hypnosis*
LECRON: *Techniques of Hypnotherapy*
LECRON: *Self Hypnotism*
LECRON: *Better Health Through Self Hypnosis*
LECRON: *How to Stop Smoking With Self Hypnosis*
MAGONET: *Hypnosis in Asthma*
SCOTT: *Hypnosis in Dermatology*
SHAW: *Hypnosis in Dentistry*
WEITZENHOFFER: *General Techniques of Hypnotism*
WOLBERG: *Hypnoanalysis*
WOLBERG: *Medical Hypnosis*
WOLPE: *Psychotherapy by Reciprocal Inhibition*

Index of Names

Index of Subjects

4
5
6 .
7 g
8 h
9 i
8 0 j